How to Pass

HIGHER
Human Biology
for CfE

Billy Dickson and Graham Moffat

HODDER
GIBSON
AN HACHETTE UK COMPANY

The Publishers would like to thank the following for permission to reproduce copyright material:

Photo credits

p.85 © Isabelle Limbach/iStockphoto/Thinkstock; p.144 © Ely William Hill in 1915, published in *Puck*, an American humour magazine, on 6 November 1915

Every effort has been made to trace all copyright holders, but if any have been inadvertently overlooked the Publishers will be pleased to make the necessary arrangements at the first opportunity.

Although every effort has been made to ensure that website addresses are correct at time of going to press, Hodder Gibson cannot be held responsible for the content of any website mentioned in this book. It is sometimes possible to find a relocated web page by typing in the address of the home page for a website in the URL window of your browser.

Orders: please contact Bookpoint Ltd, 130 Park Drive, Milton Park, Abingdon, Oxon OX14 4SE. Telephone: (44) 01235 827720. Fax: (44) 01235 400454. Lines are open 9.00–5.00, Monday to Saturday, with a 24-hour message answering service. Visit our website at www.hoddereducation.co.uk. Hodder Gibson can be contacted direct on: Tel: 0141 848 1609; Fax: 0141 889 6315; email: hoddergibson@hodder.co.uk

First published in 2015 by
Hodder Gibson, an imprint of Hodder Education,
An Hachette UK Company,
2a Christie Street
Paisley PA1 1NB

Impression number   5 4 3 2 1

Year   2019 2018 2017 2016 2015

Cover photo © vectorus–Fotolia
Illustrations by Aptara, Inc.
Typeset in CronosPro light, 13/15 Pts by Aptara, Inc.
Printed in Spain
A catalogue record for this title is available from the British Library
ISBN: 978 1 4718 4741 7

Contents

Unit 3 Neurobiology and communication

Unit 4 Immunology and public health

General introduction

Welcome to *How to Pass Higher Human Biology*!

The fact that you have opened this book and are reading it shows that you want to pass your SQA Higher Human Biology course. This is excellent because passing and passing well needs that type of attitude. It also shows you are getting down to the revision that is *essential* to pass and get the best grade possible.

The idea behind the book is to help you to pass, and if you are already on track to pass, it can help improve your grade. It can help boost a C into a B or a B into an A. It cannot do the work for you, but it can guide you in how best to use your limited time.

In producing this book we have assumed that you have followed an SQA Higher Human Biology course at school or college this year and that you have probably, but not necessarily, already studied National 5 Biology.

We recommend that you download and print a copy of the Higher Human Biology Course Assessment Notes (pages 7–56) from the SQA website at www.sqa.org.uk.

You should note that in your exam only the material included in the Mandatory Course Key Areas can be examined. Skills of scientific inquiry, described on pages 59–62 of the Notes, are also examined. You should get copies of any specimen or past papers that are available on the SQA website.

We have tried to keep the language simple and easy to understand and we have used the language of SQA Higher support materials. This is the language used in the setting of the exam papers.

Although we have covered the entire Higher course within these materials, we have tried to emphasise those areas that cause most difficulty for students. We have concentrated on support for the examination element of the course assessment, which is worth about 83% of your final grade. The other 17% is covered in your assignment and you will have support for this from school or college, although we have provided some material in the short chapter on pages 214–218.

We suggest that you use this book throughout your course. Use it at the end of each Key Area covered in class, at the end of each Unit in preparation for Unit assessment, before your preliminary examination and, finally, to revise the whole course in the lead up to your final examination.

There is a grid on page x that you can use to record and evaluate your progress as you finish each Unit.

Course assessment outline

The Higher Human Biology course is assessed in three parts: the National Units, an assignment and a course examination. It is necessary to pass *all* assessments to achieve a course award. The grading of the course award (A, B, C or D) comes from the assignment and course exam marks.

National Units

Each of the four National Units is assessed at your school or college on a pass or fail basis. There are different methods of Unit assessment. Each school or college will have its own approach but all students have to pass a knowledge test in each Unit and write up an experiment they have carried out. Your school or college will assess the Units and you will probably have a chance to try Unit assessments again if you need to. You must pass all four Units.

Assignment (20 marks)

The assignment is an open-book task that is based on some research that you have carried out in class time. The investigation will be supervised by teachers, and you will have to write up the work in the form of a report during a controlled assessment. During the write-up you will have access to your research material and notes.

The assignment has several stages:
1 Selecting a topic
2 Planning the investigation
3 Identifying resources
4 Carrying out the investigation
5 Selecting and gathering relevant information
6 Writing up an investigation report in a controlled assessment

The write-up is marked out of 20 marks, with some of the marks being for scientific inquiry skills and some for the application of knowledge.

	Marks available
Skills	15
Knowledge and understanding	5
Total	**20**

The marks are allocated as follows:

Skills, knowledge and understanding	Mark allocation
Aim	1
Applying knowledge and understanding of biology	5
Selecting information	2
Processing and presenting data/information	4
Analysing data/information	2
Conclusion(s)	1
Evaluation	3
Presentation	2

The assignment is marked by the SQA and contributes 17% of the overall grade for the course. We have provided an assignment evidence checklist on page xi–xii that will allow you to check that you are prepared for the controlled assessment.

Course examination (100 marks)

The Higher examination is a single paper consisting of a booklet of questions in two sections:

- **Section 1** contains 20 multiple-choice questions for 1 mark each.
- **Section 2** contains a mixture of restricted- and extended-response questions for a total of 80 marks. The questions range from 1 to around 10 marks and the higher-mark allocation questions offer a choice.

The majority of the marks test knowledge, with an emphasis on the application of knowledge. The remainder test the application of scientific inquiry, analysis and problem-solving skills. There will usually be an opportunity to comment on, or suggest modifications to, an experimental situation.

The course examination is marked by SQA and contributes 83% to the overall grade for the course.

The various components of the Higher assessment system are as follows:

Higher Human Biology	Assessment	Who does the assessing?
Units (pass or fail)	Unit 1 tests	School staff
	Unit 2 tests	School staff
	Unit 3 tests	School staff
	Unit 4 tests	School staff
Course (graded A–D)	Assignment (worth 17% of grade)	Marked by SQA out of 20 marks
	Examination (worth 83% of grade)	Marked by SQA out of 100 marks
	20 multiple-choice marks and 80 restricted- and extended-response marks	

About this book

Course content

The course content section is split into four units, which cover the four Units of Higher Human Biology. Each unit is divided into Key Areas. Each Key Area has the following features:

 Key points

These list and expand the content statements from the SQA specification using words and phrases needed to answer examination questions. Where a key term appears for the first time it is in **bold** and you will find it listed in the key words section at the end of each chapter and in the Glossary on pages 223–240. It is essential to read the definitions when working with ⇨

the key points. After having worked on a Key Area, the key points should be easy to understand. You might want to use the boxes to show progress. We suggest marking like this – if you are having difficulty, like this + if you have done further work and are more comfortable and this * if you are confident you have learned a particular idea. Alternatively you could traffic light them using coloured dots: red for 'not understood', orange for 'more work needed' and green for 'fully understood'.

Hints & tips

Where we offer a tip to help learning it is boxed like this. These tips can be very general or can be specific to the content of the Key Area. Many tips alert you to topics that are linked to other areas in the course and where you can read more. The tips are suggestions – don't feel you need to use them all.

Summary notes

These give a summary of the knowledge required in each Key Area. You must read these carefully. You could use a highlighter pen to emphasise certain words or phrases and you might want to add your own notes in the margin in pencil. In these summary notes we have tried to give examples of the biology from life situations. There are diagrams to illustrate many of the key learning ideas. Some areas contain separate boxes, providing relevant examples relating human biology to modern life.

Key words

These are the terms introduced in the chapter that also appear in the glossary. They could be used to produce flash cards for each Key Area at a time – maybe better than doing the whole glossary at once!

Questions

These are designed to help you assess your knowledge and understanding of the key points and should be attempted on separate paper. Mark your own work using the answers provided towards the end of each Unit. Good performance in these tests is a sign of learning and progress in the course. The questions are in two parts:

Restricted response

This part has a set of restricted-response questions. Those worth 1 mark are usually straightforward and start with *name, state* or *give*. They can usually be answered quickly with a word or two. Those worth 2 marks are often more complex and require a description or explanation. They usually require two- or three-part answers.

Extended response

This includes two extended-response questions worth between 4 and 10 marks. These questions require detailed answers. In your exam the higher-mark questions will usually offer a choice.

Practice course assessment

Schools can have widely differing ways of assessing Units.

Although the practice assessment is designed to test *Units*, it can also give you an idea of your overall progress in the *course*. We have designed the assessments to be like mini course exams, with multiple-choice, restricted-response and extended-response questions.

We have included a practice assessment linked to each Unit. The questions are intended to replicate the types to expect in the course exam. They allow you to judge how you are doing overall. Most questions test knowledge and its application and some test scientific inquiry skills. The questions are provided in roughly the same proportion as in your final exam.

Give yourself a maximum of 60 minutes to complete the tests for Units 1 and 2 and about 30 minutes for Units 3 and 4, but don't worry if you go over this suggested time. Your timing will improve with further revision and practice.

Mark your own work using the answers provided at the end of each Unit. Although Units are not graded, you could grade your work as you go along to give you an idea of how well you are doing in the course. The table below shows a suggested grading system.

Mark out of 50 (Units 1 and 2)	Mark out of 25 (Units 3 and 4)	Grade
20–24 marks	10–12 marks	D
25–30 marks	13–15 marks	C
31–35 marks	16–18 marks	B
36+ marks	19+ marks	A

Skills of scientific inquiry: three approaches

This science skills section offers three different approaches to revising and improving your skills of scientific inquiry. In the first, we offer some tips and hints for tackling exam questions, grouped under each skill area. The second approach involves four practice questions in which all the individual skills have been identified for you so that you can work to your strengths and improve weaker areas. The third approach focuses on one investigation and provides questions about the thinking that should go into experimental design. Most students should use all three sections.

Your assignment

We give an introduction to the assignment, some suggestions for suitable topics and some information, with hints, to help you complete the task. On page xi–xii is a grid that summarises assignment criteria on which you can record evidence for your controlled assessment. There are some hints and tips there too.

Your exam

We give some hints on approaches to your final exams in general as well as more specific tips for your Higher Human Biology exam.

Glossary

We have given the meanings of the special terms that occur in the Assessment Specification for Higher Human Biology in the context of the Key Areas where they first appear in the book. You could use the glossary to make flash cards. A flash card has the term on one side and the definition on the other. Get together with a friend and use these cards to test each other.

Answers

Short answers are provided for all of the questions in this book. These are intended to replicate SQA standard answers but we have tried to keep the answers short, and any instructions simple, to make them easier to use – there will often be other acceptable answers.

Record of progress and self-evaluation

Use the grid below to record and evaluate your progress as you finish each of the four Units.

Feature	As an indicator of progress, I have...	Unit 1	Unit 2	Unit 3	Unit 4
Key points	used the minus (−), plus (+), star (*) system to identify areas of strength and areas requiring further attention for each of the key points sections				
Summary notes	read and thought about the summary notes for each Key Area and used highlighters to pick out the main points				
Hints & tips	read and thought about the hints and tips and exam technique advice for each Unit				
Key words	used the key words to make a set of flash cards for each Key Area				
Questions	answered, marked and corrected the restricted-response questions at the end of each Key Area of each Unit				
	answered, marked and corrected the extended-response questions at the end of each Key Area of each Unit				
Practice course assessment	answered and marked Section 1 of the practice assessment (5 or 10 multiple-choice marks for each Unit)				
	answered and marked Section 2 of the practice assessment (20 or 40 restricted- and extended-response marks for each Unit)				
Skills of scientific inquiry	read and thought about the tips given for each of the skills for each Unit				
	answered, marked and corrected the skills questions in each Unit				
	gone through and thought about the skills areas points in context and looked at the answers to these				
Glossary	used the glossary terms and definitions to create a set of flash cards for each Unit				

Assignment evidence checklist

Your preparation for the communication stage of your assignment should allow you to produce a report that has evidence of the following assessment points.

Assessment point/out of	Evidence	Check
Topic	My topic is related to a Key Area of Higher Human Biology	
Aim/1	My aim(s) have been clearly stated and I have described what is to be investigated	
Applying knowledge and understanding of human biology/5	I have clearly explained the topic I have researched, using correct biological terms and key ideas; I have made at least five correct statements from the Key Area	
Selecting information/2	My information has been selected from a variety of sources	
	This information includes some of the following: raw data from an experiment/practical activity, extracted tables, graphs, diagrams and text	
	The information I have selected is relevant, reliable and could give similar or different perspectives; it is sufficient to make a conclusion to fulfil my aim	
Processing and presenting information/4	My information is processed and presented in a variety of forms, using calculations and units where appropriate	
	This processing includes performing calculations accurately, plotting graphs from tables, populating a table from other sources and/or summarising referenced text	
	I have made it clear where my raw or extracted data/information came from	
	My presentation of processed data/information includes appropriate formats from the following: summary, graph, table, chart or diagram (including at least one graph, table, chart or diagram)	
	I have used suitable scales, units, headings and labels	
Analysing data/information/2	My analysis includes the interpretation of data/information used in the report in order to identify relationships and trends	
Concluding/1	My conclusion(s) are clearly stated and relate to the aim(s); they are supported by the data I have included	

➭

Hints & tips

Remember RALF!
R – Referencing in full
A – Accurate calculations and plotting
L – Labels, headings and units
F – Formats appropriate

Hints & tips

If using commercial spreadsheet software like Microsoft Excel, major and minor gridlines must be included.

Hints & tips

When commenting on reliability, a reason for the comment must be given such as large sample size used, repeated trials undertaken or sourced data has been peer-reviewed.

Hints & tips

When commenting on validity, a reason for the comment must be given such as only the independent variable was changed or stating that all the other variables were controlled.

Evaluating/3	I have included an evaluation of my individual sources and an evaluation of the investigation as a whole	
	My judgements of the investigation are based on criteria, which may include the following: ● Reliability of data/information ● Validity of sources ● Evaluation of experimental procedures	
Presentation/2	My report has an appropriate structure, with an informative title and headings	
	I have given full, traceable references to at least two sources used in the report in sufficient detail to allow someone else to find them again	

Hints & tips

References may be unbiased if sourced from a scientific journal, whereas it is possible that some commercial companies may be biased by the need to sell products.

Hints & tips

Citing other sources to back up data can improve its robustness.

Unit 1 Human cells

Division and differentiation of human cells

Key points !

1 Cellular **differentiation** is the process by which a cell develops more specialised functions by expressing the genes characteristic of that type of cell. ☐

2 **Stem cells** are unspecialised **somatic cells** that can divide to make copies of themselves (self-renew) and to make cells that differentiate into specialised cells of one or more types. ☐

3 The cells of the early embryo are **pluripotent** and can make almost all of the differentiated cell types of the body. ☐

4 The cells of the early embryo can be cultured in the laboratory to give a supply of **embryonic stem cells**. ☐

5 **Tissue (adult) stem cells** are **multipotent** as they can make almost all of the cell types found in a particular tissue type. ☐

6 Tissue (adult) stem cells are involved in the growth, repair and renewal of the cells found in that tissue. ☐

7 Tissue (adult) stem cells in bone marrow differentiate into **red blood cells**, **platelets** and the various forms of **phagocytes** and **lymphocytes**. ☐

8 Somatic cells are **diploid** cells and contain two sets of homologous chromosomes. ☐

9 Diploid cells in humans have 23 pairs of homologous chromosomes. ☐

10 During cell division the nucleus of a somatic cell divides by **mitosis** to maintain the diploid chromosome number. ☐

11 Somatic cells divide by mitosis to form more somatic cells, which differentiate to form different body tissue types such as **epithelial**, **connective**, **muscle** and **nervous tissues**. ☐

12 **Mutations** in somatic cells are not passed to offspring. ☐

13 **Germline cells** divide by mitosis to produce more germline cells or by **meiosis** to produce **haploid** gametes. ☐

14 Mutations in germline cells can be passed to offspring. ☐

15 Research and **therapeutic** uses of stem cells focus on areas such as the repair of damaged or diseased organs or tissues, for example corneal transplants and skin grafts for burns. ☐

16 Stem cells can also be used as model cells to study how diseases develop or for drug testing. ☐ ⇨

⇨
17 There are **ethical issues** related to stem cell use and its regulation. ☐
18 **Cancer cells** divide excessively to produce a mass of abnormal cells called a **tumour.** ☐
19 Cancer cells do not respond to **regulatory signals** and may fail to attach to each other. ☐
20 If cancer cells fail to attach to each other they can spread through the body to form **secondary tumours.** ☐

Summary notes

The human life cycle and cell division

The human life cycle is shown in Figure 1.1. The gametes (sperm and egg cells) are haploid, which means that they each contain one complete set of human chromosomes. The zygote is diploid – it contains two complete sets of chromosomes. The zygote grows and develops by the processes of mitosis and differentiation to produce the adult body made up of many diploid cells. Some of these are germline cells, which can also undergo meiosis to produce haploid gametes. The main body tissue types are epithelial, connective, muscle and nerve tissue. The body organs are formed from a variety of these tissues.

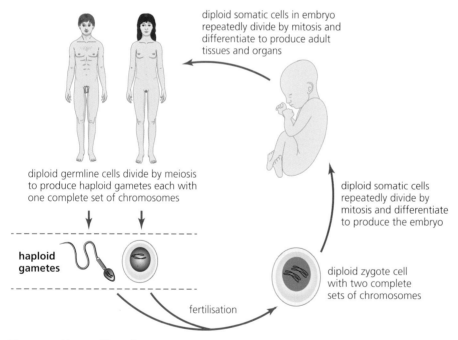

Figure 1.1 Human life cycle

Mitosis and cell division

Humans, like most living organisms, grow by producing new cells. Both somatic and germline cells can undergo mitosis. New cells are produced when the nuclei of diploid parent cells divide by mitosis and their cytoplasm is split into two.

Before mitosis, the DNA that makes up the chromosomes of a parent cell is copied exactly in a process called replication. Following replication, each chromosome appears as a double structure made up of two chromatids – each chromatid is a replicated chromosome. During mitosis, the chromatids are pulled apart and two new diploid daughter cells are produced.

Figure 1.2 shows a cell with a diploid number of four undergoing mitosis and cytoplasm splitting. Each daughter cell is diploid and identical to the parent cell because it has an exact copy of the parent cell's genetic information.

Germline cells and meiosis

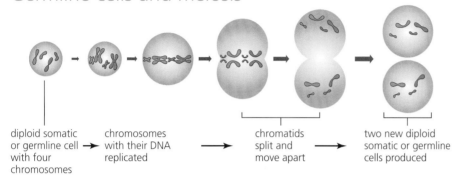

diploid somatic or germline cell with four chromosomes → chromosomes with their DNA replicated → chromatids split and move apart → two new diploid somatic or germline cells produced

Figure 1.2 Stages of mitosis in a cell with a diploid number of four

Hints & tips ⭐

There is more about replication of DNA in Key Area 1.2 on pages 13–14.

Germline cells are found in the ovaries of females and the testes of males. They can divide by mitosis to form more germline cells. They can also divide by another process called meiosis, which results in the formation of haploid gametes – eggs (ova) in ovaries and sperm in the testes.

The stages of meiosis are shown in Figure 1.3. Note that the cell is illustrated with a diploid number of four for clarity – diploid cells in humans have 46 chromosomes. The haploid gametes produced by meiosis are genetically different from each other, which leads to the variation we see in the human population.

Hints & tips ⭐

Try using eight pieces of drinking straw or wool and some sticky tape to make four model chromosomes – use them to practise the chromosome movements in mitosis and meiosis.

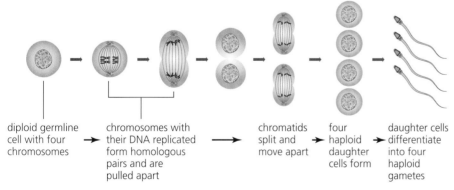

diploid germline cell with four chromosomes → chromosomes with their DNA replicated form homologous pairs and are pulled apart → chromatids split and move apart → four haploid daughter cells form → daughter cells differentiate into four haploid gametes

Figure 1.3 Stages of meiosis in a male germline cell with a diploid number of four

Cellular differentiation

The cell is the basic unit of human body structure. Different cells become specialised to carry out different functions through the process of differentiation. This process depends on the control of gene expression. Specialised cells express the genes characteristic of that cell type.

A human muscle cell expresses or switches on human muscle cell genes and therefore human muscle cells produce human muscle cell proteins. This idea is shown in Figure 1.4.

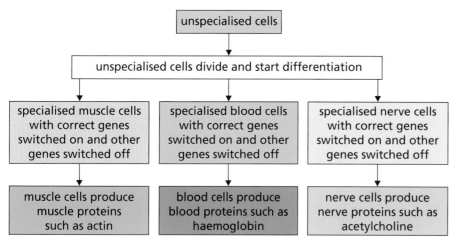

Figure 1.4 Flow chart to show differentiation in human cells

The result of differentiation is a variety of cells specialised for different functions, as shown by the examples in Figure 1.5.

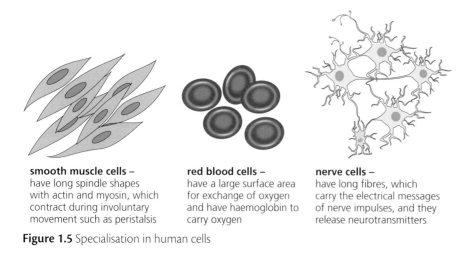

smooth muscle cells – have long spindle shapes with actin and myosin, which contract during involuntary movement such as peristalsis

red blood cells – have a large surface area for exchange of oxygen and have haemoglobin to carry oxygen

nerve cells – have long fibres, which carry the electrical messages of nerve impulses, and they release neurotransmitters

Figure 1.5 Specialisation in human cells

Hints & tips

There is more about
- *muscle cells in Key Area 1.8 on pages 48–50*
- *blood cells in Key Area 4.2 on pages 176–179*
- *nerve cells in Key Area 3.3 on pages 150–154.*

Specialisation of cells leads to the formation of a variety of tissues and organs.

Tissues

A living tissue is made from a group of cells with a similar structure and function, which all work together to do a particular job. There are four basic types of human tissue: epithelial, connective, muscle and nervous tissue, as shown in Figure 1.6.

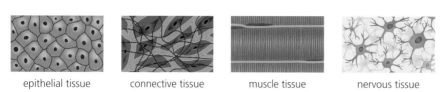

epithelial tissue   connective tissue   muscle tissue   nervous tissue

Figure 1.6 Variety of human tissues

The following table shows the location and specialised functions of the different tissues.

Human tissue	Location	Specialised function
Epithelial	Lines tubes, cavities and surfaces of structures throughout the human body; many glands contain epithelial cells	Secretion, protection, absorption, sensitivity
Connective	Found throughout the body, including in the central nervous system; located in between other tissues; examples include fatty tissue, blood and bone	Support, connection and separation of different types of tissue and organs of the body; specialised functions include storage and defence
Muscle	Makes up muscles of the body including skeletal muscle, the heart, and the smooth muscle in the digestive system	Contract and relax to bring about various movements including locomotion, heartbeat and peristalsis
Nerve	Makes up the nervous system – the brain and spinal cord in the central nervous system and the branching peripheral nerves	Allows rapid electrical processing and communication to control other body functions

Organs

An organ is made up of a group of different tissues working together to perform a particular function. Different organs carry out different functions. Examples of organs in humans include the heart and brain.

Organ systems

An organ system is made up of a group of different organs that work together to do a particular job. Examples of organ systems in humans include the circulatory system and nervous system, as shown in Figure 1.7.

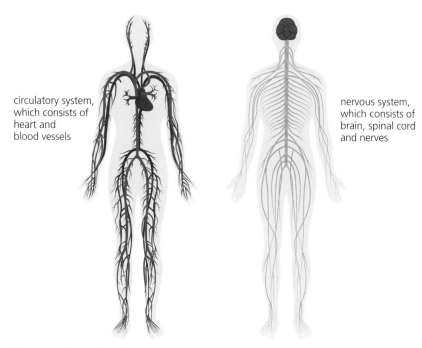

circulatory system, which consists of heart and blood vessels

nervous system, which consists of brain, spinal cord and nerves

Figure 1.7 Examples of human systems

Stem cells and their therapeutic use

Human stem cells are relatively unspecialised somatic cells. They can divide to produce cells that can differentiate into various cell types and more stem cells. In early embryos, embryonic stem cells are pluripotent, which means they can differentiate into all cell types that make up the adult organism, as shown in Figure 1.8. The inner cell mass of an early embryo at the blastocyst stage contains the pluripotent stem cells. These cells can self-renew, under the right conditions in the laboratory, to produce a supply of embryonic stem cells.

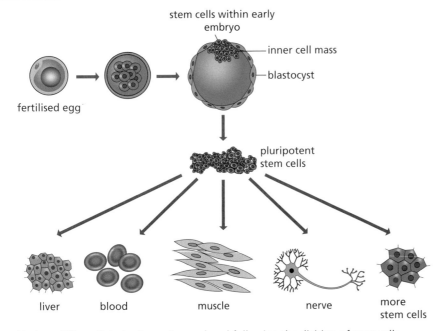

Various differentiated cells can be produced following the division of stem cells.

Figure 1.8 Embryonic stem cells

In adults, stem cells within tissues are multipotent, which means they can differentiate to replace damaged cells of the type found in that particular tissue, as shown in Figure 1.9.

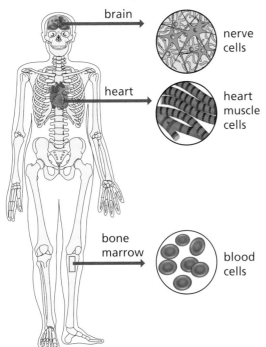

Figure 1.9 Tissue (adult) stem cells

Tissue (adult) stem cells in bone marrow differentiate into blood cells. There are several different types, including red blood cells, platelets and the various forms of phagocyte and lymphocyte, as shown in Figure 1.10.

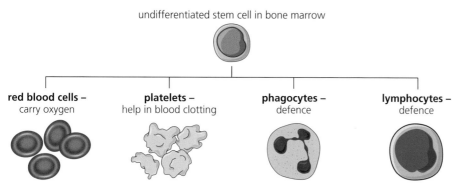

undifferentiated stem cell in bone marrow

red blood cells –
carry oxygen

platelets –
help in blood clotting

phagocytes –
defence

lymphocytes –
defence

Figure 1.10 Differentiated blood cells

Stem cell research

Stem cell research provides information on how cell processes such as growth, differentiation and gene regulation work. Stem cells can be used therapeutically to repair damaged or diseased organs and tissue. Current uses include corneal and skin grafts. They can also be used as model cells to study how diseases develop or for drug testing.

There are various ethical issues raised by stem cell research. The following table summarises some of these issues.

Ethical question	Notes
Is the prevention of suffering more important than the duty to preserve human life?	Embryonic stem cell research gives us a moral dilemma. It forces us to choose between two moral principles important to humans: the duty to prevent or ease suffering and the duty to respect the value of human life.
Is there a possibility of stem cells being used eugenically?	Embryonic stem cells might be used to change the body characteristics of already healthy and well individuals.
Could stem cells become part of a commercial trade in biological material?	It is possible that stem cells might be bought and sold commercially, and treatment could become subject to the ability of an individual to pay.

Embryonic stem cell research could lead to new medical treatments, which could save human lives and relieve human suffering. On the other hand, to obtain embryonic stem cells, an early-stage embryo has to be destroyed, meaning the loss of a potential human life. Stem cell research is strictly regulated. For example, researchers must be granted a licence to use stem cells, embryos cannot be used beyond 14 days of development and human embryos cannot be implanted into another species.

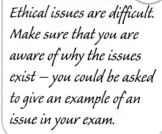

Hints & tips

There is more about
- phagocytes and lymphocytes in Key Areas 4.1 and 4.2 on pages 173 and 176–179
- platelets in Key Area 2.7 on page 108.

Hints & tips

Ethical issues are difficult. Make sure that you are aware of why the issues exist – you could be asked to give an example of an issue in your exam.

Cancer cells

Cancer cells are abnormal cells that do not respond to regulatory signals in the body and so avoid being destroyed by the immune system. They can divide rapidly and excessively to produce a mass of abnormal cells called a tumour. Normal cells are attached to each other and their surroundings in the body, but sometimes cancer cells fail to attach to each other and spread round the body in the bloodstream to form secondary tumours, as shown in Figure 1.11.

Hints & tips ⭐

There is more about inherited mutation and disease in Key Area 1.4 on pages 24–27.

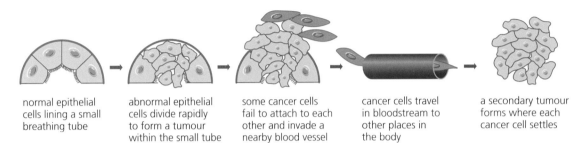

normal epithelial cells lining a small breathing tube

abnormal epithelial cells divide rapidly to form a tumour within the small tube

some cancer cells fail to attach to each other and invade a nearby blood vessel

cancer cells travel in bloodstream to other places in the body

a secondary tumour forms where each cancer cell settles

Figure 1.11 Stages of tumour and secondary tumour formation

Mutation

Mutations are changes in genetic information. Mutations in somatic cells are passed to cells that are produced when the somatic cell divides. These mutations are not passed onto offspring and so only affect the individual involved. An example could be a skin cancer that arises in a somatic skin cell, which divides many times to produce a tumour.

Mutations can arise in germline cells or be present in the germline cells of individuals with a specific mutation already present. Mutations present in germline cells can be passed onto gametes and so could be inherited by offspring. Genetic diseases such as sickle cell disease and haemophilia are inherited in families because copies of the mutated gene involved are found in gametes.

Hints & tips ⭐

Although a mutation carried in a gamete can be passed to offspring if that gamete is fertilised, the mutation could have arisen at a much earlier stage, and have been passed repeatedly down several generations of a family.

Key words

Cancer cell – grows and divides in an unregulated way to produce a tumour
Connective tissue – tissue that supports, connects or separates other body tissues
Differentiation – changes to cells that allow them to specialise for different functions
Diploid – refers to a cell having two sets of chromosomes
Embryonic stem cells – stem cells from embryos that can divide and become any type of cell
Epithelial tissue – tissue that lines tubes and surfaces within the body
Ethical issue – issue affecting human attitudes and decisions regarding various choices
Germline cell – cell that can give rise to gametes
Haploid – describes a cell having one set of chromosomes (e.g. gametes)
Lymphocyte – type of white blood cell involved in a specific immune response
Meiosis – type of cell division resulting in four haploid gametes
Mitosis – division of the nucleus of somatic or germline cells, giving two diploid daughter cells
Multipotent stem cell – stem cell that has the potential to make almost all cell types found within a particular tissue
Muscle tissue – tissue making up skeletal, smooth and cardiac muscle
Mutation – random change to a DNA sequence

⇨

Nervous tissue – tissue making up the nervous system

Phagocyte – defence white blood cell that can engulf and destroy foreign material

Platelets – blood cell fragments important in blood clotting

Pluripotent stem cell – stem cell that has the potential to make almost all differentiated cell types of the body

Red blood cell – blood cell containing haemoglobin, which can carry oxygen in the bloodstream

Regulatory signal – molecular signal that can be received by a cell to modify its activity

Secondary tumour – cancer formed from a cell transported from a primary tumour

Somatic cell – body cell that divides by mitosis to form more body cells

Stem cell – unspecialised cell that can divide and then differentiate

Therapeutic – used as part of a medical therapy

Tissue (adult) stem cells – stem cells from tissue that divide and differentiate to become cells of that tissue

Tumour – collection of cancer cells produced by excessive, uncontrolled cell division

Questions ❓

Restricted response (structured in 1- or 2-mark parts)

1 Describe what is meant by the term differentiation as applied to cells. (2)
2 Name the **four** main types of body tissue that form when somatic cells differentiate in human embryos. (2)
3 Identify the types of cell that may carry mutations that:
  a) cannot be passed to offspring (1)
  b) can be passed to offspring. (1)
4 Give **two** characteristics of human cancer cells. (2)
5 Describe how secondary cancer tumours form in the body. (2)
6 Describe **one** ethical dilemma related to the use of embryonic stem cells. (2)

Extended response (4–9 marks each)

7 Give an account of stem cells under the following headings:
  a) Embryonic and adult stem cells (5)
  b) Stem cell research and the therapeutic use of stem cells (3)
8 Compare the processes of mitosis and meiosis. (6)
9 Give an account of cells under the following headings:
  a) Somatic cells (3)
  b) Germline cells (2)
Answers are on page 51.

Structure and replication of DNA

Key points !

1 Genetic information is inherited. ☐
2 **DNA** is a substance that encodes genetic information of heredity in a chemical language. ☐
3 DNA is a very long double-stranded molecule in the shape of a **double helix**. ☐
4 Each strand is made up from chemical units called **nucleotides**. ☐
5 A nucleotide is made up of three parts: a **deoxyribose** sugar, a **phosphate** and a **base**. ☐
6 Deoxyribose molecules have five carbon atoms, which are numbered 1 to 5. ☐
7 The phosphate of one nucleotide is joined to its carbon 5 (5′) and linked to the carbon 3 (3′) of the next nucleotide in the strand to form a **3′–5′** sugar–phosphate backbone. ☐
8 There are four different DNA bases called **adenine** (A), **guanine** (G), **thymine** (T) and **cytosine** (C). ☐
9 Genetic information is encoded in the sequence of bases along the length of one of the strands of a DNA molecule. ☐
10 The nucleotides of one strand of DNA are linked to the nucleotides on the second strand through their bases – the bases form pairs joining the strands. ☐
11 Bases pair in a complementary way: adenine always pairs with thymine and guanine always pairs with cytosine. ☐
12 Base pairs are held together by **hydrogen bonds**. ☐
13 Each strand has a **sugar–phosphate backbone** with a 3′ end that starts with a deoxyribose molecule and a 5′ end that finishes with a phosphate. ☐
14 The two strands of a DNA molecule run in opposite directions and are said to be **antiparallel** to each other. ☐
15 Chromosomes consist of tightly coiled DNA, which is packaged with associated proteins. ☐
16 DNA molecules replicate prior to cell division. ☐
17 **Replication** is the process by which DNA molecules can direct the synthesis of identical copies of themselves. ☐
18 DNA unwinds and unzips to form two **template strands**. ☐
19 Replication starts at several places along the DNA molecule at the same time. ☐
20 The enzyme **DNA polymerase** adds complementary DNA nucleotides to the 3′ end of a DNA strand. ☐
21 DNA polymerase requires **primers** to start replication. ☐
22 Primers are short, complementary sequences of nucleotides that allow binding of DNA polymerase. ☐
23 The 3′–5′ **lead strand** is replicated continuously in the direction from its 3′ end towards its 5′ end. ☐
24 Nucleotides are added as fragments on the **lagging strand**. ☐
25 The replicated fragments on the lagging strand are joined together by a **ligase** enzyme. ☐

Summary notes

Deoxyribonucleic acid

Function of DNA

Genetic information is coded into the chemical language of DNA (deoxyribonucleic acid). This genetic information gives cells the ability to synthesise specific proteins, which determine the cell's structure and allow it to control metabolism. Copies of a cell's genetic information are inherited by daughter cells when it divides.

Structure of DNA

Each DNA molecule is very long and has two strands coiled into the shape of a double helix. Each strand of the double helix is made up from nucleotides. Figure 1.12 shows a single DNA nucleotide made up of a deoxyribose sugar to which a phosphate group and a nitrogenous base are attached. The carbon atoms of the deoxyribose sugar are numbered from 1 to 5, as shown in the diagram.

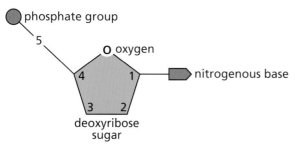

Figure 1.12 One nucleotide of DNA with the carbon atoms of the deoxyribose sugar numbered

Nucleotides are linked by their deoxyribose sugars and phosphates to form a strand with a sugar–phosphate backbone, as shown in Figure 1.13.

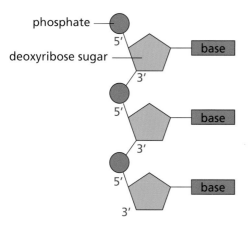

Figure 1.13 Short strand of DNA, showing three nucleotides linked by a 3'–5' sugar–phosphate backbone

Two strands are connected by hydrogen bonding between complementary pairs of bases. The base adenine (A) always pairs with thymine (T) and guanine (G) always pairs with cytosine (C), making the two strands complementary to each other, as shown in Figure 1.14. Note that the strands run in opposite directions (antiparallel) depending on the bonding through the carbon atoms of the sugar–phosphate backbone. One strand has deoxyribose **(3')** at one end of the molecule, but its complementary strand has a phosphate group **(5')** at the same end of the molecule.

Hints & tips

The DNA strands are a bit like lanes of traffic on a road – they are essentially the same but run in opposite directions. This is what is meant by the term antiparallel.

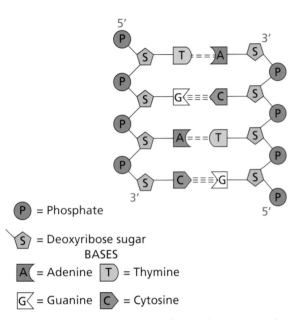

P = Phosphate

S = Deoxyribose sugar

BASES

A = Adenine T = Thymine

G = Guanine C = Cytosine

Figure 1.14 Short double strand of DNA, showing complementary base pairing and its antiparallel structure

Figure 1.15 summarises the structural features of a DNA molecule.

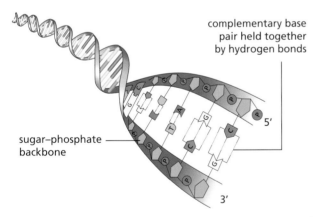

complementary base pair held together by hydrogen bonds

sugar–phosphate backbone

5'

3'

Figure 1.15 DNA, showing the double helix, sugar–phosphate backbones, complementary base pairing and the antiparallel strands

Organisation of DNA in chromosomes

In the nuclei of cells, chromosomes consist of tightly coiled DNA, which is packaged with associated proteins that help to keep the DNA strands untangled, as shown in Figure 1.16.

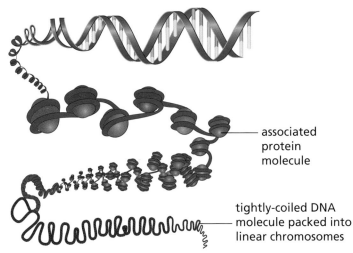

Figure 1.16 Organisation of DNA in chromosomes

associated
protein
molecule

tightly-coiled DNA
molecule packed into
linear chromosomes

Replication of DNA

DNA is the hereditary material of cells. DNA can make precise copies of itself by a process called replication. DNA replicates before cell division and copies are passed to daughter cells.

Stages in replication of DNA

The double helix of DNA is unwound by an enzyme, and the hydrogen bonds that connect the two strands are unzipped. The unwinding and unzipping forms a replication fork. Primers are short complementary sequences of nucleotides that allow DNA polymerase to bind. A primer joins the end of the 3'–5' leading template strand and DNA polymerase adds free DNA nucleotides to synthesise a complementary strand continuously.

On the lagging strand, primers are added one by one into the replication fork as it widens. DNA nucleotides are added to form fragments. These fragments are then joined by DNA ligase to form a complete complementary strand. The process requires energy, which is supplied by ATP produced by the cell's respiration. The replication process is summarised in Figure 1.17.

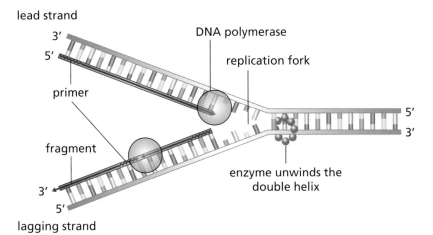

lead strand

DNA polymerase

replication fork

primer

fragment

enzyme unwinds the
double helix

lagging strand

Figure 1.17 Replication of DNA

Importance of DNA replication

When the DNA in a chromosome is being replicated many replication forks are formed at the same time. As a result, the DNA of whole chromosomes is replicated quickly and precisely, as shown in Figure 1.18.

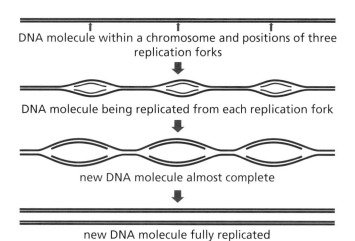

DNA molecule within a chromosome and positions of three replication forks

DNA molecule being replicated from each replication fork

new DNA molecule almost complete

new DNA molecule fully replicated

Figure 1.18 Multi-replication forks

This is important because it ensures that precise copies of the genetic material are available for cells undergoing mitosis and meiosis, and are passed on from cell to cell and from generation to generation. Figure 1.1 on page 2 shows the importance of DNA replication in the life cycle.

Key words

3'–5' – strand of nucleic acid running from a sugar to a phosphate
Adenine (A) – DNA base that pairs with thymine
Antiparallel – parallel strands in DNA that run in opposite directions in terms of chemical polarity
Base – nitrogenous substance that is a component of DNA nucleotides
Cytosine (C) – DNA base that pairs with guanine
Deoxyribose – pentose sugar that is a component of DNA nucleotides
DNA – deoxyribonucleic acid; molecule that holds the genetic code in living organisms
DNA polymerase – enzyme that unwinds and unzips DNA; adds free nucleotides during DNA replication
Double helix – the three-dimensional shape of a DNA molecule
Guanine (G) – DNA base that pairs with cytosine
Hydrogen bond – weak chemical link joining complementary base pairs in DNA
Lagging strand – DNA strand that is replicated in fragments
Lead strand – DNA strand that is replicated continuously
Ligase – enzyme that joins DNA fragments
Nucleotide – component of DNA consisting of a deoxyribose sugar, a phosphate group and a base
Phosphate – component of DNA nucleotide
Primer – short complementary strand of DNA
Replication – formation of copies of DNA molecules
Sugar–phosphate backbone – strongly bonded strand of DNA
Template strand – DNA strand on which a complementary copy is made
Thymine (T) – DNA base that pairs with adenine

Questions ?

Restricted response (structured in 1- or 2-mark parts)

1 DNA is a complex double-stranded molecule made up from nucleotide units.
   a) Describe the shape of a DNA molecule. (1)
   b) Describe how the two strands of DNA are held together. (2)
   c) Name the **three** components that make up a nucleotide. (2)
   d) Explain what is meant by the following terms, as applied to DNA structure:
      (i) complementary base pairing (1)
      (ii) antiparallel. (1)
2 Describe how DNA is organised in chromosomes. (2)

Extended response (4–9 marks each)

3 Give an account of the replication of a molecule of DNA. (7)

Answers are on page 51–52.

Key points ⚠

1 Genes are encoded into DNA and the genetic code is found in all forms of life. ☐

2 Human genes have **introns** (non-coding regions) and **exons** (coding regions). ☐

3 Genes are transcribed and translated during gene expression. ☐

4 Only a fraction of the genes in a cell are expressed. ☐

5 **Gene expression** is controlled by the regulation of **transcription** and **translation**. ☐

6 Gene expression can be influenced by intracellular and extracellular environmental factors. ☐

7 Genes are expressed to produce proteins. ☐

8 Gene expression results in the **phenotype** of an individual human. ☐

9 Proteins have a variety of structures and molecular shapes, which allows a wide range of functions. ☐

10 Proteins are formed from **polypeptides**, which are chains of amino acids held together by **peptide bonds** and folded in various ways. ☐

11 Gene expression involves three types of **RNA**, which is similar to DNA. ☐

12 RNA is single stranded, its nucleotides contain ribose instead of deoxyribose and the base **uracil (U)** replaces the thymine found in DNA. ☐

13 DNA in the nucleus is transcribed to produce **messenger RNA (mRNA)**, which carries a copy of the genetic code. ☐

14 In transcription, **RNA polymerase** moves along DNA, unwinding the double helix and aligning RNA nucleotides by complementary base pairing to form a **primary transcript**. ☐

15 Introns are removed from the primary transcript and the exons spliced to form a mature mRNA transcript. ☐

16 Alternative **RNA splicing** allows different mRNAs to be formed from the same primary transcript depending on which RNA segments are treated as exons and introns. ☐

17 Triplets of bases on mRNA are called **codons**. ☐

18 Translation of mRNA results in the production of a polypeptide. ☐

19 Most codons code for specific **amino acids**, but there are also start and stop codons, which start and stop translation. ☐

20 **Ribosomes** are made from **ribosomal RNA (rRNA)** and proteins. ☐

21 mRNA carries a copy of the DNA code from the nucleus to the ribosomes, where it is translated. ☐

22 **Transfer RNA (tRNA)** folds because of base pairing and forms a triplet **anticodon** site and an **attachment site** for a specific amino acid. ☐

23 Amino acids are carried by specific tRNA molecules. ☐

24 tRNA anticodons align to their complementary codons on mRNA. ☐

25 tRNA molecules deliver amino acids in sequence; these are then joined together by peptide bonds to form polypeptides. ☐ ⇨

⇨

26 Following polypeptide formation, tRNA exits the ribosome to collect further amino acids. ☐

27 **Post-translational modification** allows different proteins to be created by cutting and combining polypeptide chains or by adding phosphate or carbohydrate groups to the protein. ☐

28 As a result of alternative RNA splicing and post-translational modification, one gene can express many proteins. ☐

Summary notes

The genetic code

The base sequence of DNA forms the genetic code. This code is found in all forms of life, suggesting that all life evolved from a common ancestor.

Genes are the units of genetic code that make up the genotype of an organism, and are expressed to produce proteins, which form the structure and control the functions of the organism. The phenotype of an individual is the result of the proteins produced by the expression of its genes. Only a fraction of the genes in any cell are expressed. Figure 1.19 summarises how the genetic code results in the phenotype of an individual.

Hints & tips ⭐

There is more about the idea of evolutionary relationships in Key Area 1.5 on page 30.

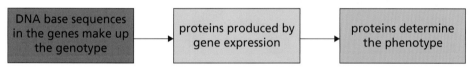

Figure 1.19 Flow chart showing how the genetic code produces the phenotype

Stages of gene expression

Genes are expressed in two main stages – transcription and translation. In transcription a copy of the gene, in the form of a molecule called mRNA, is created. In translation, a specific sequence of amino acids is built up using the mRNA codes, as shown in Figure 1.20. In human cells, post-translational modifications produce the final structure of the protein.

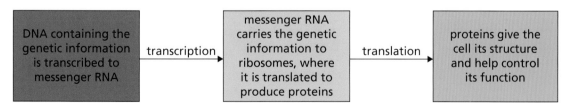

Figure 1.20 Relationships between the substances involved in gene expression

Ribonucleic acid (RNA)

Gene expression relies on various forms of RNA. RNA is very similar to DNA, but has differences mainly in the nucleotides that make it up. DNA nucleotides have deoxyribose sugar while RNA nucleotides have ribose. DNA nucleotide bases are adenine, thymine, guanine and cytosine. In RNA the base uracil (U) replaces thymine. Uracil also pairs with adenine

17

in complementary base pairing. RNA is single stranded, although there can be some base pairing of nucleotides. RNA nucleotides are shown in Figure 1.21.

There are three types of RNA. Messenger RNA (mRNA) carries a complementary copy of the genetic code from the DNA in the nucleus to the ribosomes in the cytoplasm. Transfer RNA (tRNA) carries specific amino acids to ribosomes, where they can be assembled to form polypeptide chains. Ribosomal RNA (rRNA) is combined with proteins to make up the structure of ribosomes.

Transcription

In the first step, the enzyme RNA polymerase unwinds and unzips the double helix of the gene to be expressed and aligns free RNA nucleotides against the exposed DNA nucleotides of the template strand. Complementary base pairing ensures correct positioning of RNA nucleotides, which are then joined to form a primary transcript. The primary transcript is a complementary copy of the gene made up of groups of three bases called codons, as shown in Figure 1.22.

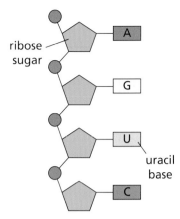

Figure 1.21 RNA nucleotides linked into a single strand and showing the differences from DNA nucleotides

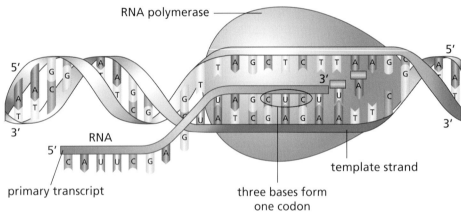

Figure 1.22 Formation of a primary transcript

Each primary transcript has introns and exons. Introns are non-coding regions and are removed from the primary transcript, leaving coding regions that are known as exons. The exons are then spliced together to form a mature mRNA transcript, as shown in Figure 1.23. Alternative splicing allows a primary transcript to form different mature mRNA molecules, depending on which sequences are treated as introns and which as exons. mRNA molecules move to the ribosomes to be translated.

Hints & tips

Introns are non-coding. Exons are coding regions that are expressed.

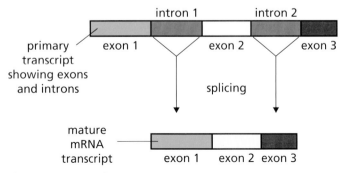

Figure 1.23 RNA splicing

Ribosomes and translation

Ribosomes made of rRNA and protein are found free in the cytoplasm of the cell or bound to the membranes of its endoplasmic reticulum (ER). A mature mRNA molecule binds onto a ribosome. tRNA molecules have a triplet of three bases called an anticodon and transport a specific amino acid to mRNA on the ribosomes. They align with the mRNA according to their anticodons, which are complementary to the codons of mRNA.

The amino acids that have been lined up bind through peptide bonds to form polypeptides. mRNA carries a start codon and a stop codon, which causes translation to start and to finish when the polypeptide is complete. The polypeptide then folds to form a protein, which is held in a three-dimensional shape by hydrogen bonds and other linkages. Translation is summarised in Figure 1.24.

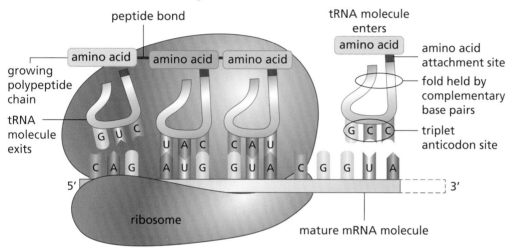

Figure 1.24 Translation of mRNA to form a polypeptide chain

Post-translational modification

Post-translational modification completes the formation of the protein by making changes to the chemical structure of the polypeptide chain. Figure 1.25 shows how the polypeptide chain of insulin is modified by the combining and cutting of the chain. Other post-translational modifications include the addition of phosphate or carbohydrate groups to a polypeptide chain.

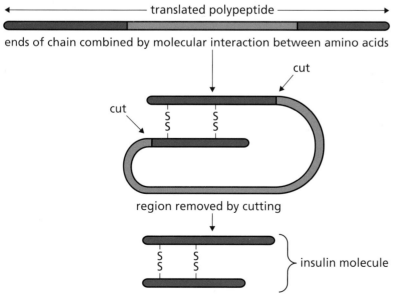

Figure 1.25 Post-translational modification of insulin

One gene, many proteins

A variety of proteins can be expressed from the same gene due to alternative RNA splicing and the various types of post-translational modification that can occur. This idea is summarised in Figure 1.26.

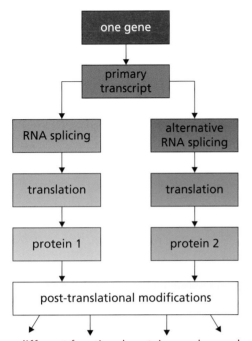

other different functional proteins can be produced

Figure 1.26 Production of different proteins from one gene

Regulation of gene expression

Some proteins, such as enzymes involved in respiration, are needed continuously in the life of cells so the genes that code for them are always switched on. Other proteins are only produced when needed and their production can be switched on and off by the regulation of the genes that code for them.

Gene expression can be influenced by the intracellular factors that make up the switching systems and extracellular factors such as hormones and amino acid supply. These factors can regulate both transcription and translation, as shown in the example in Figure 1.27, in which a specific gene is switched on. In the absence of the extracellular factors, or if the intracellular factors are not activated, the gene remains switched off and the protein is not produced.

Regulation of gene expression is important because it conserves cell resources and energy by producing proteins only when they are required.

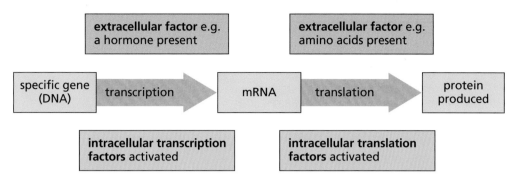

Figure 1.27 Control of gene expression by intracellular and extracellular factors

Key words

Amino acid – unit of polypeptide structure

Anticodon – sequence of three bases on tRNA that codes for a specific amino acid

Attachment site – site on a transfer RNA molecule to which a specific amino acid binds

Codon – sequence of three bases on mRNA that codes for a specific amino acid

Exon – sequence of DNA that codes for protein

Gene expression – transcription and translation of a gene to synthesise proteins

Intron – non-coding sequence of DNA

Messenger RNA (mRNA) – carries a copy of the DNA code from nucleus to ribosome

Peptide bond – strong chemical link between amino acids in the primary structure of a polypeptide

Phenotype – outward appearance of an organism

Polypeptide – short strand of amino acids

Post-translational modification – changes made to polypeptides following translation

Primary transcript – molecule made when DNA is transcribed

Ribosomal RNA (rRNA) – type of RNA that makes up ribosomes

Ribosome – site of protein synthesis; composed of rRNA and protein

RNA – ribonucleic acid; occurs in several forms in cells

RNA polymerase – enzyme involved in synthesis of primary transcripts from DNA

RNA splicing – joining of exons following the removal of introns from a primary transcript

Transcription – copying of DNA sequences to make a primary transcript

Transfer RNA (tRNA) – transfers specific amino acids to the mRNA on the ribosomes

Translation – production of a polypeptide at a ribosome using information encoded in mRNA

Uracil (U) – RNA base not found in DNA

Questions ❓

Restricted response (structured in 1- or 2-mark parts)

1 Give **two** ways by which the expression of a single gene can result in different proteins being produced. (2)
2 Give **two** structural differences between DNA and RNA molecules. (2)
3 Human genes are made up from base sequences known as introns and exons. State how introns and exons differ. (1)
4 Describe **two** post-translational modifications of polypeptides produced by human cells. (2)
5 Explain the importance of the regulation of gene expression. (1)

Extended response (4–9 marks each)

6 Give an account of gene expression under the following headings:
 a) Transcription of DNA (4)
 b) Translation of mature mRNA (4)

Answers are on page 52.

Genes and proteins in health and disease

Key points ❗

1. **Proteins** are made up from chains of amino acids called polypeptides. ☐
2. Polypeptide chains are held in their three-dimensional shapes by hydrogen bonds and other **molecular interactions** between individual amino acids. ☐
3. Protein function depends on the three-dimensional shapes of the protein's molecules. ☐
4. Protein functions include acting as structural units, enzymes, some hormones and antibodies. ☐
5. Mutations are random changes in genetic information. ☐
6. Mutations can alter genes or **chromosomes**. ☐
7. Mutations of genes result in no protein or an altered protein being expressed. ☐
8. Single gene mutations affect DNA nucleotide sequences and include **deletion, insertion** and **substitution** of nucleotides. ☐
9. Single nucleotide substitutions include **missense, nonsense** and **splice-site mutations**. ☐
10. Nucleotide insertions or deletions result in **frameshift mutations** or expansion of a **nucleotide sequence repeat**. ☐
11. Mutations are important in evolution. ☐
12. Mutations of regulatory sequences can alter gene expression. ☐
13. Splice-site mutations can alter post-transcription processing. ☐
14. Chromosome mutations that involve alterations to the structure of a chromosome include **duplication, deletion** (of genes) and **translocation**. ☐
15. Some human diseases, such as **haemophilia** and **sickle cell disease**, are caused by mutations. ☐

Summary notes

Structure and function of proteins

Protein molecules are polypeptide chains. A polypeptide is a chain of amino acids held together by peptide bonds. The polypeptide is folded to give a protein with a three-dimensional shape held in place by hydrogen bonds and other interactions. The shape of a protein is linked to its function. Protein functions include structural components of cells, enzymes, certain hormones and antibodies, as shown in the following table.

Protein group	Function	Example
Structural component of cells	Building block of cell structure	Actin and myosin form structural fibres in muscle cells, which allow contraction
Enzyme	Speeds up the rate of chemical reactions	Pepsin speeds up the breakdown of protein in the stomach during digestion
Hormone	Chemical messengers involved in regulation	Insulin is involved in the regulation of glucose levels in blood
Antibody	Defensive substance that provides immunity to specific diseases	Measles immunoglobulin specifically recognises measles antigens and renders them inactive

Mutation

Mutations are rare, random changes to DNA sequences. The following table shows different types of mutation and their effects.

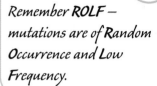

Hints & tips

Remember ROLF – mutations are of Random Occurrence and Low Frequency.

Mutation	Effect
...of genes	Changes the base order within a gene and so alters the amino acid sequence of the protein coded for
...of chromosomes	Affects the structure or number of chromosomes present in cells

Hints & tips

Single gene mutations are a bit like spelling errors in the genetic code.

Gene mutations

Gene mutations occur within genes and involve changes to the DNA nucleotide sequence, which alters the sequence of bases on the DNA.

The following table provides descriptions of various gene mutations and their effects.

Hints & tips

Remember SID – Substitution, Insertion and Deletion.

Single gene mutation	Description	Example of nucleotide base sequence change	Impact on protein structure
Substitution	One nucleotide removed from a DNA sequence and replaced by another with a different base	Normal sequence: ...ATGTCCATG... Following mutation: ...ATG**G**CCATG...	Minor impact since there is a maximum of one amino acid changed in the protein structure – called **mis**sense Major impact could result if mutation results in production or loss of a stop codon – called **non**sense
Insertion	Additional nucleotide added into a DNA sequence	Normal sequence: ...ATGTCCATG... Following mutation: ...ATGT**G**CCATG...	Major effect on protein likely since all amino acids coded for after the mutation could be affected Sometimes called frameshift mutations
Deletion	Nucleotide removed from a DNA sequence but not replaced with another	Normal sequence: ...ATGTCCATG... Following mutation: ...ATG_CCATG...	

Mutation in nucleotide sequence repeats

Nucleotide sequence repeats occur throughout the human genome and consist of multiple copies of sequences of nucleotides of various lengths, from one nucleotide to many. Insertion can cause expansion of a sequence repeat and some of these can cause phenotypic effects.

Examples

Fragile X syndrome

Fragile X syndrome is caused by expansion of the CGG DNA triplet repeat in a gene found on the X chromosome. Fragile X causes intellectual disability, especially in boys.

Huntington's disease

Huntington's disease (HD) is caused by expansion of a CAG DNA triplet repeat in a gene that codes for a protein whose absence can lead to the neurological degeneration linked to HD in humans.

Splice-site mutation

A single gene mutation at a splice site could result in an intron being left in the mature mRNA and so contributing to protein structure. This could result in an altered protein that would not function normally, as shown in Figure 1.28.

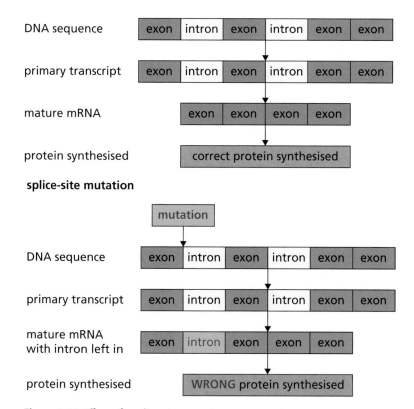

Figure 1.28 Effect of a splice-site mutation on a protein

The effect of gene mutations on health

Some mutations cause either the absence of a protein or presence of a protein that does not function. Examples of diseases caused by these types of mutation are sickle cell disease (SCD) and haemophilia.

Examples

Sickle cell disease (SCD)

Haemoglobin is a protein that carries oxygen in the blood. Each person has two copies of the haemoglobin gene, each of which codes for half of their haemoglobin.

About 5000 years ago, a single gene mutation of the gene is thought to have arisen in Africa. This involved a substitution, which resulted in a form of haemoglobin with one amino acid different from the normal form. This abnormal haemoglobin leads to the collapsing of the red blood cells that contain it when conditions become acidic during exercise. The collapsed cells stick in narrow blood vessels. The result is the breathlessness and pain that are symptoms of sickle cell disease.

Individuals with two copies of the mutation have a seriously debilitating condition called sickle cell anaemia. Individuals with one copy of the normal gene and one copy of the mutated gene have sickle cell trait and show less severe symptoms of the disease. In some parts of Africa, it is an advantage to have sickle cell trait because it protects individuals from malaria parasites. The parasites live inside red blood cells and their acidic waste products cause cells to collapse and target them for destruction by white blood cells. The mutation is now common in parts of Africa and demonstrates the importance of mutation in evolution.

Haemophilia

Haemophilia is a group of sex-linked, inherited conditions that impair the body's ability to control blood clotting or coagulation, which normally stops the bleeding when a blood vessel is broken. Haemophilia A involves deficiency of the blood clotting protein called factor VIII. It is the commonest form of the condition and occurs in about 1 in 5000–10 000 male births. A person with haemophilia can bleed excessively from a minor cut and this could be life-threatening. Modern treatment includes injections of factor VIII.

Chromosome mutation

Some mutations affect the structure of chromosomes present in the cells of living organisms. These arise when pieces of one chromosome break off and are lost or join back into the chromosome complement in a different way. Chromosome mutations are often lethal because of the substantial changes they make to genetic information. However, some give rise to serious health implications, as shown in the following table.

Hints & tips

You are not required to know about the effects on health of a specific mutation, but it's probably worth learning about SCD and haemophilia because you could use the information in an extended response. The inheritance of these conditions is dealt with in Key Area 2.4 on page 89.

Chromosome mutation	Description	Diagram	Example or effect
Deletion	Detached genes are lost completely	A B C D E F G H →deletion→ A B C E F G H	Cri du chat syndrome in humans involves a loss of part of chromosome 5
Duplication	A set of genes from one chromosome becomes attached to its matching chromosome, leading to repeated genes	A B C D E F G H →duplication→ A B C B C D E F G H	Some duplications can be highly detrimental; others can be important in evolution
Translocation	Detached genes become attached to a different chromosome in the complement	A B C D E F G H M N O C D E F G H →translocation→ M N O P Q R A B P Q R	One type of Down syndrome in humans is caused in this way

Key words

Chromosome – rod-like structure that contains the genetic material of an organism encoded into DNA

Deletion (of genes) – chromosome mutation in which a sequence of genes is lost from a chromosome

Deletion (of nucleotides) – single-gene mutation involving removal of a nucleotide from a sequence

Duplication – chromosome mutation in which a sequence of genes is repeated on a chromosome

Frameshift mutation – gene mutation in which all amino acids coded for after the mutation are affected

Haemophilia – inherited disease in which blood clotting fails or is very slow

Insertion – single-gene mutation in which an additional nucleotide is placed into a sequence

Missense – substitution mutation; a single nucleotide change results in a codon for a different amino acid

Molecular interactions – various chemical links (e.g. sulfur bridge, ionic bond, van der Waals forces) joining amino acids and giving protein molecules their shape

Nonsense – substitution mutation in which a codon is changed to a stop codon, shortening the resulting protein

Nucleotide sequence repeat – repeated sequence of nucleotides, which can be expanded by some gene mutations

Protein – large molecule made up of chains of amino acids linked by peptide bonds

Sickle cell disease – disease caused by a substitution mutation in the gene encoding haemoglobin

Splice-site mutation – mutation at a point where coding and non-coding regions meet in a section of DNA

Substitution – single-gene mutation in which one nucleotide is replaced by another

Translocation – chromosome mutation in which part of a chromosome becomes attached to another

Hints & tips

Remember **DDT** –
Deletion, Duplication and
Translocation.

Questions ?

Restricted response (structured in 1- or 2-mark parts)

1   Proteins are chains of amino acids folded into three-dimensional shapes.
    a) Name the bonds that hold the amino acids together in sequence.   (1)
    b) Give **one** example of a bond that holds the chains of amino acids in three-dimensional shapes.   (1)
2   The table below shows the effects of some gene mutations on base sequences in DNA.

Original base sequence of gene	Number	Effect of mutation on base sequence
...TTACGCTAC...	1	...TACGCTAC...
	2	...TTACGGCTAC...
	3	...TGACGCTAC...

   a) Name mutations 1–3.   (2)
   b) Describe the effects of mutations 1 and 3 on the structure of the polypeptide coded for by the original gene.   (2)
3   Give the meaning of the following types of mutation:
   a) missense mutation   (1)
   b) splice-site mutation.   (1)

Extended response (4–9 marks each)

4   Describe the effects of named single gene mutations on the amino acid sequences in proteins they code for.   (7)
5   Give an account of the types of structural mutation to chromosomes and their effects.   (4)
6   Give an account of the effects of mutation on health under the following headings:
   a) Sickle cell disease   (3)
   b) Haemophilia   (3)

Answers are on page 52–53.

Human genomics

Key points !

1 The **genome** of an organism is the genetic information that is encoded into its DNA and can be inherited by its offspring. ☐

2 A genome is defined as the genes that code for proteins and other DNA sequences that do not code for proteins. ☐

3 DNA can be sequenced to determine the order of bases along its molecule. ☐

4 Comparison of **sequence data** requires **bioinformatics**, which involves computer and statistical analysis. ☐

5 **Systematics** compares human **genome sequence data** and the genomes of other species to provide information on evolutionary relationships and origins. ☐

6 **Personalised medicine** is based on an individual's genome. ☐

7 Analysis of an individual's genome can lead to personalised medicine through understanding of the genetic component of disease risk. ☐

8 The **polymerase chain reaction (PCR)** is a laboratory technique for the amplification of DNA. ☐

9 PCR uses primers complementary to specific target sequences at the two ends of the DNA region to be amplified. ☐

10 In PCR, heating separates the two strands of the DNA to be amplified. ☐

11 In PCR, the separated strands are then cooled to allow primers to bind to target sequences. ☐

12 **Heat-tolerant DNA polymerase** (Taq polymerase) replicates the region of DNA that has been primed. ☐

13 Repeated cycles of heating and cooling amplify the region of DNA. ☐

14 **DNA probes** are short, single-stranded fragments of DNA that are complementary to a specific DNA sequence. ☐

15 In PCR, arrays of DNA probes are used to detect the presence of specific sequences in strands of DNA. ☐

16 A cycle of PCR doubles the number of copies of a region of DNA. ☐

17 Fragments of DNA can be separated by **gel electrophoresis**. ☐

18 **Fluorescent labelling** allows detection of DNA fragments amplified by PCR and separated by electrophoresis. ☐

19 In **DNA profiling**, individuals can be identified through comparison of regions of their genome, which have variable numbers of **repetitive DNA sequences**. ☐

Summary notes

The human genome

The genome of a human individual is the total genetic information encoded into the base sequence of DNA. The genome contains those sequences that code for protein (genes) and those that do not. The non-coding sequences include those that regulate transcription, those that are transcribed into RNA but not translated and some non-coding

DNA sequences that have no known function. Humans pass copies of their genome to their offspring. The following table summarises the human genome structure.

Part of genome	Function of sequences
Coding sequences (genes)	Code for amino acid sequence in proteins
Non-coding sequences	Regulate transcription by turning genes on or off Transcribed but not translated (e.g. rRNA, tRNA) No known function

The Human Genome Project (HGP) was started in the 1990s and aimed to work out the sequences of the three billion base pairs in human DNA. The project used DNA from several individuals to produce an average human sequence. Publication of the results began in 2001.

Systematics

Systematics uses sequence data to provide information on the evolutionary relationships between humans and other species, allowing **phylogenetic** diagrams to be constructed, as shown in Figure 1.29.

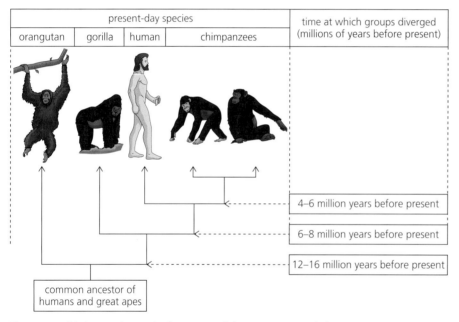

Figure 1.29 Phylogenetic tree for humans and the great apes, and the approximate times at which the different groups diverged

Personalised medicine

It is possible to sequence the genome of an individual human being. Many diseases have a genetic risk component and so personal genomics could lead to personalised medicine through increased information on the likelihood of a treatment being successful in a specific individual.

There is significant difficulty in distinguishing between neutral mutations and potentially harmful mutations in genes and in regulatory genetic sequences, which makes relating genomic data to personalised medicine more problematic.

Figure 1.30 shows the effects of the genotype of a group of patients with liver disease on treatment with a new, potentially beneficial drug – this highlights the problem. If patient genotype could be related to the effects of the drug before treatment, this could maximise the benefits of the treatment by identification of the group for whom the drug would be most beneficial.

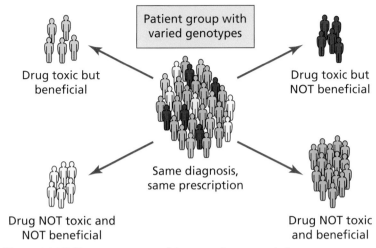

Figure 1.30 Different outcomes of the same drug on varied genotypes

Polymerase chain reaction

The polymerase chain reaction (PCR) is a laboratory technique used to produce billions of copies of a specific target sequence of DNA. The technique is carried out *in vitro*, which means that it happens outside the body of the organism in laboratory apparatus, and involves cycles of heating and cooling, as shown in Figure 1.31.

PCR involves exposing DNA to a series of temperature changes, known as thermal cycling. First the DNA is denatured at 90° C, which separates the strands. Cooling to below 60° C then allows primers to bind to the target sequences. The temperature is then raised to over 70° C, when heat-tolerant DNA polymerase is used to synthesise new strands from free DNA nucleotides. These steps can be automated in a thermal cycling machine. Many repeated cycles allow millions of copies of the target sequence to be produced.

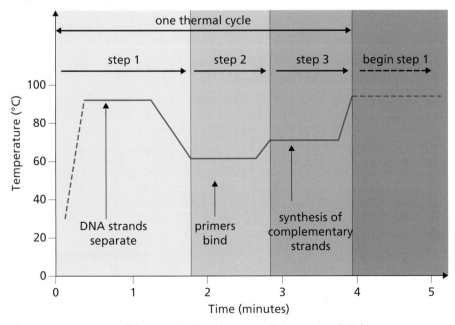

Figure 1.31 Summary of the steps in the polymerase chain reaction (PCR)

Figure 1.32 shows the pattern of amplification of a target sequence of DNA by the PCR process.

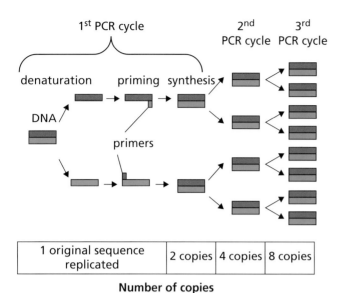

1 original sequence replicated	2 copies	4 copies	8 copies

Number of copies

Figure 1.32 Pattern of amplification of a target sequence of DNA

Applications of PCR

PCR has a variety of applications. It can be used to amplify tiny quantities of DNA from human sources such as blood or semen. This amplified material might then be enough to carry out DNA profiling, as outlined below.

DNA profiling and repetitive DNA sequences

Although humans share 99.9% of their DNA, the remaining 0.1% is unique to individuals. No two people, apart from monozygotic twins, are thought to have this 0.1% completely in common. DNA profiling is a method of identifying an individual from their DNA sequences. Throughout the human genome, multiple copies of sequences of DNA commonly occur. These are called repetitive sequences and are highly variable from one person to another. It is these variable repetitive sequences that are looked for in DNA profiling, allowing DNA samples to be individually matched.

Profiling involves isolating and amplifying DNA. It is first cut with enzymes to form fragments, then treated with an array of pieces of DNA called probes to target specific sequences to which they are complementary. Fluorescent labels are used to reveal sequences that have been found. The labelled sequences are passed through electrophoresis gel, which separates them to create the DNA 'fingerprint', as shown in Figure 1.33.

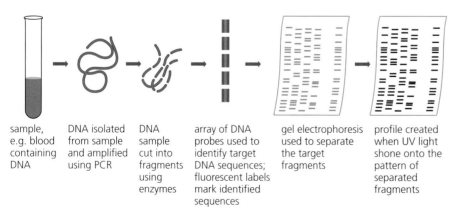

| sample, e.g. blood containing DNA | DNA isolated from sample and amplified using PCR | DNA sample cut into fragments using enzymes | array of DNA probes used to identify target DNA sequences; fluorescent labels mark identified sequences | gel electrophoresis used to separate the target fragments | profile created when UV light shone onto the pattern of separated fragments |

Figure 1.33 Stages in DNA profiling

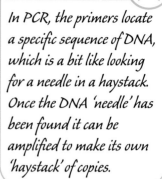

Example 🚩

DNA samples 1 and 2 in Figure 1.34 were obtained from the scene of a crime.

Samples 3 and 4 were obtained from two individuals suspected to have been involved in the crime. As can be seen, Suspect 1's DNA profile matches the unknown DNA from the crime scene, which makes it certain that the suspect was present at the scene – unless the suspect has an identical twin! This information could be helpful in investigating the crime.

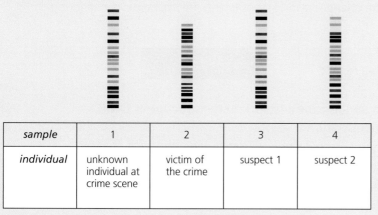

sample	1	2	3	4
individual	unknown individual at crime scene	victim of the crime	suspect 1	suspect 2

Figure 1.34 Matching DNA samples using DNA profiling

Key words

Bioinformatics – use of computers and statistics in analysis of sequence data
DNA probe – short piece of DNA complementary to a target sequence of DNA
DNA profiling – use of DNA probes to produce a 'fingerprint' of an individual's DNA
Fluorescent labelling – method of making a fragment of DNA show up under ultraviolet light
Gel electrophoresis – method for the separation of DNA fragments using an electric current in a gel
Genome – total genetic material present in an organism
Genome sequence data – information about the nucleotide sequence of the entire human genome
Heat-tolerant DNA polymerase – enzyme from bacteria in hot springs, used in PCR
Personalised medicine – development in which treatment is based on an individual's genome
Phylogenetics – study of evolutionary relatedness of species
Polymerase chain reaction (PCR) – method of amplifying sequences of DNA
Repetitive DNA sequence – sequence of DNA that is repeated many times; these are highly individual
Sequence data – information concerning amino acid or nucleotide base sequences
Systematics – study of the diversification of living organisms past and present

Questions ?

Restricted response (structured in 1- or 2-mark parts)

1 Describe what is meant by the genome of an organism. (2)
2 Give the meanings of the following terms:
   a) sequence data (1)
   b) bioinformatics. (1)
3 Describe the basis for personalised medicine. (2)
4 The flow chart below shows temperature changes during steps in the polymerase chain reaction (PCR) procedure.

step 1		step 2		step 3
DNA heated to 90°C	→	DNA cooled to 55°C	→	DNA heated to 70°C

   a) Describe the effect of the increase in temperature at step 1 on the structure of DNA. (1)
   b) State the need for the reduction in temperature at step 2. (1)
   c) Explain why the DNA polymerase used in step 3 can function at 70°C, although the high temperature would denature most enzymes. (1)
   d) State the number of DNA molecules that would be present after one molecule of DNA has passed through seven thermal cycles of PCR. (1)
   e) Describe **one** application of the PCR procedure. (1)

Extended response (4–9 marks each)

5 Give an account of DNA profiling and its applications. (6)
Answers are on page 53.

Metabolic pathways

Summary notes

Metabolism

Control of metabolic pathways

Enzymes are coded for by genes. Each step in a metabolic pathway is controlled by a specific enzyme. A metabolic block may occur due to a gene mutation resulting in the absence of a functional enzyme.

Figure 1.35 shows genetic control of an enzyme-catalysed metabolic pathway. In this pathway, metabolite A is converted to metabolite B by enzyme 1. Enzyme 2 is non-functional because of a mutation in gene 2, so a metabolic block occurs that prevents the formation of metabolite C.

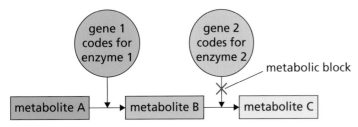

Figure 1.35 Enzyme-catalysed metabolic pathway

Enzyme action

Enzymes are biological catalysts that speed up the rates of chemical reactions by lowering the activation energy required for the reactions to proceed.

Activation energy

The energy required to initiate a reaction is called its activation energy (E_A). Before a substrate can change into a product, the substrate must overcome this energy barrier. For example, in the breakdown of hydrogen peroxide:

$E_A = 86\,kJ\,mol^{-1}$ without an enzyme

$E_A = 1\,kJ\,mol^{-1}$ with the enzyme catalase

High temperatures often supply the activation energy in non-living situations, but in cells enzymes reduce the activation energy needed for a reaction to occur, as shown in Figure 1.36.

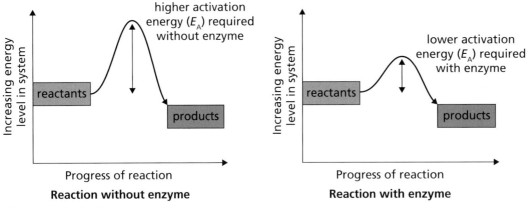

Figure 1.36 Activation energy

Induced fit

The active site of an enzyme is the location on its surface where substrate molecules bind and the chemical reaction takes place. Enzymes are specific and only act on one substrate because substrate molecules are complementary in shape to the enzyme's active site. Substrates are chemically attracted to the active site – they are said to have an affinity for it.

As the substrate starts to bind, the active site changes shape to fit the substrate more closely, increasing the rate of reaction, as shown in Figure 1.37.

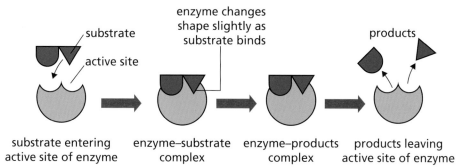

| substrate entering active site of enzyme | enzyme–substrate complex | enzyme–products complex | products leaving active site of enzyme |

Figure 1.37 The induced fit model of enzyme action

The active site orientates the substrate molecules and promotes the chemical reaction through the lowering of the activation energy required, as shown in Figure 1.38.

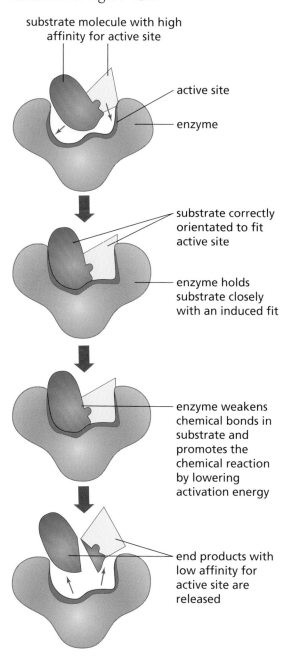

substrate molecule with high affinity for active site

active site

enzyme

substrate correctly orientated to fit active site

enzyme holds substrate closely with an induced fit

enzyme weakens chemical bonds in substrate and promotes the chemical reaction by lowering activation energy

end products with low affinity for active site are released

Figure 1.38 The role of the active site in orientating reactants

After the reaction takes place, the product, being a different shape from the substrate, moves away because it has low affinity for the active site. The active site returns to its original shape.

Rates of enzyme reaction

The maximum rate at which any reaction can proceed depends on, among other things, the concentration of substrate molecules, as shown in Figure 1.39. An increase in substrate concentration drives the reaction in the direction of the end product and increases the rate of the reaction.

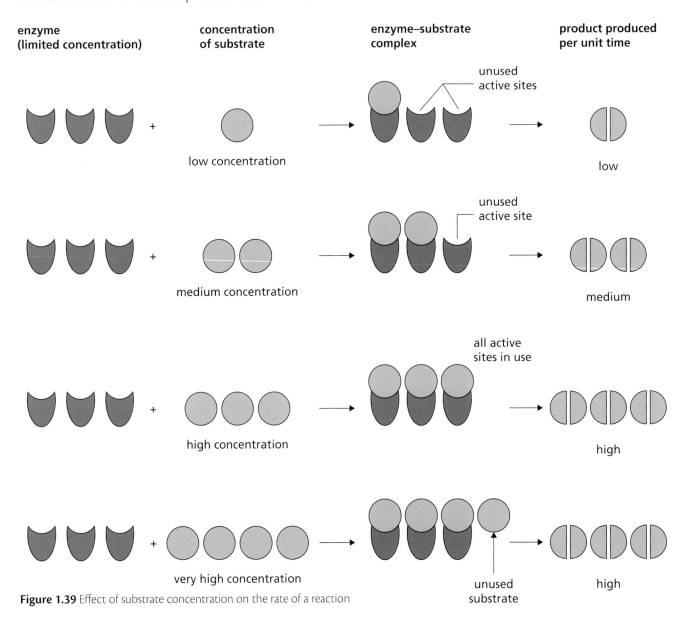

Figure 1.39 Effect of substrate concentration on the rate of a reaction

Multi-enzyme complexes

Some enzymes involved in a particular metabolic pathway occur grouped together in a membrane as a multi-enzyme complex. This helps ensure that the chemical reactions proceed in the correct order. For example, in respiration, the pyruvate dehydrogenase complex contains three enzymes, which act together to convert pyruvate into acetyl coenzyme A.

Hints & tips

There is more about the conversion of pyruvate to acetyl coenzyme A in Key Area 1.7 on page 44.

Control of metabolic pathways through the regulation of enzyme action

Many metabolic reactions are reversible and the concentration of the substrate and product affect the direction and rate of the reaction.

Inhibitors

An inhibitor is a substance that reduces the rate of an enzyme reaction. Inhibitors occur naturally but are also produced artificially and have applications in medicine (drugs) and agriculture (pesticides). There are two kinds of inhibitor.

Competitive inhibitors

Competitive inhibitors are molecules with a similar structural shape to the normal substrate of the enzyme, and so can fit into its active site. They compete with substrate molecules for a position in the active site on the enzyme. Figure 1.40 shows the effect of a competitive inhibitor on the activity of an enzyme.

competitive inhibitor absent

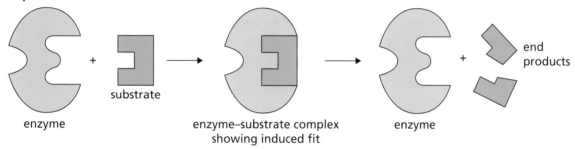

competitive inhibitor present

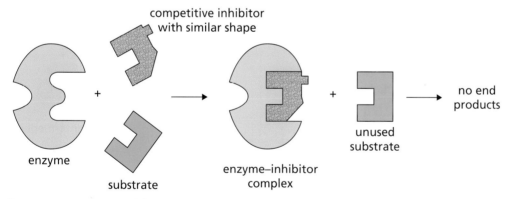

Figure 1.40 Competitive inhibition

With some of the active sites occupied and blocked by the inhibitor, the rate of the reaction is reduced. However, if the substrate concentration is increased, the chance of the substrate binding to the enzyme is increased and the rate of the reaction can return to normal, as shown in Figure 1.41.

Non-competitive inhibitors

Non-competitive inhibitors are molecules with a quite different structure from the substrate molecule. They do not fit into the active site of the enzyme but bind to

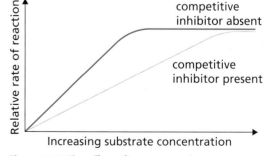

Figure 1.41 The effect of increasing substrate concentration on competitive inhibition

another part of the enzyme molecule. This changes the shape of the active site, so that it can no longer combine with the substrate molecule. Figure 1.42 shows the effect of a non-competitive inhibitor on the activity of an enzyme.

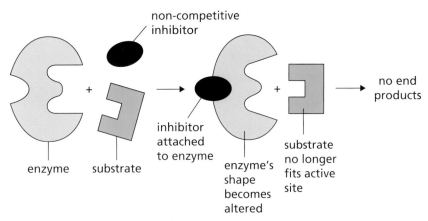

Figure 1.42 Non-competitive inhibition

Non-competitive inhibitors reduce the amount of active enzyme and have a similar effect to decreasing the enzyme concentration. Cyanide, heavy metal ions and some insecticides are examples of non-competitive inhibitors. Increasing the substrate concentration does not increase the reaction rate in the presence of a non-competitive inhibitor and the effect of the inhibitor is permanent.

Feedback inhibition

Feedback inhibition occurs when an end product inhibits the activity of an enzyme that catalysed a reaction earlier in the pathway that produced it, as shown in Figure 1.43.

Signal molecules

Extracellular signal molecules originate outside a target cell and can bring about changes which regulate the action of enzymes. Adrenaline is a hormone released from adrenal glands in response to stress situations. It travels and binds to liver cells where it signals the start of a series of events that result in the activation of an intracellular signal molecule. This molecule is an intracellular signal that activates the enzyme which converts glycogen to glucose. The glucose can then be used as an energy source to allow the body to react to the stimulus that caused the adrenaline to be released in the first place. This is shown in Figure 1.44 opposite.

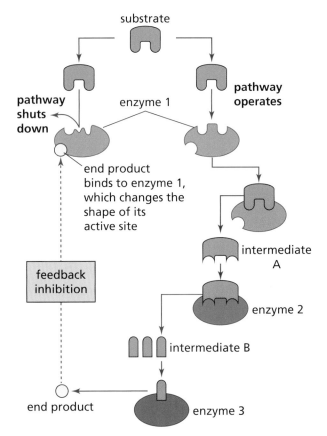

Figure 1.43 Example of feedback inhibition

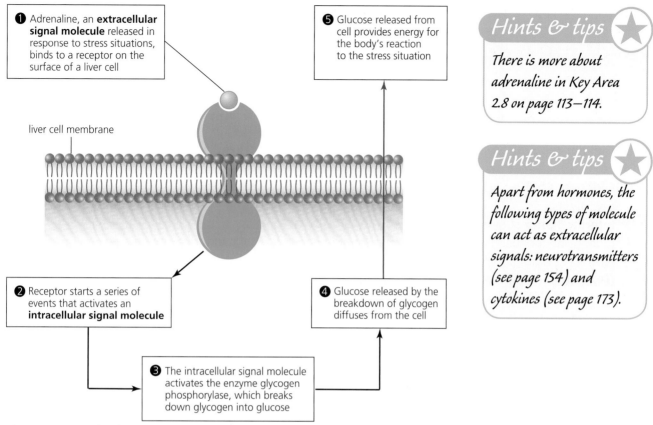

❶ Adrenaline, an **extracellular signal molecule** released in response to stress situations, binds to a receptor on the surface of a liver cell

❺ Glucose released from cell provides energy for the body's reaction to the stress situation

Hints & tips

There is more about adrenaline in Key Area 2.8 on page 113–114.

Hints & tips

Apart from hormones, the following types of molecule can act as extracellular signals: neurotransmitters (see page 154) and cytokines (see page 173).

liver cell membrane

❷ Receptor starts a series of events that activates an **intracellular signal molecule**

❹ Glucose released by the breakdown of glycogen diffuses from the cell

❸ The intracellular signal molecule activates the enzyme glycogen phosphorylase, which breaks down glycogen into glucose

Figure 1.44 Example of the effect of extracellular and intracellular signal molecules on liver cell function

Key words

Activation energy – input of energy required to start a chemical reaction
Active site – region on an enzyme molecule where the substrate binds
Anabolic – metabolic pathways that consume energy in synthesis of complex molecules
Catabolic – metabolic activity that releases energy in breakdown reactions
Competitive inhibition – slowing of reaction rate due to the presence of a substance resembling the substrate
Feedback inhibition – enzyme inhibition caused by the presence of an end product of a metabolic pathway
Induced fit – change to an enzyme's active site brought about by its substrate
Metabolic pathway – enzyme-controlled sequence of chemical reactions in a cell
Non-competitive inhibition – enzyme inhibition by a substance that permanently alters the active site of the enzyme
Product – substance resulting from an enzyme-catalysed reaction
Signal molecule – molecule that brings about changes in a cell's metabolism
Substrate – substance on which an enzyme works

Questions ❓

Restricted response (structured in 1- or 2-mark parts)

1 Describe the role of genes in the control of metabolic pathways. (2)
2 a) Explain what is meant by the induced fit model of enzyme action. (2)
  b) Describe the effect of an increase in substrate concentration on the direction and rate of an enzyme reaction. (2)
  c) Explain how enzymes speed up the rate of reactions in metabolic pathways. (2)

Extended response (4–9 marks each)

3 Give an account of enzyme action and of the effects of competitive and non-competitive inhibition. (9)
Answers are on page 53–54.

Key points

1 **Cellular respiration** is the release of energy from food molecules in cells. ☐

2 **Glucose** is broken down to **pyruvate** in the cytoplasm of cells during **glycolysis**. ☐

3 **Intermediates** of glycolysis are **phosphorylated** by **ATP** (adenosine triphosphate) in an energy investment phase. ☐

4 ATP is generated in glycolysis by the addition of inorganic **phosphate (Pi)** to **ADP** (adenosine diphosphate) in an energy pay-off phase. ☐

5 **Phosphofructokinase (PFK)** is an enzyme that catalyses the irreversible transfer of a phosphate (Pi) from ATP to fructose-6-phosphate in glycolysis. ☐

6 PFK is the key regulatory enzyme for glycolysis and when ATP and citrate levels are high in the cell, the cell no longer needs metabolic energy production to occur and PFK's activity is inhibited. ☐

7 The **citric acid cycle** occurs in the **matrix** of the **mitochondria**. ☐

8 In the presence of oxygen, pyruvate is broken down to an **acetyl group**. ☐

9 An acetyl group combines with **coenzyme A** to be transferred to the citric acid cycle as acetyl coenzyme A. ☐

10 Acetyl coenzyme A combines with **oxaloacetate** to form **citrate**. ☐

11 Oxaloacetate is regenerated by enzyme-mediated reactions in the citric acid cycle. ☐

12 Some ATP is generated during the citric acid cycle. ☐

13 Carbon dioxide is released from the citric acid cycle. ☐

14 **Dehydrogenases** remove hydrogen and electrons from intermediates in the citric acid cycle. ☐

15 Hydrogen and electrons are passed to coenzymes **NAD** and **FAD** to produce NADH and $FADH_2$ in glycolysis and the citric acid cycle. ☐

16 NADH and $FADH_2$ release hydrogen and high-energy electrons to the **electron transport chain** on inner mitochondrial membranes. ☐

17 **High-energy electrons** are used to pump hydrogen ions across a mitochondrial membrane. ☐

18 Return flow of hydrogen ions through the inner mitochondrial membrane synthesises ATP, using the membrane protein **ATP synthase**. ☐

19 Most ATP is generated from the electron transport chain. ☐

20 The final electron acceptor is oxygen, which combines with hydrogen ions and electrons to form water. ☐

21 In the absence of oxygen, pyruvate from glycolysis follows a **fermentation** pathway. ☐

22 Other than glucose, **alternative respiratory substrates** include starch, glycogen, other sugars, amino acids and fats. ☐

Summary notes

Cellular respiration

The metabolic pathways of cellular respiration are of central importance to human cells. They yield energy and are connected to many other pathways.

Transfer of energy via ATP

ATP is a substance that is involved in the transfer of chemical energy in cells. ATP is built up or regenerated from ADP and inorganic phosphate (Pi) using the energy released from cellular respiration. Respiration converts the chemical energy stored in glucose into chemical energy stored in ATP.

ATP is used to transfer the chemical energy from cellular respiration to synthetic pathways and other cellular processes where energy is required, for example contraction of muscle fibres, DNA replication and protein synthesis. The energy held in the ATP is released when it is broken down into ADP + Pi. Figure 1.45 shows the transfer of chemical energy by ATP from cellular respiration to protein synthesis.

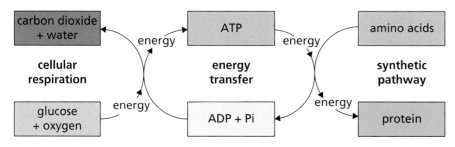

Figure 1.45 Role of ATP in energy transfer

Synthesis of ATP in respiration

During cellular respiration, glucose is broken down in a series of enzyme-controlled stages. Hydrogen and high-energy electrons are removed by dehydrogenase enzymes and used in the synthesis of ATP.

Stages in aerobic respiration

The three stages of respiration take place in different parts of the cell.

1 Glycolysis

Glycolysis is a series of enzyme-controlled reactions that take place in the cytoplasm of the cell.

During glycolysis, glucose is broken down to pyruvate in the absence of oxygen.

The phosphorylation of intermediates in glycolysis uses two molecules of ATP and is described as an energy investment phase. The later reactions in glycolysis result in the direct regeneration of four molecules of ATP for every glucose molecule and are referred to as the energy pay-off stage, giving a net gain of 2ATP. During the energy pay-off phase,

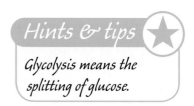

Hints & tips

Glycolysis means the splitting of glucose.

dehydrogenase enzymes remove hydrogen ions (H^+), which combine with the hydrogen carrier NAD to form NADH. If oxygen is present, NADH transports hydrogen to the electron transport chain, which leads to the production of more ATP. Figure 1.46 shows features of glycolysis.

The remaining two stages of cellular respiration occur in mitochondria as shown in Figure 1.47.

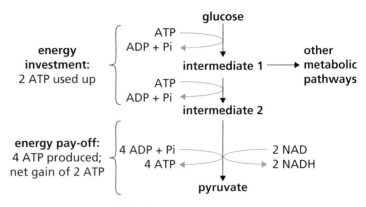

Figure 1.46 Features of glycolysis

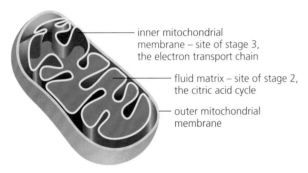

Figure 1.47 A mitochondrion, showing the sites of stages in cellular respiration

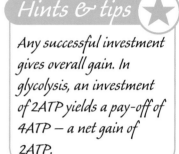

Hints & tips

Any successful investment gives overall gain. In glycolysis, an investment of 2ATP yields a pay-off of 4ATP – a net gain of 2ATP.

2 Citric acid cycle

If oxygen is available, pyruvate progresses to the citric acid cycle. This stage takes place in the central matrix of the mitochondria. Pyruvate enters the mitochondria and is broken down by enzymes to an acetyl group and carbon dioxide (CO_2).

The acetyl group then combines with coenzyme A to be transferred to the citric acid cycle as acetyl coenzyme A. Acetyl coenzyme A combines with oxaloacetate to form citrate (citric acid). The citrate then undergoes a series of enzyme-mediated steps, resulting in the generation of one ATP molecule, the release of carbon dioxide and the regeneration of oxaloacetate in the matrix of the mitochondria. During the citric acid cycle, dehydrogenase enzymes remove hydrogen ions (H^+) and high-energy electrons, which combine with the coenzymes NAD and FAD to form NADH and $FADH_2$. Figure 1.48 shows the stages involved in the citric acid cycle.

Phosphofructokinase (PFK)

PFK is an enzyme that is important in the regulation of glycolysis. It catalyses an irreversible reaction in the glycolysis pathway, which essentially ensures that the pathway is switched on.

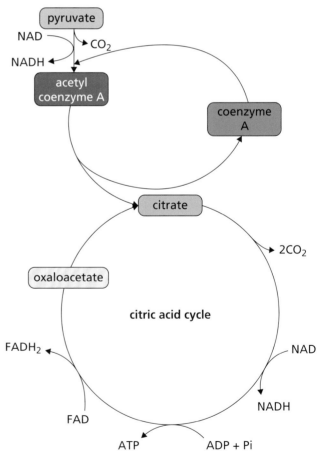

Figure 1.48 Citric acid cycle

PFK activity is inhibited by ATP and citrate. High levels of ATP and citrate indicate that phosphorylation and the rate of the citric acid cycle are sufficient to meet the cell's energy demand, so the inhibition of glycolysis saves cell resources. When ATP and citrate levels are lower, PFK is not inhibited and glycolysis proceeds as normal, ensuring an adequate supply of ATP to meet the cell's energy needs. ATP and citrate act to synchronise glycolysis with the citric acid cycle and ensure that the supply of ATP to the cell is regulated, as shown in Figure 1.49.

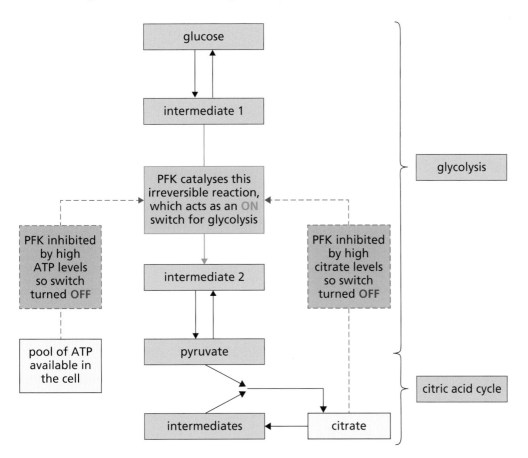

Figure 1.49 Synchronisation of glycolysis with the citric acid cycle by PFK

3 Electron transport chain

NADH and FADH$_2$ transport and pass on hydrogen ions and high-energy electrons to the electron transport chain. This final stage in aerobic respiration takes place on inner membranes of the mitochondria.

The electron transport chain is a collection of proteins called electron acceptors attached to the membrane. NADH and FADH$_2$ release the high-energy electrons to the electron transport chain where they pass down the chain of electron acceptors, releasing their energy. The energy is used to pump the hydrogen ions (H$^+$) across the inner mitochondrial membrane from the matrix side of the mitochondria into the space between its membranes. The return flow of the hydrogen ions (H$^+$) back into the matrix drives the enzyme ATP synthase, which results in the synthesis of ATP from ADP + Pi. This stage produces most of the ATP generated by cellular respiration. Oxygen is the final acceptor of hydrogen ions and electrons, forming water.

Figure 1.50 shows the stages involved in the electron transport chain.

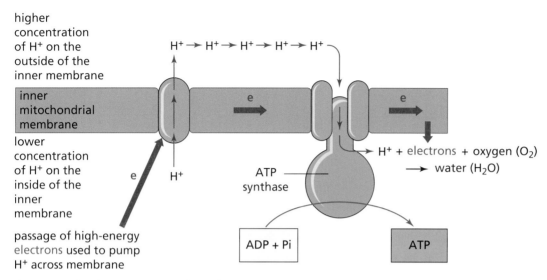

Figure 1.50 The electron transport chain of respiration

Fermentation

Glycolysis can occur in the presence or absence of oxygen. Pyruvate progresses into the citric acid cycle in the presence of oxygen. In the absence of oxygen the pyruvate undergoes reactions called fermentation, resulting in the production of lactic acid as a final metabolic product. Fermentation is an inefficient method of energy release in cells because much energy remains in the lactic acid molecules and is unavailable to the cell at that stage.

Substrates for respiration

Starch and glycogen are broken down to glucose for use as a respiratory substrate. Starch can be found in the diet and glycogen is a storage carbohydrate found in the liver and muscles.

Alternative respiratory substrates

Other sugar molecules can be converted to glucose or intermediates in glycolysis. Proteins can be broken down to amino acids, which are converted to intermediates of glycolysis or the citric acid cycle. Body bulk protein can be broken down for use during extreme starvation. Fats can also be broken down to intermediates of glycolysis and the citric acid cycle.

> *Hints & tips*
>
> You can read more about lactic acid metabolism in Key Area 1.8 on pages 48–49.

> *Hints & tips*
>
> There is more about glycogen in Key Area 2.8 on page 114.

Key words

Acetyl group – produced by breakdown of pyruvate; joins with oxaloacetate in the citric acid cycle
ADP – adenosine diphosphate; molecule that is phosphorylated to produce ATP
Alternative respiratory substrates – substrates for respiration other than glucose
ATP – adenosine triphosphate; molecule used for energy transfer in cells
ATP synthase – membrane-bound enzyme that synthesises ATP
Cellular respiration – release of energy from respiratory substrates
Citrate – citric acid; first substance produced in the citric acid cycle
Citric acid cycle – second stage of aerobic respiration occurring in the matrix of mitochondria

Coenzyme A – substance that carries acetyl groups into the citric acid cycle
Dehydrogenase – enzymes that remove hydrogen from their substrates; important in the citric acid cycle
Electron transport chain – group of proteins embedded in membranes of mitochondria and chloroplasts
FAD – hydrogen carrier important in the citric acid cycle
Fermentation – progression of pyruvate in the absence of oxygen
Glucose – sugar that is the main respiratory substrate in cells
Glycolysis – first stage in cellular respiration
High-energy electrons – electrons that can yield energy as they pass through an electron transport chain
Intermediate – substance in a metabolic pathway between the original substrate and the end product
Matrix – central cavity of a mitochondrion in which the citric acid cycle occurs
Mitochondrion – cell organelle in which the aerobic stages of respiration occur (plural: mitochondria)
NAD – hydrogen carrier important in the citric acid cycle
Oxaloacetate – substance that combines with the acetyl group in the citric acid cycle to form citrate
Phosphate (Pi) – inorganic phosphate used to phosphorylate ADP
Phosphofructokinase (PFK) – enzyme that regulates glycolysis and synchronises it with the citric acid cycle
Phosphorylation – addition of phosphate to a substance
Pyruvate – the end product of glycolysis

Questions ?

Restricted response (structured in 1- or 2-mark parts)

1 a) Explain why the phosphorylation of intermediates in glycolysis is
    described as an energy investment phase. (2)
   b) State the role of dehydrogenase enzymes in glycolysis and the citric
      acid cycle. (1)
   c) Describe the importance of phosphofructokinase in the regulation
      of glycolysis. (2)
   d) Describe the role of the coenzymes NAD and FAD. (2)
2 a) Name the enzyme embedded in the inner membrane of a
      mitochondrion that is responsible for the regeneration of ATP. (1)
   b) Describe the role of the high-energy electrons transported to the
      electron transport chain. (2)
   c) State the role of oxygen in the electron transport chain. (1)
   d) Name **two** alternative respiratory substrates. (1)

Extended response (4–9 marks each)

3 Give an account of respiration under the following headings:
   a) Glycolysis (3)
   b) The citric acid cycle (6)
4 Give an account of the electron transport chain in respiration. (8)
5 Give an account of respiration under the following headings:
   a) The role of ATP within the cell (4)
   b) The use of alternative respiratory substrates (4)

Answers are on page 54–55.

1 **Creatine phosphate (CP)** breaks down to release energy and phosphate, which are used to convert ADP to ATP at a fast rate, and therefore helps support strenuous exercise in muscle cells. ☐

2 After around 10 seconds of strenuous exercise, creatine phosphate supply in muscle cells runs out. ☐

3 Levels of creatine phosphate are restored when energy demand on muscle cells is low. ☐

4 In oxygen-deficient conditions pyruvate from glycolysis is converted to **lactic acid**. ☐

5 Lactic acid can build up in muscle cells when oxygen is in short supply during strenuous exercise. ☐

6 Lactic acid build-up in muscle cells can cause **muscle fatigue** and an **oxygen debt**. ☐

7 Oxygen debt can be repaid in a recovery period following strenuous exercise, during which time lactic acid is broken down. ☐

8 **Skeletal muscle** contracts to bring about the movements of strenuous exercise. ☐

9 Skeletal muscle has **slow-twitch (type 1) fibres** and **fast-twitch (type 2) fibres**. ☐

10 Slow-twitch fibres contract more slowly but can sustain contractions for longer and are effective for endurance activities. ☐

11 Fast-twitch fibres contract more quickly over short periods and are effective for short bursts of strenuous activity. ☐

Summary notes

Creatine phosphate is a substance that acts as a reserve of phosphates and energy in muscle and brain cells. It can be broken down rapidly to release phosphate and energy during the first few seconds of intense muscular effort. Excess ATP can be used to regenerate creatine phosphate during low-energy-demand rest periods, as shown in Figure 1.51.

Lactic acid metabolism

After a short period of strenuous exercise, the demand for oxygen by muscle becomes too much to be completely supplied by breathing in and delivery by the bloodstream. When oxygen supply is deficient, muscle cells convert pyruvate from glycolysis to lactic acid in a process called fermentation. This is beneficial because the process produces NAD needed in glycolysis and allows exercise to continue.

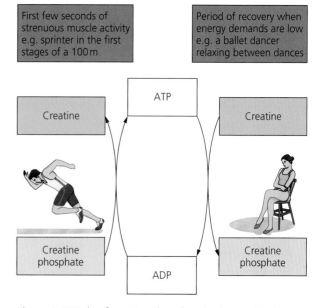

First few seconds of strenuous muscle activity e.g. sprinter in the first stages of a 100 m

Period of recovery when energy demands are low e.g. a ballet dancer relaxing between dances

ATP

Creatine

Creatine

Creatine phosphate

ADP

Creatine phosphate

Figure 1.51 Role of creatine phosphate in the production of ATP

Lactic acid builds up if it is produced faster than it can be removed during extended periods of strenuous exercise. The build up of lactic acid lowers the pH of muscle cells and causes acidosis, which makes the muscle tissue become painful. During the recovery period following exercise, muscle cells become well oxygenated, which allows lactic acid to be converted back to pyruvate and then pass on into the citric acid cycle. This is shown in Figure 1.52.

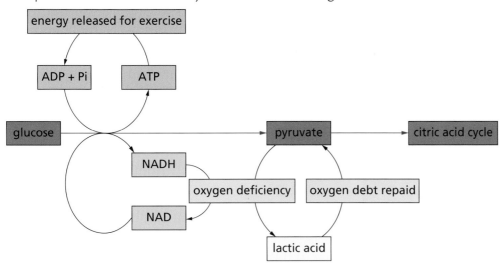

Figure 1.52 Summary of lactic acid metabolism

Skeletal muscle

Skeletal muscle is connected to the skeleton by tendons and contracts to cause movement during exercise. There are two types of skeletal muscle fibre, type 1 (slow twitch) and type 2 (fast twitch).

Slow-twitch muscle fibres are good for endurance activities like marathon running or long-distance cycling. They can sustain contractions over a long period of time. Slow-twitch muscle is dense with capillaries and is rich in mitochondria and the oxygen-carrying protein **myoglobin**, giving the muscle tissue its characteristic dark red colour. The slow-twitch fibres can take up more oxygen and sustain activity for longer by using stored fats as a main energy source.

Fast-twitch muscles are good for rapid movements like sprinting and high jumping. Fast-twitch fibres have fewer capillaries and mitochondria, and less myoglobin. They contract more quickly and powerfully, but fatigue very quickly, sustaining only short bursts of activity before muscle contraction becomes painful due to build-up of lactic acid. They contribute most to muscle strength and have greater potential for increase in mass.

The characteristics of the two different muscle fibre types are compared in the following table.

Characteristic	Fast-twitch fibres	Slow-twitch fibres
Type of activities	Strength and speed	Stamina and endurance
Blood supply	Fewer blood vessels	Many blood vessels
Energy release	Small amounts quickly	Large amounts more slowly
Mitochondria	Fewer	More
Myoglobin	Less	More
Energy source	Glycolysis only	Glycolysis, citric acid cycle and the electron transport chain

Most human muscles have a mixture of both slow- and fast-twitch muscle fibres. The main muscle in the calf and the muscles of the back that are involved in maintaining posture contain mainly slow-twitch muscle fibres. The muscles that move the eyes are made up of fast-twitch muscle fibres. Figure 1.53 shows that different types of training can affect the proportions of the two fibre types in an individual's body.

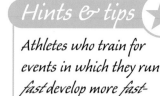

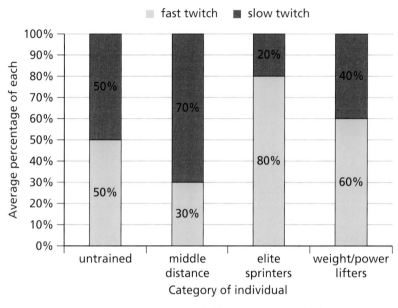

Figure 1.53 Proportions of different muscle fibres in various individuals

Key words

Creatine phosphate (CP) – molecule that serves as a source of phosphate and energy in muscle cells
Fast-twitch (type 2) fibre – type of muscle fibre used in short bursts of activity
Lactic acid – produced by the fermentation of pyruvate in mammalian muscle cells
Muscle fatigue – painful condition caused by the accumulation of lactic acid in muscles
Myoglobin – protein in muscle tissue that can bind with oxygen
Oxygen debt – builds up during fermentation in muscle cells
Skeletal muscle – muscle attached to the skeleton that brings about locomotion
Slow-twitch (type 1) fibre – type of muscle fibre used in endurance activities

Questions ?

Restricted response (structured in 1- or 2-mark parts)

1 Describe the role of creatine phosphate in cells. (2)
2 Describe fermentation in human muscle cells. (2)

Extended response (4–9 marks each)

3 Give an account of lactic acid metabolism in muscle cells. (4)
4 Give an account of skeletal muscles under the following headings:
   a) Slow-twitch muscle fibres (3)
   b) Fast-twitch muscle fibres (3)
Answers are on page 55.

Answers

Key Area 1.1

Restricted response

1 changes to cells involving expression of certain genes; to allow the cell to specialise in a specific function [2]
2 epithelium, connective, nervous, muscle [all 4 = 2; 3/2 = 1]
3 a) somatic cell [1]
   b) germline cells/gametes [1]
4 do not respond to regulatory signals; divide repeatedly and excessively [2]
5 cancer cells that do not attach to other cells; enter the bloodstream and are carried to other areas [2]
6 to obtain embryonic stem cells an embryo must be killed; but the requirement to preserve life through medicine is a moral duty [others possible] [2]

Extended response

7 a) stem cells can continue to divide; can differentiate into specialised cells; embryonic stem cells are pluripotent/can become almost any kind of cell; adult stem cells are multipotent/can become more limited cell types; adult stem cells divide and differentiate to replenish cells that need to be replaced; adult stem cells in bone marrow give rise to various types of blood cell [any 5 = 5]
   b) stem cells can be used as model cells to study how diseases develop; stem cells can be used for drug testing; stem cells can be used in the repair of damaged tissues; stem cells can be used in the repair of diseased tissues [any 3 = 3]
8 mitosis can give rise to somatic cells and germline cells; mitosis maintains chromosome number in the daughter cells; mitosis produces two daughter cells; mitosis produces genetically identical cells; mitosis produces diploid daughter cells [any 3 = 3]
   meiosis gives rise to gametes; meiosis halves the chromosome number in daughter cells; meiosis produces four daughter cells; meiosis produces genetically varied daughter cells; meiosis produces haploid daughter cells [any 3 = 3]
9 a) somatic cells form different types of body tissue [1]
   two examples of tissues formed from somatic cells:
   epithelial tissue; connective tissue; muscle tissue; nervous tissue [any 2 = 1]
   body organs are formed from a variety/combination of these tissues; somatic cells divide by mitosis (to maintain the diploid chromosome number) [1]
   [any 3 = 3]
   b) (nucleus of a) germline cell can divide by mitosis to produce more germline cells/diploid cells; germline cell can divide by meiosis to produce haploid gametes/cells; mutations in germline cells can be passed on to offspring (whereas mutations in somatic cells can not) [any 2 = 2]

Answers

Key Area 1.2

Restricted response

1 a) double helix [1]
   b) hydrogen bonds; between bases [2]
   c) deoxyribose sugar, phosphate, base [all 3 = 2, 2/1 = 1]
   d) (i) bases pair with each other specifically/A pairs with T and C pairs with G [1]
      (ii) the two DNA strands run in opposite directions [1]
2 DNA is tightly coiled; DNA is packaged with associated proteins ⇒ [2]

Extended response

3   DNA uncoils and unzips; primers bind at end of lead template strand; DNA polymerase adds complementary DNA nucleotides to lead strand continuously; primers bind to lagging strand in many places; DNA polymerase adds complementary DNA nucleotides to lagging strand in fragments; fragments joined by ligase; replication occurs at several positions/at many replication forks on a DNA molecule at the same time; replication requires energy/ATP   [any 7 = 7]

Answers

Key Area 1.3

Restricted response

1   alternative RNA splicing; post-translational modifications   [2]
2   DNA double stranded *and* RNA single stranded; DNA contains deoxyribose *and* RNA contains ribose; DNA contains thymine *and* thymine is replaced by uracil in RNA   [any 2 = 2]
3   introns are non-coding regions *and* exons are coding regions   [1]
4   cutting *and* combining chains; adding carbohydrates; adding phosphates   [any 2 = 2]
5   energy and resources are conserved   [1]

Extended response

6   a) DNA unwinds and unzips; RNA polymerase adds complementary RNA nucleotides; (to make a) primary transcript; introns removed; exons spliced to make mRNA   [any 4 = 4]
    b) mRNA goes to ribosome; tRNA carries specific amino acids; anti codons on tRNA align with codons on mRNA; amino acids aligned in correct sequence; amino acids linked by peptide bonds   [any 4 = 4]

Answers

Key Area 1.4

Restricted response

1   a) peptide   [1]
    b) hydrogen *or* other named interaction e.g. sulfur bridge, ionic bond, van der Waals forces   [1]
2   a) 1 deletion, 2 insertion, 3 substitution   [all 3 = 2, 2/1 = 1]
    b) 1 – deletion gives frameshift effect with major changes to amino acid sequence *or* all amino acids changed after the mutation; 3 – substitution results in missense and gives minor changes to polypeptide *or* only one amino acid changed *or* results in nonsense if stop codon affected   [2]
3   a) substitution mutation/single nucleotide change resulting in a codon for a different amino acid   [1]
    b) mutation that can result in mRNA with the wrong introns or exons   [1]

Extended response

4   substitution involves swapping one nucleotide for another; substitutions can be missense in which a change in one codon results in a different amino acid being used; substitutions can be nonsense in which a codon is changed to a stop codon, making the protein shorter; deletion involves the removal of a nucleotide from the sequence; insertion involves the addition of a nucleotide to the sequence; deletion/insertion give frameshift effects to amino acid sequence in the protein; frameshift mutations lead to many amino acids being changed, which has a major effect on protein structure   [any 7 = 7; must match]

⇨

5 deletion; involves loss of a section/genes from a chromosome; translocation; involves a section/genes from one chromosome joining to another; duplication; involves a section/genes from one chromosome being copied within the chromosome [any 4 = 4; must match]

6 a) caused by substitution in the gene coding for haemoglobin; abnormal haemoglobin produced causes blood cell collapse during exercise; collapsed cells can't carry oxygen, leading to breathlessness; collapsed cells become trapped in capillaries, producing pain [any 3 = 3]

b) caused by mutation in the gene coding for blood clotting factor; absence of normal clotting factor causes failure of blood to clot; excessive bleeding occurs from cuts; excessive blood loss can be fatal [any 3 = 3]

Answers

Key Area 1.5

Restricted response

1 the DNA sequences in genes; and non-coding regions [2]

2 a) the DNA base sequences within a genome [1]

b) the use of computer technology and statistics to analyse DNA sequences [1]

3 an individual's genome may be analysed; and drug therapy matched to the genome to gain best outcome from treatment [2]

4 a) double helix split apart/denatured [1]

b) allows primers to bind [1]

c) enzyme derives from bacteria from hot springs adapted to high temperatures [1]

d) 128 molecules [1]

e) amplify DNA from crime scenes [others possible] [1]

Extended response

5 DNA sample treated with an array of DNA probes; specific sequences detected by the probes; fluorescent labelling allows the detection under UV light of the identified sequences; sequences can be separated (by electrophoresis) to give a DNA profile; individuals vary in the numbers of sequence repeats their DNA contains; profiles are unique to individuals; allows identification of individuals from their DNA in forensics; allows parents of a child to be identified [any 6 = 6]

Answers

Key Area 1.6

Restricted response

1 each step in a metabolic pathway is controlled by a specific enzyme; each enzyme is coded for by a gene [2]

2 a) enzyme is flexible and so the active site can change shape; substrate induces the active site to change shape; active site can alter the position or orientate the substrate molecules so that they fit more closely [any 2 = 2]

b) increase in substrate concentration drives the chemical reaction in the direction of the end product; increases the rate of reaction [2]

c) active site can alter the position of/orientate the substrate molecules so that they fit more closely; activation energy is lowered when an enzyme is involved [2]

⇨

Extended response

3 enzyme activity depends on the flexible/dynamic shape of enzyme molecules; substrate has an affinity for the active site; induced fit; active site orientates the reactants; enzymes lower the activation energy; products have a low affinity for the active site; substrate and product concentrations affect the direction and rate of reactions *or* increasing the substrate concentration increases/speeds up/drives forward the rate of the reaction; enzymes may act in groups/multi-enzyme complexes [any 6 = 6]

competitive inhibition – the inhibitor resembles the substrate molecule; inhibition is reduced by increase in substrate concentration; non-competitive inhibition – the shape of the active site is changed; product inhibition/feedback inhibition [any 3 = 3]

Answers

Key Area 1.7

Restricted response

1 a) phosphorylation of intermediates in glycolysis uses 2 ATP; later reactions in glycolysis result in the direct regeneration of 4 ATP for every glucose molecule and so this gives a net gain of 2 ATP [2]

   b) dehydrogenase enzymes remove hydrogen ions from the substrate along with high-energy electrons [1]

   c) PFK catalyses an irreversible reaction within glycolysis; the action of PFK is regulated by the levels of ATP and citrate in the cell, synchronising glycolysis with the citric acid cycle [2]

   d) NAD and FAD transport H^+ and high-energy electrons; to the electron transport chain [2]

2 a) ATP synthase [1]

   b) high-energy electrons pass down the chain of electron acceptors; releasing their energy, which is then used to pump hydrogen ions (H^+) across the inner mitochondrial membrane [2]

   c) oxygen acts as the final electron acceptor and combines with hydrogen ions and electrons to form water [1]

   d) other sugars; glycogen; starch; fats; amino acids [any 2 = 1]

Extended response

3 a) glycolysis is the breakdown of glucose to pyruvate; 2 ATP molecules are used to phosphorylate intermediates in glycolysis; an energy investment phase; 4 ATP molecules are produced/generated/made in a pay-off stage [any 3 = 3]

   b) if oxygen is available/in aerobic conditions pyruvate progresses to the citric acid cycle; pyruvate is converted/broken down to an acetyl group; acetyl group combines with coenzyme A; acetyl (coenzyme A) combines with oxaloacetate to form citrate; citric acid cycle is enzyme controlled/involves dehydrogenases; ATP generated/synthesised/produced/released at substrate level in the citric acid cycle; carbon dioxide is released from the citric acid cycle; oxaloacetate is regenerated; NAD/NADH/$NADH_2$/FAD/FADH/$FADH_2$ transports electrons/transports hydrogen ions to the electron transport chain [any 6 = 6]

⇒

4 electron transport chain takes place on the inner membranes of the mitochondria; electron transport chain is a collection of proteins attached to a membrane; NADH and FADH$_2$ release the high-energy electrons to the electron transport chain on the inner mitochondrial membrane; electrons cascade down the chain of electron acceptors, releasing their energy; energy is used to pump hydrogen ions (H$^+$) across the inner mitochondrial membrane; return flow of the hydrogen ions (H$^+$) back into the matrix drives the enzyme ATP synthase; synthesis of ATP from ADP + Pi; this stage produces most of the ATP generated by cellular respiration; final electron acceptor is oxygen; oxygen combines with hydrogen ions and electrons to form water [any 8 = 8]

5 a) ATP produced by phosphorylation/when Pi added to ADP; acts as a source of immediate energy for cells; made during respiration; used up during energy-requiring processes/muscle contraction/protein synthesis; mass in cell remains constant [any 4 = 4]

   b) substrates are used instead of/as an alternative to glucose/when glucose not available; examples from starch/glycogen/other sugars/amino acids/fats; glycogen is a storage carbohydrate from liver/muscles; glycogen used between meals; amino acids can be released from body bulk protein; these amino acids can be used during extreme starvation; other sugars/amino acids can enter respiration pathways/glycolysis/citric acid cycle [any 4 = 4]

Answers

Key Area 1.8

Restricted response

1 creatine phosphate breaks down to release energy and phosphate; used to convert ADP to ATP at a fast rate [2]

2 in the absence of sufficient oxygen; pyruvate converted to lactic acid [2]

Extended response

3 during exercise (muscles) do not have enough oxygen for (aerobic) respiration/the electron transport chain; pyruvate/pyruvic acid converted to lactic acid; transfer of hydrogen from NADH (produced during glycolysis); regenerates NAD needed to maintain ATP production by glycolysis; lactic acid builds up (in muscles) causing fatigue/an oxygen debt; lactic acid is converted back into pyruvate/pyruvic acid [any 4 = 4]

4 a) slow-twitch muscle fibres contract slowly but maintain contractions for a long time; they rely on aerobic respiration (to generate ATP); they have many mitochondria/a large blood supply/a high concentration of myoglobin; their (main) storage fuel/energy source is fats; good for endurance activities/example [any 3 = 3]

   b) fast-twitch muscle fibres contract quickly but cannot maintain contractions for a long time; they generate ATP through glycolysis; they have few mitochondria and a low blood supply; their (main) storage fuels/energy sources are glycogen and creatine phosphate; good for short bursts of intense activity/example [any 3 = 3]

Practice Course Assessment: Unit 1 (50 marks)

Section A (10 marks)

1 The diagram below shows how a molecule might be biosynthesised from building blocks in a metabolic pathway.

building blocks   biosynthesised molecule

Which line in the table below correctly describes the metabolic process shown in the diagram and the energy relationship involved in the reaction?

	Metabolic process	Energy relationship
A	Anabolic	Energy used
B	Anabolic	Energy released
C	Catabolic	Energy used
D	Catabolic	Energy released

2 The diagram below shows a metabolic pathway that is controlled by end product inhibition.

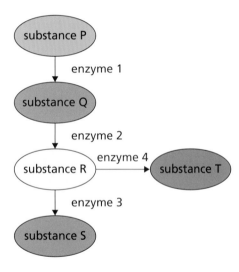

For substance S to bring about end product inhibition of the complete pathway, with which of the following must it interact?

A substance P

B substance Q

C enzyme 1

D enzyme 3

3 During fermentation in muscle fibres, pyruvate is

A converted to citrate

B broken down by the mitochondria

C broken down to carbon dioxide and water

D converted to lactic acid.

4   The graph below shows temperature changes involved in one cycle of the polymerase chain reaction (PCR).

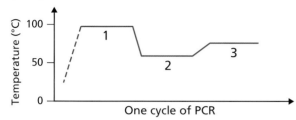

Which line in the table below identifies the main events occurring in each region of the graph?

	Main event occurring during PCR cycle		
	1	2	3
A	Primers bind to target sequences on DNA	DNA polymerase replicates regions of DNA	DNA strands separate
B	DNA strands separate	DNA polymerase replicates regions of DNA	Primers bind to target sequences on DNA
C	DNA strands separate	Primers bind to target sequences on DNA	DNA polymerase replicates regions of DNA
D	Primers bind to target sequences on DNA	DNA strands separate	DNA polymerase replicates regions of DNA

5   The list below shows steps in the synthesis of the protein mucin.
1   Transcription of DNA
2   Adding a carbohydrate group
3   RNA splicing
4   Translation of mRNA
In which order would these steps occur?
A   1 3 4 2   C   3 1 2 4
B   1 4 2 3   D   3 4 2 1

Questions 6 and 7 refer to the graph, which shows changes in the number of human stem cells present in a culture over a period of 16 days. Also shown is the level of activity of an enzyme found in stem cell cytoplasm over the same period.

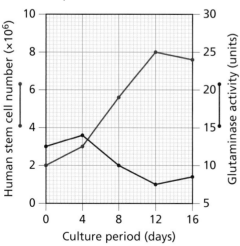

6 How many units of enzyme activity were recorded when the number of cells was at 25% of its maximum over the 16-day period?

A 2   C 10

B 3   D 12.5

7 What was the percentage decrease in enzyme activity between days 8 and 12 of the period?

A 5   C 50

B 25   D 100

8 Bioinformatics is the

A comparison of genome sequence data

B development of personalised medicine

C use of computer technology in studying DNA sequence data

D study of evolutionary relationships between animal groups.

9 Which of the following is a gene mutation that has frameshift effects?

A substitution   C duplication

B deletion   D translocation

10 Which line in the table below correctly matches athletes with the fibre types their muscles are likely to contain?

	Athlete	Fast-twitch fibres	Slow-twitch fibres
A	Sprinter	High %	Low %
B	Marathon runner	Low %	Low %
C	Sprinter	Low %	High %
D	Marathon runner	High %	Low %

Section B (40 marks)

1 The diagram shows a short section of a DNA molecule.

a) Name components X and Y, which make up the backbone of one of the strands of the molecule. (1)

b) The two strands are antiparallel.
Describe what is meant by this term. (1)

c) Name the type of bond that connects the base pairs in DNA. (1)

d) Give **one** feature of a DNA molecule that is **not** shown by this diagram. (1)

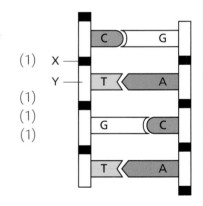

2 The diagram below shows a primary transcript that is processed to produce a mature messenger RNA molecule.

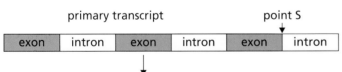

primary transcript   point S

mature messenger RNA molecule produced

a) Name the enzyme that adds RNA nucleotides to form a primary transcript. (1)

b) Describe what happens to the primary transcript to produce the mature messenger RNA. (2)

c) State the effect of a splice-site mutation at point S on the structure of the mature mRNA produced. (1)

d) Name the sites in a cell where proteins are synthesised. (1)

3   The diagram below shows the sequence of bases in some mRNA codons and the amino acids for which they code.

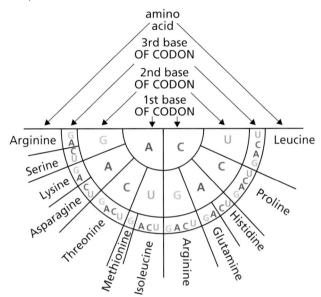

a) Give the mRNA codon that codes for the amino acid methionine. (1)
b) Name the amino acids specified by codons that have cytosine (C) as their second base. (1)
c) Name the amino acid which could be carried by a tRNA molecule with the anticodon GUA. (1)
d) A mutation caused a codon to change from AGG to CGG. Describe the impact this would have on the structure of the protein produced as a result and explain your answer. (2)

4   The graph below shows how the rate of an enzyme-catalysed reaction varies with the substrate concentration and how the reaction is affected by a competitive and a non-competitive inhibitor.

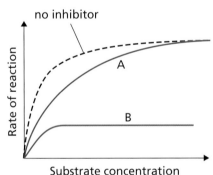

a) Describe the rate of reaction in the absence of an inhibitor. (2)
b) State which line shows the effect of the competitive inhibitor and explain the inhibitor's effect. (2)
c) Explain how a non-competitive inhibitor affects an enzyme. (1)

5 The diagram below shows part of the electron transport chain attached to the inner membrane of a mitochondrion.

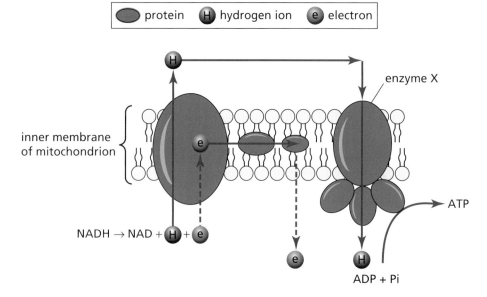

a) Describe the role of the high-energy electrons that pass down the electron transport chain. (1)
b) Describe the events involved in the synthesis of ATP as shown in the diagram above. (2)
c) State the role of oxygen in the electron transport chain. (1)

6 a) Copy and complete the table below to show the differences between embryonic and adult stem cells. (2)

	Embryonic stem cells	Adult stem cells
Location	In early embryo tissue	
Potential following cell division		Can differentiate into cells of one type of tissue

b) Describe **one** ethical issue that can arise when considering the use of embryonic stem cells in research or medicine. (2)

7 a) Copy and complete the table below, which shows information about features of mitosis and meiosis. (2)

Information	Mitosis	Meiosis
Occurs in somatic cells	Yes	
Occurs in germline cells		Yes
Chromosome complement of parent cells		Diploid
Chromosome complement of daughter cells	Diploid	

b) Cancer cells can sometimes form secondary tumours. Describe the formation of a secondary tumour. (2)

⇒
Question 8 contains a choice.

8 *Either* A Give an account of aerobic respiration under the following headings:
   a) Glycolysis   (3)
   b) The citric acid cycle   (6)
   Or B Give an account of DNA in cells under the following headings:
   a) DNA structure   (5)
   b) DNA replication   (4)

Answers to Practice Course Assessment: Unit 1

Section A

1 A, **2** C, **3** D, **4** C, **5** A, **6** D, **7** B, **8** C, **9** B, **10** A

Section B

1 a) X phosphate, Y deoxyribose   [1]
   b) each strand runs in the opposite direction from the other   [1]
   c) hydrogen bond   [1]
   d) double helix shape   [1]
2 a) RNA polymerase   [1]
   b) introns removed; exons spliced together   [2]
   c) intron left in mRNA   [1]
   d) ribosomes   [1]
3 a) AUG   [1]
   b) threonine *and* proline   [1]
   c) histidine   [1]
   d) there would be no impact/protein unchanged; mutation is silent/AGG codes for same
      amino acid as CGG   [2]
4 a) as substrate concentration increases from zero, rate of reaction increases rapidly; as
      concentration of substrate increases more, rate of reaction increases more slowly   [2]
   b) line A; inhibitor reduces reaction rates because it occupies active sites   [2]
   c) attaches to enzyme surface *and* permanently alters active site shape   [1]
5 a) provide energy to push H ions through the inner membrane   [1]
   b) return of H ions through ATP synthase; ATP synthase catalyses $ADP + Pi \rightarrow ATP$ [2]
   c) acts as a final acceptor of hydrogen *and* electrons   [1]
6 a) within adult tissues; can differentiate into almost any type of cell   [2]
   b) moral duty to preserve life; embryos killed to obtain stem cells; other answers
      possible   [any 2 = 2]
7 a) no; yes; diploid; haploid   [all 4 = 2, 3/2 = 1]
   b) tumour cell fails to attach; travels in bloodstream to site of secondary tumour   [2]
8 A a) glycolysis is the breakdown of glucose to pyruvate; glycolysis occurs in the cytoplasm;
         glycolysis is regulated by action of phosphofructokinase; 2 ATP molecules are used
         (to phosphorylate intermediates in glycolysis); in an energy investment phase; 4 ATP
         molecules are produced/generated/made in a pay-off stage   [any 3 = 3]
      b) if oxygen is available/in aerobic conditions pyruvate progresses to the citric acid cycle; in the
         matrix of the mitochondria; pyruvate is converted/broken down to an acetyl group; acetyl
         group combines with coenzyme A; acetyl (coenzyme A) combines with oxaloacetate to
         form citrate; citric acid cycle is enzyme controlled/involves dehydrogenases; ATP generated/
         synthesised/produced/released at substrate level in the citric acid cycle; carbon dioxide is
         released from the citric acid cycle; oxaloacetate is regenerated; NAD/NADH/$NADH_2$/FAD/
         FADH/$FADH_2$ transports electrons/transports hydrogen ions to the electron transport
         chain   [any 6 = 6]
                                                                                             ⇨

B a) double-stranded helix; strands made up of nucleotides; nucleotide composed of deoxyribose, phosphate and base; each strand has a sugar–phosphate backbone; strands connected through bases by H bonds; bases complementary/A pairs with T and G pairs with C; strands antiparallel/run in opposite directions; each strand has phosphate at 5' end and sugar at 3' end   [any 5 = 5]

   b) double helix (uncoils and) unzips; primers add onto template strands; primers allow DNA polymerase/enzyme to bind; DNA polymerase adds complementary DNA nucleotide to templates; one/lead strand replicated continuously; other/lagging strand replicated in fragments; fragments joined by ligase   [any 4 = 4]

Unit 2 Physiology and health

The structure and function of reproductive organs and gametes

Key points !

1 **Gametes** are produced from germline cells by meiosis. ☐
2 Sperm are produced in the **seminiferous tubules** in the **testes**. ☐
3 The **interstitial cells** of the testes produce the hormone **testosterone**. ☐
4 The **prostate gland** and **seminal vesicles** secrete fluids that maintain the motility and viability of the sperm. ☐
5 The **ovaries** contain immature ova (egg cells) in various stages of development. ☐
6 Each ovum is surrounded by a **follicle** that protects the maturing ovum and secretes hormones. ☐
7 Mature ova are released into the **oviduct** where they may be fertilised by sperm to form a **zygote**. ☐
8 A zygote undergoes mitosis to produce a **blastocyst**, which implants into the **endometrium** and develops into an embryo. ☐

Summary notes

Reproductive organs, gametes and fertilisation

Gametes are produced from the germline cells found in reproductive organs. Diploid ($2n$) germline cells divide by mitosis to form more diploid germline cells or by meiosis to produce haploid (n) gametes, as shown in Figure 2.1.

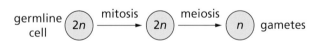

Figure 2.1 Division of germline cells by mitosis and meiosis

Hints & tips ★

There is more about mitosis, meiosis and germline cells in Key Area 1.1 on pages 2–3.

Male reproductive organs

The testes are male reproductive organs. The coiled seminiferous tubules in the testes produce sperm cells. The seminiferous tubules are lined with germline cells, which divide first by mitosis and then meiosis to produce male gametes – the sperm cells. The interstitial cells, found between the seminiferous tubules of the testes, produce the hormone testosterone. Testosterone stimulates sperm production in the seminiferous tubules. Some features of the male reproductive organs are shown in Figure 2.2.

Hints & tips

There is more about testosterone in Key Area 2.2 on pages 69–70.

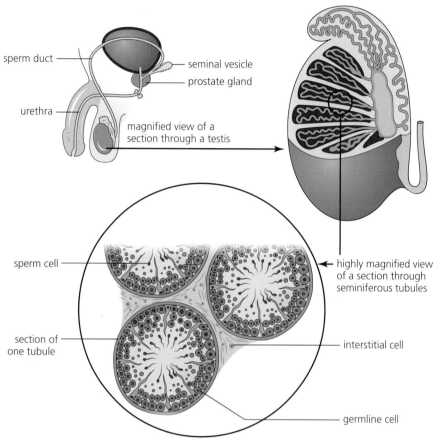

Figure 2.2 Some features of the reproductive system in males

Prostate gland and seminal vesicles

Testosterone activates the prostate gland and seminal vesicles to secrete fluids. These fluids are added to sperm cells released from the testes and maintain the motility and viability of the sperm cells. The following table provides a summary of the roles of the prostate gland and seminal vesicles.

Gland	Secretion	Role
Prostate	Enzymes	Keep fluid at correct consistency for efficient swimming of sperm cells
Seminal vesicles	Fructose (high-energy sugar)	Respired to provide the energy for the sperm cells to swim
	Prostaglandins	Cause muscles in the female reproductive system to contract, helping move the sperm cells towards the oviduct

Female reproductive organs

The ovaries are female reproductive organs. Ovaries produce and release ova (egg cells) and the hormones **oestrogen** and **progesterone**. The ovaries contain germline cells, which develop into immature ova. Each

*Hints & tips*

There is more about oestrogen and progesterone in Key Area 2.2 on pages 70–72.

ovum is surrounded by a follicle that protects the maturing ovum and secretes oestrogen. Ovulation is the release of a mature ovum into an oviduct, where it may be fertilised by a sperm cell to form a zygote. The zygote divides by mitosis to form a blastocyst, which continues along the oviduct and enters the uterus, where it implants into the endometrium to complete its development into an embryo.

Following ovulation, the follicle develops into a **corpus luteum**, which secretes progesterone.

Figure 2.3 shows the structure and function of some parts of the female reproductive system. The section of the ovary has been simplified to show the maturation of a single follicle.

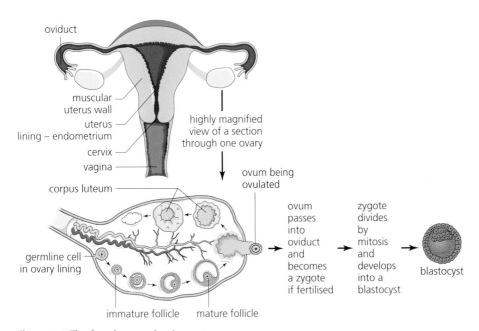

Figure 2.3 The female reproductive system

The following table summarises functions of parts of the female reproductive system.

Structure	Function
Ovary	Female reproductive organ that contains germline cells
Follicle	Structure that surrounds an ovum and secretes the hormone oestrogen
Corpus luteum	Develops from the follicle following ovulation and secretes the hormone progesterone
Ovum	Female gamete
Oviduct	Site of fertilisation and zygote formation
Uterus	Site of implantation of blastocyst and of embryo development
Cervix	Secretes cervical mucus, important in fertility

Key words

Blastocyst – cellular structure that implants and becomes the embryo and the placenta

Corpus luteum – formed from a follicle after ovulation; produces progesterone

Endometrium – inner lining of the uterus

Follicle – cluster of cells in the ovary that matures to release an ovum

Gamete – sex cell containing the haploid chromosome number

Interstitial cells – cells in testes found between the seminiferous tubules; produce ICSH

Oestrogen – hormone produced by the ovary that helps in the repair and thickening of the endometrium after menstruation

Ovaries – female sex organs in which ova are produced

Oviduct – fine tube connecting an ovary to the uterus; location of fertilisation

Progesterone – hormone produced by the ovary that thickens and vascularises the endometrium

Prostate gland – produces fluid that makes up part of the semen

Seminal vesicles – glands producing fluid that forms part of the semen

Seminiferous tubules – very narrow tubes in the testes in which sperm cells are produced

Testes – male sex organs responsible for the production of sperm

Testosterone – steroid hormone produced by interstitial cells

Zygote – fertilised egg cell

Questions

Restricted response (structured in 1- or 2-mark parts)

1 Name the structures in which sperm cells are produced. (1)
2 Name the cells which secrete testosterone. (1)
3 State the function of testosterone. (2)
4 Describe the location and function of the germline cells in the testes. (2)
5 Describe the roles of the secretions from
  a) the seminal vesicles (2)
  b) the prostate gland. (1)
6 Name the structure that develops from the follicle after ovulation. (1)
7 Give the location of fertilisation in the female reproductive system. (1)
8 Name the hormones produced by
  a) the follicle (1)
  b) the corpus luteum. (1)
9 Describe what is meant by the term blastocyst. (1)

Extended response (4–9 marks each)

10 Give an account of gamete production in the testes. (5)

Answers are on page 118.

Hormonal control of reproduction

Key points !

1 **Hormones** are chemical messengers produced by the **endocrine glands** (ductless glands). ☐

2 Hormones are released directly into the bloodstream and travel to their target tissue or organ where they have their effect. ☐

3 Hormones control the onset of puberty, sperm production and the **menstrual cycle**. ☐

4 At puberty, the **hypothalamus** in the brain secretes a releaser hormone that targets the **pituitary gland**. ☐

5 The pituitary gland is stimulated to release one hormone called **follicle stimulating hormone (FSH)**, and a second hormone called **luteinising hormone (LH)** in women and **interstitial cell stimulating hormone (ICSH)** in men. ☐

6 In males, FSH promotes sperm production in the seminiferous tubules of the testes and ICSH stimulates the interstitial cells in the testes to produce the male sex hormone called testosterone. ☐

7 Testosterone stimulates sperm production in the seminiferous tubules and also activates the prostate gland and the seminal vesicles to produce their fluid secretions. ☐

8 Overproduction of testosterone is prevented by a negative feedback mechanism. ☐

9 High testosterone levels inhibit the secretion of FSH and ICSH from the pituitary gland, resulting in a decrease in the production of testosterone by the interstitial cells. ☐

10 The menstrual cycle takes approximately 28 days with the first day of menstruation regarded as day one of the cycle. ☐

11 The pituitary hormones FSH and LH and the ovarian hormones oestrogen and progesterone are associated with the menstrual cycle. ☐

12 In the **follicular phase** (first half of the cycle), FSH stimulates the development and maturation of a follicle surrounding the ovum and the production of the sex hormone oestrogen by the follicle. ☐

13 Oestrogen stimulates the repair and vascularisation of the endometrium, thickening it and preparing it for implantation. ☐

14 High levels of oestrogen stimulate the secretion of LH by the pituitary gland. ☐

15 In the **luteal phase** (second half of the cycle), a surge in LH triggers ovulation and then stimulates the development of the corpus luteum from the follicle. ☐

16 LH also stimulates the corpus luteum to secrete the sex hormone progesterone. ☐

17 Progesterone promotes the further development and vascularisation of the endometrium, preparing it for implantation of a blastocyst, if fertilisation occurs. ☐

18 High levels of oestrogen and progesterone inhibit the secretion of FSH and LH by the pituitary gland, which prevents further follicles from developing. ☐

⇨

⇒

19 The inhibition of FSH and LH by high levels of oestrogen and progesterone is an example of **negative feedback** control. ☐

20 If fertilisation does not occur, there is a drop in LH levels, which causes the corpus luteum to break down, in turn causing a decrease in progesterone and oestrogen levels. ☐

21 The decrease in oestrogen and progesterone levels causes the endometrium to break down and triggers the start of **menstruation**. ☐

Summary notes

Hormonal onset of puberty

Puberty is the sequence of physical changes in which an individual's body develops from a child's into an adult's capable of reproduction. At puberty, the hypothalamus in the brain secretes a releaser hormone that targets the pituitary gland. The releaser hormone stimulates the pituitary gland to secrete follicle stimulating hormone (FSH) and luteinising hormone (LH), which is known as interstitial cell stimulating hormone (ICSH) in men. These hormones trigger the start of menstrual cycles in women and production of sperm by men.

Sperm production by males

In males, FSH promotes sperm production in the seminiferous tubules of the testes. ICSH (LH) in the male stimulates the release of testosterone from the interstitial cells of the testes. Figure 2.4 shows the effect of FSH and ICSH on the testes.

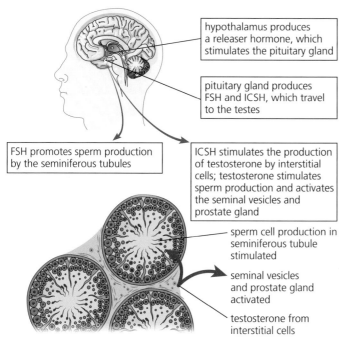

Figure 2.4 The effect of FSH and ICSH on the testes

Hormonal control of sperm production and negative feedback

ICSH stimulates the interstitial cells to produce testosterone, which in turn stimulates sperm cell production in the seminiferous tubules. When the testosterone level in the blood increases above a certain level, it inhibits the secretion of FSH and ICSH from the pituitary gland. This decreases the level of testosterone produced by the interstitial cells. When the testosterone level drops it no longer inhibits the FSH and ICSH and so testosterone production starts up again, as shown in Figure 2.5.

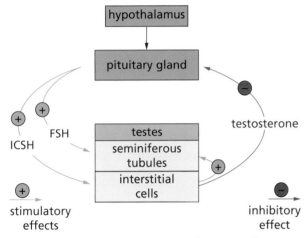

Figure 2.5 Negative feedback control of sperm production in males

Menstrual cycle in females

In females, FSH initiates gamete release through the development of follicles in the ovaries and the production of oestrogen from the follicles. The LH triggers ovulation. After ovulation, LH stimulates the corpus luteum to release the hormone progesterone as shown in Figure 2.6.

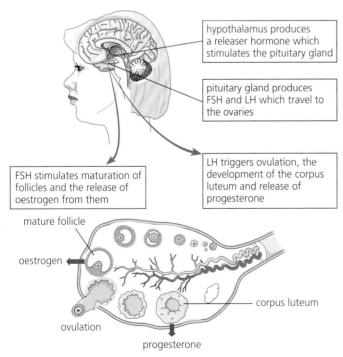

Figure 2.6 The effect of FSH and LH on the ovaries

Hormonal control of the menstrual cycle

The menstrual cycle occurs over approximately 28-day periods in the ovary and uterus and can be divided into two phases, shown in Figure 2.7.

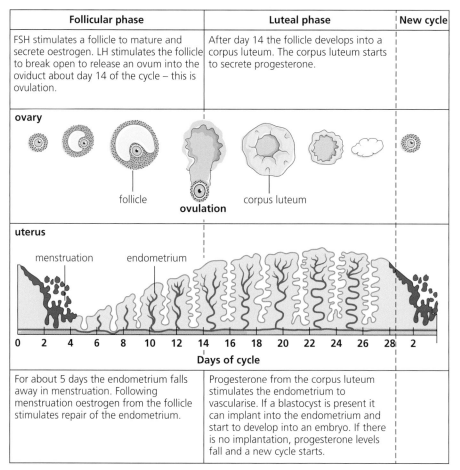

Follicular phase	Luteal phase	New cycle
FSH stimulates a follicle to mature and secrete oestrogen. LH stimulates the follicle to break open to release an ovum into the oviduct about day 14 of the cycle – this is ovulation.	After day 14 the follicle develops into a corpus luteum. The corpus luteum starts to secrete progesterone.	
ovary follicle ovulation corpus luteum		
uterus menstruation endometrium Days of cycle 0 2 4 6 8 10 12 14 16 18 20 22 24 26 28 2		
For about 5 days the endometrium falls away in menstruation. Following menstruation oestrogen from the follicle stimulates repair of the endometrium.	Progesterone from the corpus luteum stimulates the endometrium to vascularise. If a blastocyst is present it can implant into the endometrium and start to develop into an embryo. If there is no implantation, progesterone levels fall and a new cycle starts.	

Figure 2.7 Stages of the menstrual cycle

Follicular phase

FSH stimulates the development of a follicle and the production of oestrogen by the follicle in the follicular phase. Oestrogen stimulates repair of the endometrium, preparing it for implantation, and affects the consistency of cervical mucus by making it more easily penetrated by sperm. Peak levels of oestrogen act on the pituitary gland and stimulate a surge in the secretion of LH, which triggers ovulation.

Luteal phase

In the luteal phase the remaining cells of the follicle develop into a corpus luteum and start to secrete progesterone. Progesterone promotes vascularisation of the endometrium, preparing it to receive a blastocyst if fertilisation occurs. Progesterone also causes thickening of the cervical mucus.

A blastocyst develops from a zygote. This is a pre-implantation embryo consisting of a thin-walled hollow sphere of 16–40 cells, which usually implants in the endometrium of the uterus 8–13 days after fertilisation.

Hints & tips

*For the follicular phase, remember the **4Fs**:*
Follicular phase
First half
FSH
Follicle development

Hints & tips

There is more about the blastocyst in Key Area 1.1 on page 6.

Hints & tips

*For the luteal phase, remember **LOL**:*
Luteal phase
Ovulation
LH

Negative feedback

High progesterone levels have a negative feedback effect on the pituitary gland, resulting in the inhibition of FSH and LH. The inhibition of FSH prevents further follicles from developing. The lack of LH leads to degeneration of the corpus luteum, with a subsequent drop in progesterone levels, leading to menstruation and allowing the cycle to start again.

The following table shows a summary of the hormones associated with the menstrual cycle, their sites of production and functions.

Hormone	Site of production	Function
FSH	Pituitary gland	Stimulates the development and maturation of a follicle surrounding the ovum, and the production of the sex hormone oestrogen by the follicle
LH	Pituitary gland	Triggers ovulation and then stimulates the development of the corpus luteum from the follicle
Oestrogen	Ovaries	Stimulates the repair of the endometrium, thickening it and preparing it for implantation
Progesterone	Ovaries	Promotes the vascularisation of the endometrium, finally preparing it for implantation of a blastocyst if fertilisation occurs

No fertilisation

If fertilisation does not take place, the corpus luteum degenerates and the progesterone and oestrogen levels decrease. Low levels of progesterone and oestrogen result in the onset of menstruation, with the loss of the inner layer of the endometrium, along with some blood.

Fertilisation and pregnancy

If fertilisation does occur, the corpus luteum continues to produce progesterone, which maintains the endometrium and prevents a miscarriage. The placenta takes over the production of progesterone a few weeks into pregnancy. The inhibitory effect of high progesterone levels results in a drop in the levels of FSH and LH from the pituitary.

Summary of negative feedback effects in reproduction

The following table summarises the role of negative feedback in reproduction.

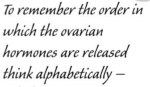

Hints & tips

To remember the order in which the pituitary hormones are released:
- *F for **FSH** – **F** for First hormone released*
- *L for **LH** – **L** for Last hormone released*

Hints & tips

To remember the order in which the ovarian hormones are released think alphabetically – O before P.

Negative feedback control in the hormonal control of reproduction	Notes
Negative feedback control of testosterone	Overproduction of testosterone is prevented by a negative feedback mechanism High testosterone levels inhibit the secretion of FSH and ICSH from the pituitary gland, resulting in a decrease in the production of testosterone by the interstitial cells
Negative feedback control of FSH and LH	High levels of oestrogen and progesterone inhibit the secretion of FSH and LH by the pituitary gland, which prevents further follicles from developing

Key words

Endocrine gland – gland that produces and releases hormones

Follicle stimulating hormone (FSH) – pituitary hormone that controls development of follicles in ovaries and sperm production in males

Follicular phase – first stage in the menstrual cycle during which a follicle develops

Hormone – protein released by an endocrine gland into the blood that acts as a chemical messenger

Hypothalamus – region of the mammalian brain that secretes releaser hormone at puberty

Interstitial cell stimulating hormone (ICSH) – hormone from interstitial cells that stimulates sperm production in seminiferous tubules

Luteal phase – second stage of the menstrual cycle in which a corpus luteum is present

Luteinising hormone (LH) – pituitary hormone that triggers ovulation and corpus luteum development

Menstrual cycle – approximately 28-day cycle in the middle of which ovulation occurs

Menstruation – removal of the endometrium and an unfertilised egg cell at the end of a menstrual cycle

Negative feedback – system of maintaining a steady state in various body systems

Pituitary gland – gland in the brain that releases many hormones

Questions ?

Restricted response (structured in 1- or 2-mark parts)

1 Describe the role of ICSH. (1)
2 Describe the role of the pituitary gland in male reproduction. (2)
3 Describe the effect of testosterone on the testes of an adult male. (1)
4 Explain how the concentration of testosterone in the blood is prevented from becoming too high. (2)
5 Describe the role of the corpus luteum. (1)
6 Describe the role of the following hormones in the menstrual cycle:
   a) FSH (2)
   b) LH. (2)
7 Describe the role of oestrogen and progesterone in the menstrual cycle. (2)
8 Describe the changes in the concentrations of progesterone and FSH in a woman's blood if she becomes pregnant. (2)
9 Explain what prevents further development of follicles when an embryo is developing in the uterus. (2)

Extended response (4–9 marks each)

10 Give an account of the role of pituitary and ovarian hormones in the menstrual cycle. (6)
11 Write notes on negative feedback in the control of male reproduction. (9)
12 Give an account of the events that take place in the first half of the menstrual cycle. (9)

Answers are on page 118–119.

Key points ⓘ

1 Infertility treatments and contraception are based on the biology of fertility. ☐

2 Males are continuously fertile due to relatively constant levels of pituitary hormones. ☐

3 Females' fertility is cyclical and the most fertile period – the time with the highest likelihood of pregnancy resulting from sexual intercourse – is from a few days before until 1–2 days after ovulation. ☐

4 The time of ovulation can be estimated by the number of days after menstruation, a slight rise in body temperature on the day of ovulation and the thinning of cervical mucus. ☐

5 Female infertility may be due to failure to ovulate, which is usually the result of a hormone imbalance. ☐

6 Ovulatory or fertility drugs can be used to stimulate ovulation. ☐

7 Some ovulatory drugs work by preventing the negative feedback effect of oestrogen on FSH secretion. ☐

8 Some ovulatory drugs mimic the action of FSH and LH. ☐

9 Ovulatory drugs can cause super ovulation, which can result in multiple births. ☐

10 Ovulatory drugs can be used to collect ova for **in vitro** fertilisation **(IVF)** programmes. ☐

11 **Artificial insemination** is a treatment in which semen is inserted into the female reproductive tract without intercourse having taken place. ☐

12 Artificial insemination is particularly useful where the male has a low sperm count. ☐

13 Artificial insemination involves collecting and combining several samples of semen over a period of time. ☐

14 If a male partner is infertile (sterile), sperm from a donor may be used in artificial insemination. ☐

15 IVF involves the surgical removal of eggs from ovaries after hormone stimulation, mixing with sperm to achieve fertilisation, incubation of zygotes and uterine implantation. ☐

16 **Intracytoplasmic sperm injection (ICSI)** can be used during IVF treatment, if mature sperm are defective or very low in number. ☐

17 ICSI involves the head of a sperm being drawn into a needle and injected directly into the egg to achieve fertilisation. ☐

18 **Pre-implantation genetic diagnosis (PGD)** is used in conjunction with IVF to identify single gene disorders and chromosome abnormalities. ☐

19 Methods of contraception act by preventing fertilisation or implantation. ☐

20 Contraception is the intentional prevention of pregnancy (conception) by natural or artificial methods. ☐

21 Contraception includes both physical and chemical methods. ☐

22 Physical methods of contraception include barrier methods, avoiding fertile periods, intra-uterine devices and sterilisation procedures. ☐ ⇨

> 23 Chemical contraceptives are based on combinations of synthetic progesterone and oestrogen that mimic negative feedback, preventing the release of FSH/LH, inhibiting follicular development, ovulation and implantation (morning after pills) or causing thickening of the cervical mucus (mini pill). ☐
> 24 There are risks and ethical issues associated with fertility treatments. ☐

Summary notes

Fertility

Infertility treatments and contraception are based on the biology of fertility.

Fertile periods

A fertile period is when a male is capable of fathering a child or a female of conceiving and becoming pregnant.

Male fertility

Males are continuously fertile and continuously produce sperm from puberty onwards. Negative feedback control ensures that the pituitary hormones FSH and ICSH are maintained at a relatively constant level, which results in a steady production of testosterone and resulting sperm production.

Female fertility

Fertility in females is cyclical – they are fertile for a few days every month. Females are most likely to conceive in a fertile period, which lasts approximately 5 days around the time of ovulation. The time of ovulation can be estimated by counting the number of days after menstruation, the slight rise in body temperature on the day of ovulation and the thinning of the cervical mucus. Figure 2.8 shows the changes in body temperature that occur through an average menstrual cycle, and the timing of menstrual cycle events.

> **Hints & tips**
>
> *There is more about the action of FSH, ICSH and testosterone in Key Area 2.2 on pages 69–70.*

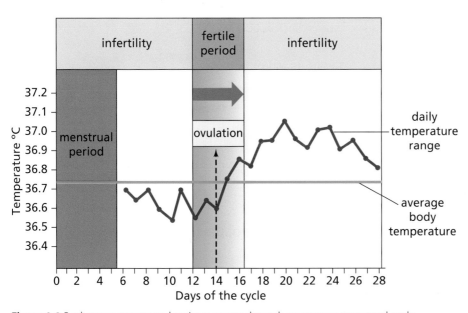

Figure 2.8 Body temperature and various events through an average menstrual cycle

The fertile period can be calculated and used to increase the chances of conceiving (becoming pregnant) or as a means of contraception through the timing of intercourse.

Infertility

Male and female infertility can arise due to factors such as age, genetics, disease, or health and lifestyle reasons, including anorexia, obesity, drug misuse, smoking, stress and poor diet.

Treatments for infertility

Stimulating ovulation

Female infertility can be due to failure to ovulate, caused by the failure of the pituitary gland to secrete FSH or LH. This can be treated with drugs that mimic FSH and LH or with drugs that interfere with the normal negative feedback control, by blocking the oestrogen receptors in the pituitary. These ovulatory drugs can cause super ovulation, which can result in multiple births. They can also be used to allow the collection of ova (eggs) for use in *in vitro* fertilisation (IVF) programmes.

The following table provides information on the stimulation of ovulation by drug treatment.

Ovulatory drug treatment	
Type	How they work
Drugs preventing negative feedback control	Ovulation is stimulated by drugs that prevent the negative feedback effect of oestrogen on FSH secretion, which means that FSH continues to be released and eggs produced
Drugs that mimic FSH and LH	These drugs mimic FSH and LH and so result in follicular development and ovulation

> **Hints & tips** ⭐
>
> It is vital that you have a really good understanding of the actions of the hormones involved in these processes — why not use a few flash cards?

> **Hints & tips** ⭐
>
> There is more about the hormonal control of the menstrual cycle in Key Area 2.2 on pages 70–72.

Artificial insemination

Artificial insemination is a treatment in which semen is collected and inserted into the female reproductive tract without intercourse having taken place.

Artificial insemination is particularly useful where the male has a low sperm count. Several samples of semen are collected and combined over a period of time. If a male partner is sterile, a donor may be used. This is called donor insemination. Figure 2.9 shows the technique of artificial insemination.

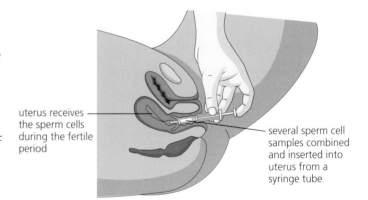

uterus receives the sperm cells during the fertile period

several sperm cell samples combined and inserted into uterus from a syringe tube

Figure 2.9 Technique of artificial insemination

In vitro fertilisation (IVF)

This treatment can be used when infertility is caused by blockage of the oviducts, which may have resulted from infection, such as pelvic inflammatory disease (PID) or the sexually transmitted *Chlamydia trachomatis*. Other causes of blockage are due to infection which can result from procedures like abortion, miscarriage or caesarean section.

Ova are surgically removed from the ovaries after stimulation by hormones. The ova are mixed with sperm cells in a culture dish outside the female's body. The fertilised eggs are then incubated until they have formed embryos of at least eight cells. Pre-implantation genetic diagnosis (PGD) is used to identify single gene disorders and chromosome abnormalities. The most suitable embryos are selected and transferred to the prepared uterus for implantation. Any unused embryos can be frozen and stored for later use. Figure 2.10 shows stages in the IVF procedure.

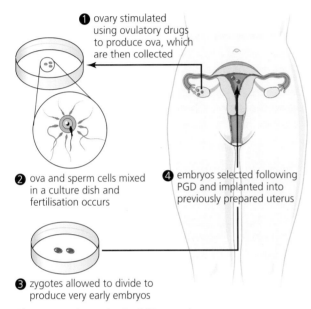

❶ ovary stimulated using ovulatory drugs to produce ova, which are then collected

❷ ova and sperm cells mixed in a culture dish and fertilisation occurs

❸ zygotes allowed to divide to produce very early embryos

❹ embryos selected following PGD and implanted into previously prepared uterus

Figure 2.10 Stages in the IVF procedure

Intracytoplasmic sperm injection (ICSI)

The success of fertilisation in the IVF procedure depends on the presence of a very high number of active sperm. With ICSI only one sperm per ovum is needed and can be used if mature sperm are either defective or very low in number. The head of an active sperm cell from a sample is drawn into a needle, then injected directly into the ovum to achieve fertilisation (Figure 2.11).

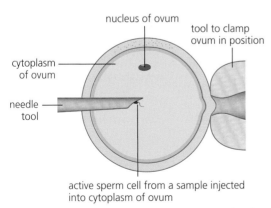

nucleus of ovum

tool to clamp ovum in position

cytoplasm of ovum

needle tool

active sperm cell from a sample injected into cytoplasm of ovum

Figure 2.11 Intracytoplasmic sperm injection (ICSI)

The following table summarises some of the main causes and treatments of female infertility.

Female infertility	
Cause	Treatment
Endometriosis, which can cause blocked tubes and ovulation problems	Surgery to remove abnormal tissue or unblock tubes Fertility drugs with artificial insemination for mild endometriosis or *in vitro* fertilisation (IVF) for more severe cases
Ovulation problems	Ovulation-stimulating drugs and IVF with fertility drugs
Poor egg quality	Egg or embryo donation
Polycystic ovary syndrome (PCOS) – a hormone imbalance that disrupts ovulation; the ovaries develop many small cysts instead of ripening and maturing one egg each cycle	Ovulation-stimulating drugs and IVF
Female tube blockages	Surgery to open tubes, or if tubes are too badly damaged to repair, IVF is an option

The following table summarises some of the main causes and treatments of male infertility.

Male infertility	
Cause	Treatment
Male sperm tube blockages	Surgery to correct tube blockages
Low or no sperm counts, poor sperm motility (the ability to move) and abnormally shaped sperm	Fertility drugs may boost sperm production Other options include artificial insemination or intra-uterine insemination (IUI), injecting sperm directly into the egg (ICSI) or donor insemination
Sperm allergy – some men have an immune reaction to their own semen, which causes them to produce anti-sperm antibodies that damage their sperm; this is most common after a vasectomy and becomes an issue for males having vasectomy reversal procedures	Artificial insemination, IVF, ICSI

Screening and pre-implantation genetic diagnosis (PGD)

As part of the IVF and ICSI procedures, cells from the embryos can be removed and tested for genetic abnormalities. Pre-implantation genetic diagnosis (PGD) is used in conjunction with IVF to identify single gene disorders and chromosome abnormalities. These tests are carried out to select the most suitable embryos for insemination and implantation.

Contraception

Contraception is the intentional prevention of pregnancy by natural or artificial methods, including both physical and chemical methods.

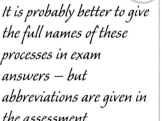

Hints & tips

It is probably better to give the full names of these processes in exam answers — but abbreviations are given in the assessment specification, so they should be acceptable.

Physical methods of contraception

Physical methods of contraception include barrier methods, avoiding fertile periods, intra-uterine devices and sterilisation procedures.

Barrier methods

Barrier methods include condom, diaphragm and cervical cap, and work by preventing the sperm entering the uterus and reaching an ovum.

Hints & tips

Read about calculating the fertile period on pages 75–76.

> ### Examples
>
> The following table provides a summary of physical methods of contraception.
>
> | Physical methods of contraception | |
> |---|---|
> | **Method** | **How it works** |
> | Condom | Prevents sperm being released into the female; can be used with spermicidal gels |
> | Diaphragm/cervical cap | Prevents sperm entering the uterus; can be used with spermicidal gels |
> | Calendar-based methods | Based on calculating the fertile period around ovulation and avoiding intercourse for a few days before and after ovulation |
> | Intra-uterine device (IUD) | Creates hostile environment for implantation to occur |
> | Vasectomy | Male sterilisation procedure preventing the release of sperm |
> | Tubal ligation | Female sterilisation procedure preventing the release of eggs |

Intra-uterine device (IUD)

An intra-uterine device (IUD or coil) is a small structure that is often T-shaped with metallic copper parts. It is fitted into the uterus to prevent the implantation of an embryo in the endometrium. Figure 2.12 shows an example.

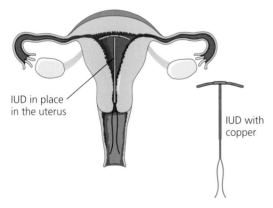

IUD in place in the uterus

IUD with copper

Figure 2.12 An intra-uterine device (IUD)

Sterilisation

Sterilisation procedures are usually irreversible and include vasectomy in males and tubal ligation in females. Sterilisation in males involves cutting and closing the sperm tube (vas deferens) of each testis. Sterilisation in females involves cutting or closing each oviduct (fallopian tube). Figure 2.13 shows sterilisation by vasectomy and tubal ligation.

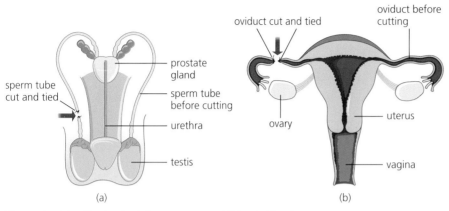

Figure 2.13 Sterilisation by (a) vasectomy and (b) tubal ligation

Chemical methods of contraception

Chemical contraceptives are based on combinations of synthetic versions of oestrogen and progesterone that mimic negative feedback, stopping the release of FSH/LH and hence suppressing ovulation ('the pill', or combination contraceptive pill), preventing implantation ('morning-after pill') or causing thickening of the cervical mucus ('mini pill'), so preventing sperm from entering the uterus and reaching the ovum.

Morning-after pills, also known as emergency contraceptive pills (ECPs), contain high levels of synthetic oestrogen and progesterone and are taken only after sexual intercourse has taken place.

Examples

The following table summarises some chemical methods of contraception and how they work.

Chemical methods of contraception	
Method	How it works
Combination contraceptive pill	Contains synthetic progesterone and oestrogen, which inhibit secretion of FSH and LH by the pituitary gland
Mini pill	Contains synthetic progesterone, which can inhibit ovulation and causes thickening of cervical mucus, preventing the entry of sperm and fertilisation
Morning-after pill (emergency contraceptive pill)	Contains a high dose of synthetic progesterone and oestrogen, decreasing chances of ovulation and implantation and thickening cervical mucus to prevent entry of sperm

Risks and ethics

Risk associated with the use of fertility drugs

The use of ovulatory drugs carries some risk of multiple pregnancies. Another risk that comes with fertility drug use is ovarian hyperstimulation syndrome (OHSS), which occurs when the ovaries become unusually enlarged, filling with fluid. When ovulation occurs, the fluid is released into the body, causing complications and, in rare cases, leading to blood clots and kidney failure. Ovulatory drug treatments can also slightly increase the chance of ovarian cysts.

Ethics and pre-implantation genetic diagnosis (PGD)

Some people support pre-implantation genetic diagnosis (PGD) as it offers reassurance to couples who are at high risk of having a child with a genetic disease. Some of these individuals may choose to remain childless without the help of PGD.

Supporters claim that a reduced frequency of genetic diseases and disorders is of great benefit to society as a whole. People opposed to PGD claim that it is morally wrong to interfere with conception. They argue that these procedures are really just selective breeding in humans and could lead to designer babies.

Ethics associated with the use of fertility drugs

There are several ethical issues associated with infertility and its treatment, as shown in the following table.

Issue	Ethical question
Economic	Should unlimited treatment be available on the NHS?
	Should health insurance companies be obliged to cover infertility treatment?
	Could the medical resources be better allocated elsewhere?
Legal	What is the legal status of embryos fertilised *in vitro* but not transferred?
	Should embryos not transferred be destroyed – is that just abortion?
Medical	Is there a link between IVF-based multiple births and premature birth and later health problems?
	Is it right to allow potential Y-chromosome abnormalities to be passed on using ICSI?
Religious	Are IVF and other treatments at odds with various commonly held beliefs?

Key words

Artificial insemination (AI) – insertion of donated sperm directly into the uterus

***In vitro* fertilisation (IVF)** – medical procedure involving fertilisation of eggs by sperm in laboratory containers

Intracytoplasmic sperm injection (ICSI) – injection of sperm directly into an egg during IVF

Pre-implantation genetic diagnosis (PGD) – genetic profiling of embryos prior to implantation during fertility treatments

Questions

Restricted response (structured in 1- or 2-mark parts)

1 Give the meaning of the terms cyclical fertility and continuous fertility. (2)
2 Describe how the fertile period of a female can be calculated. (2)
3 Name the method of fertility treatment that would be appropriate for a woman with blocked oviducts. (1)
4 Describe a treatment that may be used when female infertility is due to failure to ovulate. (1)
5 Give **one** risk associated with the use of ovulatory drugs. (1)
6 Give **two** physical methods of contraception. (2)
7 Explain the mechanism of action of the combined contraceptive pill. (2)
8 Explain how the mini pill works. (2)
9 Explain how the morning-after pill works. (2)
10 Describe the process of artificial insemination in the treatment of infertility. (2)
11 Describe the steps involved in intracytoplasmic sperm injection (ICSI). (2)
12 Explain why ICSI is sometimes used in conjunction with IVF. (2)
13 Explain why pre-implantation genetic diagnosis (PGD) is used in conjunction with IVF. (1)

Extended response (4–9 marks each)

14 Explain the biological basis for the stimulation of ovulation by ovulatory drugs. (5)
15 Describe the process of *in vitro* fertilisation (IVF). (4)
16 Discuss procedures that can be used to treat male infertility. (5)
17 Give an account of the causes and treatment of female infertility. (9)
18 Write notes on:
    a) risks associated with fertility treatments (2)
    b) ethics associated with fertility treatments. (2)

Answers are on page 119–120.

Ante- and postnatal screening

Key points !

1 Antenatal or prenatal screening involves testing for diseases or conditions in a **fetus** or **embryo** before it is born. ☐

2 **Antenatal screening** identifies the risk of a disorder so that further tests and a **prenatal diagnosis** can be offered. ☐

3 Common antenatal testing procedures include **ultrasound scanning**, **amniocentesis**, **chorionic villus sampling (CVS)** and **rhesus antibody testing**. ☐

4 An ultrasound scanner is used to produce an ultrasound image on a computer screen. ☐

5 Ultrasound scanners can be used to produce a pregnancy or gestational dating scan, which is used to determine the stage of pregnancy and the date that the baby is due. ☐

6 Ultrasound imaging is also used to produce an **anomaly scan**, which is used to detect the presence of serious physical problems in the fetus. ☐

7 Biochemical tests are carried out to detect marker chemicals that are produced during normal physiological changes that take place during pregnancy. ☐

8 Tests, such as ultrasound imaging, that indicate the possible presence of a disorder or condition are called screening procedures. ☐

9 Diagnostic tests, like amniocentesis and CVS, can confirm the presence of conditions such as Down syndrome. ☐

10 Cells from an amniocentesis sample or CVS can be cultured to obtain sufficient cells to produce a **karyotype**. ☐

11 A karyotype is an image of an individual's chromosomes, arranged in homologous pairs. ☐

12 A karyotype is used to identify anomalies in the numbers or structure of chromosomes. ☐

13 Diagnostic tests, like amniocentesis and CVS, are invasive and carry a small risk of inducing miscarriage. ☐

14 CVS can be carried out earlier than amniocentesis, but has a higher risk of inducing miscarriage. ☐

15 Rhesus antibody testing is carried out early in a pregnancy to determine the rhesus status of the mother, to ensure that she shows no immune response to her fetus. ☐

16 In the event of a second pregnancy, complications can arise if a mother is rhesus negative and the fetus is rhesus positive. ☐

17 Anti-rhesus antibodies are given to rhesus negative mothers after a sensitising event such as the birth of the baby. ☐

18 **Postnatal screening** involves health checks that are carried out after the birth of the baby. These are aimed at detecting certain conditions or abnormalities. ☐

19 Postnatal diagnostic testing is used to detect metabolic disorders such as **phenylketonuria (PKU)**. ☐

20 PKU is an inborn error of metabolism caused by an **autosomal recessive** genetic disorder. ☐

⇨

⇒

21 Individuals with PKU cannot metabolise excess phenylalanine. ☐
22 If PKU is not detected soon after birth the baby's mental development can be affected. ☐
23 Individuals with PKU are placed on a restricted diet that lacks the amino acid phenylalanine. ☐
24 **Pedigree charts** (family trees) are compiled and used to analyse patterns of inheritance in genetic screening and counselling. ☐
25 Pedigree charts are constructed to provide information and advice in situations where there is the possibility of passing on a genetic disorder to potential offspring. ☐
26 Pedigree charts can be used to analyse patterns of inheritance involving autosomal recessive, **autosomal dominant, incomplete dominance** and **sex-linked recessive** single gene disorders. ☐
27 **Alleles** are forms of the same gene; **homozygous** individuals have two copies of the same allele and **heterozygous** individuals have copies of two different alleles. ☐
28 An autosomal recessive disorder, such as cystic fibrosis, is expressed relatively rarely in the offspring. It affects males and females equally and may skip generations. ☐
29 An autosomal dominant disorder such as Huntington's disease (HD) shows up in every generation and affects males and females equally. ☐
30 In examples of autosomal incomplete dominance, the fully expressed form of the condition is rare, the partly expressed form is more common and males and females are affected equally. ☐
31 In sex-linked recessive disorders, males are affected more than females. Male offspring receive the condition from their mother; fathers cannot pass the condition on to their sons and female offspring can only be affected if the father has the condition and the mother is at least a carrier. ☐

Summary notes

Antenatal screening

Antenatal or prenatal screening involves assessing the health and general well-being of the mother and testing for diseases or conditions in an embryo or fetus before it is born.

The purpose of antenatal screening is to detect the risk of disorders such as Down syndrome, spina bifida, cystic fibrosis and muscular dystrophy. Antenatal screening can also be used to determine the sex of the baby. Results of screening can allow further tests and a prenatal diagnosis to be offered.

Antenatal tests

Common antenatal testing procedures include ultrasound imaging, amniocentesis, chorionic villus sampling (CVS), rhesus antibody testing and various other biochemical tests.

Ultrasound imaging

Dating scans, for pregnancy stage and due date, are used with tests for marker chemicals, which vary normally during pregnancy. The first scan is carried out at around 8–14 weeks of the pregnancy and is called a dating scan as it is used to determine the age of the fetus and the expected delivery date (Figure 2.14).

A second scan is also offered at 18–20 weeks, when the fetus is much larger. This is known as an anomaly scan and is used to identify any aspects of physical development of the limbs and vital organs that are unusual.

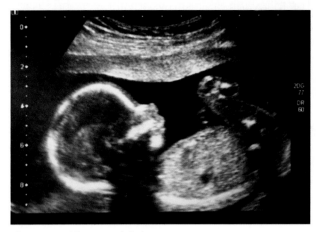

Figure 2.14 Ultrasound dating scan

Biochemical tests

The health of the mother and the fetus can be monitored by biochemical tests that detect marker chemicals produced during the normal physiological changes of pregnancy.

Diagnostic testing

Medical conditions can be detected by a range of marker chemicals that indicate a condition but need not necessarily be part of that condition. As a result of routine screening, or for individuals in high-risk categories, further tests may be offered.

In deciding to proceed with these tests, the element of risk will be assessed, as will the decisions the individuals concerned are likely to make if a test is positive. Tests include amniocentesis and chorionic villus sampling (CVS) from the placenta. Figure 2.15 shows the stages in amniocentesis and CVS.

(a) amniocentesis

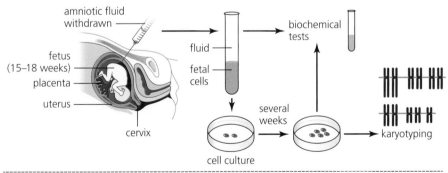

(b) chorionic villus sampling (CVS)

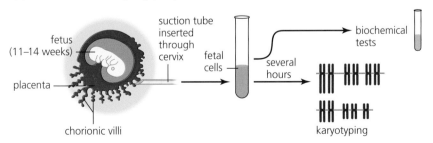

Figure 2.15 Stages of (a) amniocentesis and (b) chorionic villus sampling (CVS)

The following table shows advantages and disadvantages associated with amniocentesis and CVS.

Test	Amniocentesis	Chorionic villus sampling
Timing (week of pregnancy)	15th–18th	11th–14th
Advantages	Prenatal diagnosis possible Detects neural tube defect	Prenatal diagnosis possible Gives results earlier in pregnancy
Disadvantages	Small risk of miscarriage Gives results later in pregnancy	Does not detect neural tube defects Small risk of miscarriage May carry risk of defects of fingers and toes if carried out too early

Karyotypes

Cells from amniocentesis or from CVS can be used to produce karyotypes. A karyotype is an image of an individual's chromosomes, arranged in homologous pairs. The karyotype is used to identify anomalies in terms of the numbers or structure of chromosomes (Figure 2.16).

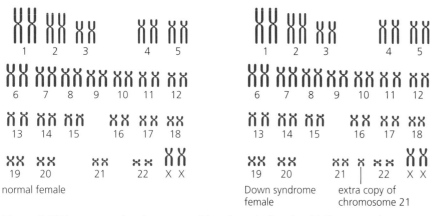

Figure 2.16 Karyotypes showing a normal female and a female with Down syndrome

Rhesus antibody testing

Generally mothers show no immune response to their fetus, although sensitisation to rhesus antigens can occur. This condition arises when the mother is rhesus negative and the fetus rhesus positive. Red blood cells from the fetus cross the placenta and trigger the release of antibodies by the mother. These antibodies can cross back into the fetal blood circulation and cause the blood to clot. Figure 2.17 shows sensitisation to rhesus antigens in a rhesus negative mother.

Treatment

Anti-rhesus antibodies can be given to rhesus negative mothers after a potentially sensitising event and after the first pregnancy so that the fetal rhesus positive red blood cells are destroyed before the mother's immune system can discover them. This protects any potential rhesus negative baby.

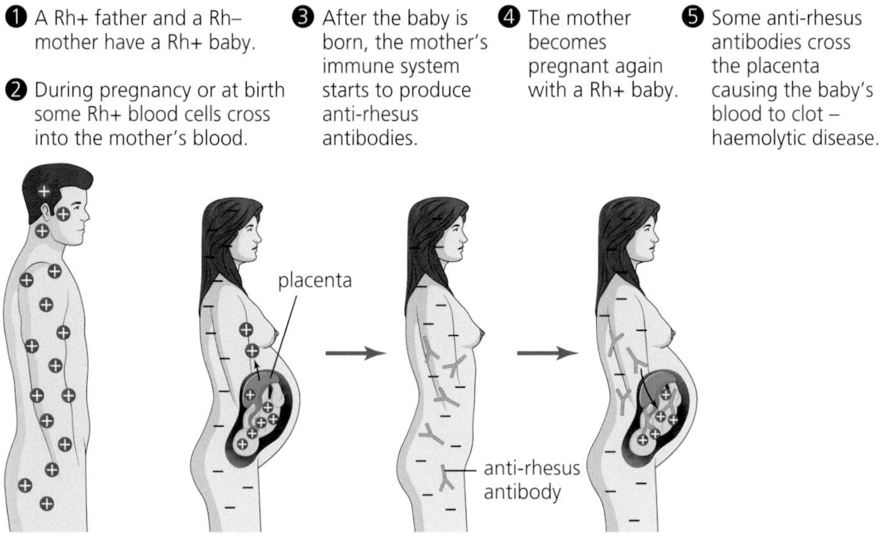

① A Rh+ father and a Rh– mother have a Rh+ baby.

② During pregnancy or at birth some Rh+ blood cells cross into the mother's blood.

❸ After the baby is born, the mother's immune system starts to produce anti-rhesus antibodies.

❹ The mother becomes pregnant again with a Rh+ baby.

❺ Some anti-rhesus antibodies cross the placenta causing the baby's blood to clot – haemolytic disease.

placenta

anti-rhesus antibody

Figure 2.17 Sensitisation to rhesus antigens in a rhesus negative mother

The following table summarises some examples of antenatal screening procedures and their functions.

Antenatal screening	
Procedure	Function
Ultrasound scan	Used to produce a pregnancy or gestational dating scan, determining the stage of pregnancy and the date that the baby is due
	Used to produce an anomaly scan to detect the presence of serious physical problems in the fetus
Biochemical tests	Carried out to detect marker chemicals that are produced during the normal physiological changes that take place during pregnancy
Amniocentesis	Diagnostic test involving the culture of cells to produce a karyotype
	Used to confirm a range of conditions such as Down syndrome
Chorionic villus sampling (CVS)	Diagnostic test used immediately to produce a karyotype to confirm a range of conditions such as Down syndrome
Rhesus antibody testing	Diagnostic test used to check for the presence of rhesus antibodies in a rhesus negative mother

Postnatal screening

Postnatal screening involves health checks that are carried out after the birth of the baby, aimed at detecting certain conditions or abnormalities. Postnatal diagnostic testing is used to detect metabolic disorders such as phenylketonuria (PKU). Figure 2.18 shows the heel prick test for PKU in newborn babies.

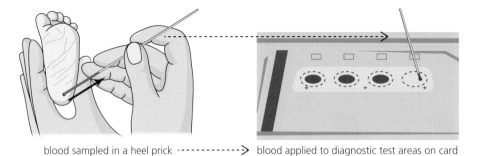

blood sampled in a heel prick ···········> blood applied to diagnostic test areas on card

Figure 2.18 The heel prick (Guthrie) test for PKU

Phenylketonuria (PKU)

Phenylketonuria (PKU) is an inborn error of metabolism caused by an autosomal recessive genetic disorder. This involves a mutation of the gene encoding the enzyme that converts the amino acid phenylalanine to the amino acid called tyrosine. As a result, individuals with PKU cannot metabolise the amino acid phenylalanine. The phenylalanine converts to phenylpyruvate, which affects the baby's mental development after birth. Infants with PKU are placed on a restricted diet that lacks the amino acid phenylalanine. Figure 2.19 provides a summary of PKU.

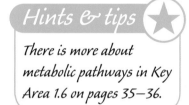

Hints & tips

There is more about metabolic pathways in Key Area 1.6 on pages 35–36.

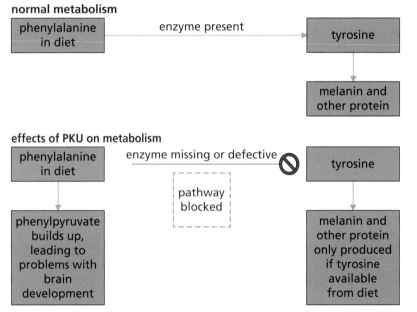

Figure 2.19 Effects of PKU on metabolism

Pedigree charts

A pattern of inheritance can be revealed by collecting information about a particular characteristic from family members and using it to construct a family tree or pedigree chart, as shown in Figure 2.20. If phenotypes are known, most of the genotypes of the individuals can be determined. Construction of a family tree may be carried out by a genetic counsellor and the information used to advise parents about inheritance patterns in their family.

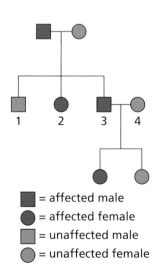

■ = affected male
● = affected female
▢ = unaffected male
○ = unaffected female

Figure 2.20 Example of a pedigree chart with a key and some individuals numbered for reference

Autosomal recessive

An autosomal recessive disorder such as cystic fibrosis (CF) is expressed relatively rarely in offspring, affects males and females equally and may skip generations through carriers. Figure 2.21 shows the inheritance of CF in a family. Note that carriers of the condition do *not* show the condition but they can pass it to their offspring.

Autosomal dominant

An autosomal dominant condition such as Huntington's disease (HD) can be common in a family. It affects males and females equally and an individual cannot carry the condition without being affected. Figure 2.22 shows the inheritance of HD.

Autosomal incomplete dominance

In examples of autosomal incomplete dominance, the fully expressed form of the condition is rare, the partly expressed form is more common and males and females are affected equally. Figure 2.23 shows the inheritance of sickle cell disease (SCD) in a family. Note that carriers have a less severe form of the disease called sickle cell trait, while those with two alleles have the more severe sickle cell anaemia.

In the pedigree chart shown individual **x** has sickle cell anaemia because she has received an allele for the condition from each of her parents, whereas individual **z** has sickle cell trait through receiving only one allele for the condition from her parents. Individual **y** has no allele for the condition and so she does not have SCD.

Sex-linked recessive

In sex-linked recessive conditions such as haemophilia, males are more commonly affected than females. Male offspring inherit the condition from their mother. Fathers cannot pass the condition on to their sons and female offspring can only be affected if the father has the condition and the mother is at least a carrier. Figure 2.24 shows inheritance of haemophilia in a family.

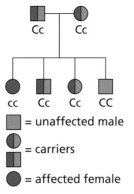

= unaffected male

= carriers

= affected female

Figure 2.21 CF in a family tree

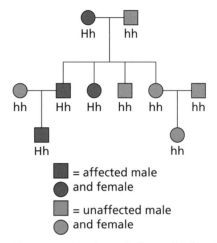

= affected male and female

= unaffected male and female

Figure 2.22 Huntington's disease (HD) in a family tree

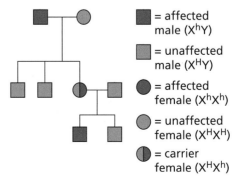

= unaffected female

= severely affected female

= mildly affected female

= unaffected male

= severely affected male

= mildly affected male

Figure 2.23 Sickle cell disease (SCD) in a family tree

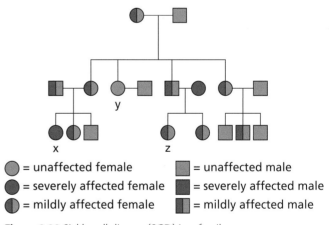

= affected male (X^hY)

= unaffected male (X^HY)

= affected female (X^hX^h)

= unaffected female (X^HX^H)

= carrier female (X^HX^h)

Figure 2.24 Haemophilia in a family tree

Key words

Allele – form of a gene coding for a version of a characteristic

Amniocentesis – prenatal test to assess health of fetus using cells from amniotic fluid

Anomaly scan – antenatal ultrasound scan that checks for physical abnormalities

Antenatal screening – use of tests to identify risk of a disorder before birth

Autosomal dominant – allele on chromosomes 1–22; always expressed in phenotype

Autosomal recessive – allele on chromosomes 1–22; expressed in phenotype if the genotype is homozygous for the recessive allele

Chorionic villus sampling (CVS) – prenatal test to assess health of the fetus using cells from the placenta

Embryo – stage of development up to about 8 weeks that leads to the formation of a fetus

Fetus – stage of a baby after 8 weeks of development

Heterozygous – having two different alleles of the same gene

Homozygous – having two identical alleles of the same gene

Incomplete dominance – when an allele is not completely masked by a dominant allele, thus affecting an individual's phenotype

Karyotype – display of matched chromosomes produced for medical purposes

Pedigree chart – diagram showing the occurrence of phenotypes of a particular gene in a family tree

Phenylketonuria (PKU) – metabolic disorder that is tested for by postnatal screening

Postnatal screening – diagnostic testing of newborn babies

Prenatal diagnosis – identification of the risk of disorders in unborn babies

Rhesus antibody testing – testing to show if a person carries rhesus antibodies in their blood

Sex-linked recessive – recessive allele carried on the X chromosome

Ultrasound scanning – diagnostic procedure used for various prenatal checks, such as establishing the stage of pregnancy and the date that the baby is due

Questions

Restricted response (structured in 1- or 2-mark parts)

1 Explain the purpose of antenatal screening. (2)
2 Give **two** examples of antenatal screening procedures. (2)
3 Give **two** uses of ultrasound imaging obtained by the use of ultrasound scanners. (2)
4 Give the name of an image of an individual's chromosomes arranged in homologous pairs. (1)
5 Explain the difference between a screening test and a diagnostic test. (2)
6 Explain why rhesus antibody testing is carried out early in a pregnancy. (1)
7 Give **one** characteristic of a pedigree chart that would suggest to a geneticist that the condition or disorder was autosomal recessive. (1)
8 Give **one** characteristic of a pedigree chart that would suggest to a geneticist that the condition or disorder was sex-linked and recessive. (1)

Extended response (4–9 marks each)

9 Explain why anti-rhesus antibodies are given to rhesus negative mothers after a sensitising event or after birth. (4)
10 Discuss the advantages and disadvantages of amniocentesis and chorionic villus sampling as diagnostic techniques. (4)
11 Explain the use of pedigree charts in genetic screening and counselling. (4)
12 Phenylketonuria (PKU) is an inborn error of metabolism detected by postnatal screening. Write notes on:
   a) the cause of PKU (3)
   b) the importance of detecting this metabolic disorder and the treatment given to an individual with PKU. (2)
13 Discuss the screening and testing procedures that may be carried out as part of antenatal care. (9)

Answers are on page 120–121.

The structure and function of arteries, capillaries and veins

Key points !

1 Blood circulates from the heart through blood vessels called **arteries**, **arterioles**, **capillaries**, **venules** and finally **veins**, before returning to the heart. ☐

2 Blood vessels are tubes with walls composed of different tissues dependent on the function of the vessel. ☐

3 The central space or cavity of the blood vessels is called the **lumen**. ☐

4 The lumen is lined with a layer of cells called the **endothelium**. ☐

5 The endothelium lining the central lumen of blood vessels is surrounded by layers of tissue that differ between arteries, capillaries and veins. ☐

6 Arteries carry blood away from the heart. ☐

7 Blood is pumped through arteries at a high pressure. ☐

8 Arteries have an outer layer of connective tissue containing elastic fibres and a thick middle layer containing smooth muscle with more elastic fibres. ☐

9 The thick elastic walls of the arteries stretch and recoil to accommodate the surge of blood after each contraction of the heart. ☐

10 The smooth muscle in the walls of arterioles can contract or relax, causing **vasoconstriction** and **vasodilation** to control blood flow. ☐

11 The ability of the arterioles to vasoconstrict or vasodilate allows the changing demands of the body's tissues to be met. ☐

12 During exercise the arterioles supplying the muscles vasodilate, which increases the blood flow. ☐

13 During exercise the arterioles supplying the abdominal organs vasoconstrict, which reduces the blood flow to them. ☐

14 Arteries branch into smaller blood vessels called arterioles. ☐

15 The arterioles branch into smaller blood vessels called capillaries. ☐

16 The blood is transported from the arterioles to the venules by passing through a dense network or bed of capillaries. ☐

17 Capillary walls are only one cell thick, which allows quick and efficient exchange of materials. ☐

18 Capillaries allow exchange of substances with tissues. ☐

19 Capillaries merge into one another, producing wider blood vessels called venules, which finally form veins. ☐

20 Veins carry blood towards the heart. ☐

21 Veins have an outer layer of connective tissue containing elastic fibres but a much thinner muscular wall than arteries. ☐

22 The lumen of a vein is relatively wider than that of an artery. ☐

23 Valves are present in veins to prevent the backflow of blood. ☐

24 Valves are needed as the blood is flowing back to the heart at low pressure and generally against the force of gravity. ☐

⇨

⇒

25 Blood in the arterioles is at a higher pressure than the blood in the capillaries. ☐
26 Higher blood pressure at the arteriole end of the capillary bed results in **pressure filtration**, forcing the **plasma**, with small soluble molecules, out of the capillaries into the tissues. ☐
27 **Tissue fluid** is similar to blood plasma but does not contain plasma proteins. ☐
28 Tissue fluid contains glucose, oxygen and dissolved substances, which supply the tissues with all their requirements. ☐
29 Useful molecules such as glucose and oxygen diffuse into cells and carbon dioxide and waste substances diffuse out of the cells and into the tissue fluid to be excreted. ☐
30 Tissue fluid re-enters the capillaries at the venule end of the capillary bed by **osmosis**. ☐
31 Pressure filtration forces more water out of the capillaries than re-enters by osmosis. ☐
32 Excess tissue fluid enters the lymph vessels and passes into the **lymphatic system**. ☐
33 **Lymph vessels** have thin walls and valves. ☐
34 The lymphatic system returns the **lymph fluid** to the circulatory system. ☐

Summary notes

Circulation

The heart together with blood vessels and the blood they contain form the cardiovascular system. Blood circulates from the heart through blood vessels called arteries, arterioles, capillaries, venules and veins before returning to the heart (Figure 2.25).

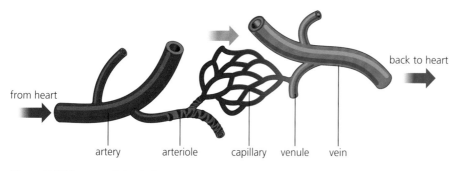

from heart   back to heart

artery   arteriole   capillary   venule   vein

Figure 2.25 Pattern of circulation

Blood vessels

The central space within a blood vessel is called the lumen. The lumen is lined with a layer of cells called the endothelium. The layers of tissue outside the endothelium are different in the different blood vessels.

Arteries

Arteries carry blood at high pressure away from the heart. Arterioles are the smallest arteries and supply blood to the capillaries. They have thick walls and a relatively narrow central lumen. The outer wall is made of tissue with elastic fibres. The inner wall contains smooth muscle with elastic fibres, as shown in Figure 2.26.

Contractions of the heart force surges of high-pressure blood into the arteries. The elastic fibres in the outer and middle layers allow the artery walls to stretch as these surges of blood pass through them. These fibres then recoil between beats, so maintaining the high pressure of blood in the arteries.

Contraction of the smooth muscle in the middle layer of the artery wall decreases the diameter of the central lumen. This is called vasoconstriction. Vasoconstriction of the arteries and arterioles decreases the flow of blood into the capillaries. Relaxation of the smooth muscle in the middle layer of the artery wall causes the opposite effect, called vasodilation. Vasodilation increases the diameter of the central lumen and increases the blood flow into the capillaries.

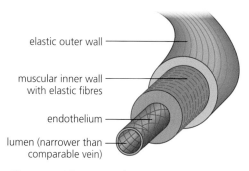

elastic outer wall

muscular inner wall with elastic fibres

endothelium

lumen (narrower than comparable vein)

Figure 2.26 Structure of an artery

Hints & tips

Remember: **A** for **Artery** and for **Away** from heart.

Veins

Veins carry blood at low pressure back to the heart. Venules are the smallest veins that remove blood from the capillaries, where exchange of materials with tissues has taken place. Veins have an outer wall containing elastic fibres but a much thinner inner muscular wall than arteries. The lumen of a vein is relatively wider than that of an artery of equivalent diameter.

Veins have valves that prevent backflow of blood flowing to the heart at low pressure and generally against the force of gravity. Figure 2.27 shows the structure of a vein.

Hints & tips

Remember: Ve**IN**s carry blood **IN**to the heart. Veins have **V**alves.

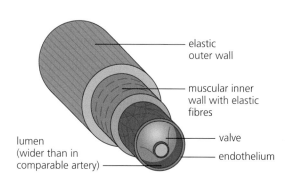

elastic outer wall

muscular inner wall with elastic fibres

lumen (wider than in comparable artery)

valve

endothelium

Figure 2.27 Structure of a vein

Capillaries

Capillaries allow the exchange of substances carried in the blood with the tissues of the body. Capillaries have a lumen and very thin walls – only the endothelium. This allows quick and efficient exchange of materials to occur between the blood inside and the surrounding body tissues. Figure 2.28 shows the structure of a capillary.

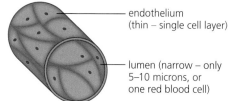

endothelium (thin – single cell layer)

lumen (narrow – only 5–10 microns, or one red blood cell)

Figure 2.28 Structure of a capillary

93

The following table summarises the structure and function of arteries, veins and capillaries.

Blood vessel	Function	Structure of wall	Lumen	Valves
Arteries	Carry blood away from the heart at a high pressure	Outer wall of elastic fibres and an inner wall containing smooth muscle with some elastic fibres	Relatively narrow	Absent
Veins	Carry blood towards the heart at lower pressure	Outer wall of elastic fibres but a much thinner inner muscular wall than arteries	Relatively wide	Present to prevent the backflow of blood
Capillaries	Allow rapid and efficient exchange of substances with tissues	Capillary walls are only one cell thick	Very narrow	Absent

The exchange of materials between tissue fluid and cells

Capillaries occur in networks called capillary beds, which run in between cells of the body tissues. The high pressure of arteriole blood causes pressure filtration, leading to the capillaries exuding plasma. This becomes the tissue fluid, which bathes the cells. Tissue fluid then exchanges material with the cells and returns to the capillaries by osmosis and diffusion. Excess tissue fluid drains into lymph vessels and is now called lymph (Figure 2.29).

Hints & tips

Remember: CaPillArieS allow materials to PASs through them.

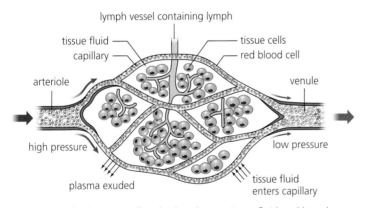

Figure 2.29 Fluids in a capillary bed – plasma, tissue fluid and lymph

The role of lymph vessels

More fluid passes out of the capillaries due to pressure filtration than diffuses back by osmosis and diffusion. Excess tissue fluid that does not pass into the capillaries enters the lymph vessels and passes into the lymphatic system. The tissue fluid entering the lymph vessels is now called lymph. The pressure of the lymph fluid is even lower than that of the blood in the veins.

Like veins, lymph vessels contain valves and surrounding skeletal muscles squeeze the lymph through the valves of the lymph vessels as the body moves. The lymphatic system returns the lymph fluid back into the bloodstream. Returning lymph passes through a series of lymph nodes, which contain lymphocytes and other cells of the immune system. The nodes act as filters, removing foreign particles from the lymph fluid. Figure 2.30 shows the lymphatic system.

Hints & tips ★

There is more about lymphocytes and the immune system in Key Area 4.2 on pages 176—179.

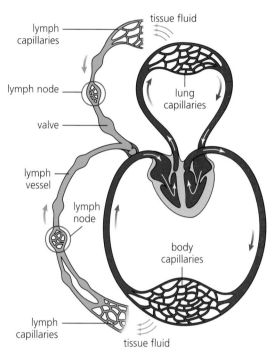

Figure 2.30 The lymphatic system

Key words

Arteriole – branch of an artery leading to capillaries

Artery – blood vessel that carries blood away from the heart

Capillary – narrow, thin-walled blood vessel that exchanges materials with the tissues

Endothelium – layer of cells that lines the inner surface of blood vessels

Lumen – central channel of a tube such as a blood vessel

Lymph fluid – fluid made up from tissue fluid collected into lymph vessels, which circulates the body

Lymphatic system – system of vessels and nodes that deals with lymph in the body

Lymph vessels – tiny vessels in which lymph circulates around the body

Osmosis – water movement from high water concentration to lower water concentration through a selectively permeable membrane

Plasma – liquid component of the blood

Pressure filtration – passage of molecules through membranes under pressure

Tissue fluid – fluid which bathes cells in tissues; derived from blood

Vasoconstriction – narrowing of blood vessels to reduce blood flow

Vasodilation – widening of blood vessels to increase blood flow

Vein – blood vessel with valves that transports blood back to the heart

Venule – small branch of a vein

Questions ❓

Restricted response (structured in 1- or 2-mark parts)

1 Give the name of the central space or cavity in a blood vessel. (1)
2 Name the layer of cells that forms the inner lining of a blood vessel. (1)
3 Define an artery. (1)
4 Define a vein. (1)
5 Explain why veins require valves. (2)
6 Give **two** structural differences between an artery and a vein. (2)
7 Describe the structure and function of a capillary. (2)
8 Explain the process of pressure filtration in the capillary beds. (2)
9 Describe how tissue fluid differs from blood plasma. (1)
10 Describe the role of tissue fluid. (1)
11 Describe how tissue fluid re-enters the capillaries at the venule end of the capillary bed. (1)
12 Describe the role of the lymph vessels. (1)
13 Explain the importance of vasoconstriction and vasodilation in arteries. (2)

Extended response (4–9 marks each)

14 Write notes on the structure and function of the arteries, veins and capillaries. (9)
15 Describe the exchange of substances between plasma and body cells. (9)

Answers are on page 121–122.

Key points !

1 The heart has four chambers (right atrium, right ventricle, left atrium and left ventricle) and works as a double pump. ☐

2 The right side collects **deoxygenated blood** from the body and pumps it to the lungs to collect oxygen. ☐

3 The left side collects **oxygenated blood** from the lungs and pumps it to the body. ☐

4 The walls of the heart are made of **cardiac muscle** that can contract continuously without causing fatigue. ☐

5 Deoxygenated blood returning from the body via the vena cava fills the right atrium (during **atrial diastole**). ☐

6 The build-up of pressure during atrial diastole forces open the **atrio-ventricular (AV) valve** and blood flows into the right ventricle during **ventricular diastole**. ☐

7 The right atrium contracts, forcing all the blood into the right ventricle **(atrial systole)**. ☐

8 Once full, the right ventricle's muscular walls contract **(ventricular systole)**, closing the AV valve and forcing the blood up through the **semi-lunar valve** and out through the pulmonary artery to the lungs. ☐

9 Oxygenated blood returning from the lungs via the pulmonary vein fills the left atrium (during atrial diastole). ☐

10 The build-up of pressure during atrial diastole forces open the atrio-ventricular valve and blood flows into the left ventricle. The atrium contracts forcing all the blood into the ventricle (atrial systole). ☐

11 Once full, the left ventricle's muscular walls contract (ventricular systole), closing the AV valve and forcing the blood up through the semi-lunar valve and out through the aorta to the body's organs. ☐

12 The opening and closing of the atrio-ventricular (AV) and semi-lunar (SL) valves are responsible for the heart sounds heard with a stethoscope. ☐

13 **Cardiac output** is the volume of blood pumped out by either ventricle (out of the heart) per minute. ☐

14 **Stroke volume** is the volume of blood pumped out by either ventricle during one systole. ☐

15 Cardiac output is determined by heart rate and stroke volume (CO = HR × SV). ☐

16 The **cardiac cycle** is the pattern of contraction **(systole)** and relaxation **(diastole)** of the heart muscle in one complete heartbeat. ☐

17 The heartbeat originates in the heart itself. ☐

18 The **sino-atrial node (SAN)**, also known as the pacemaker, is situated in the wall of the right atrium. ☐

19 The SAN ensures that both atria contract simultaneously by sending out electrical impulses that are carried through the muscular walls of the atria. ☐

20 The sino-atrial node (SAN) or pacemaker sets the rate at which cardiac muscle cells contract. ☐

⇨

21 The timing of cardiac cells contracting is controlled by the electrical impulse from the SAN spreading through the atria to the **atrio-ventricular node (AVN)** and through the ventricles. ☐

22 The electrical impulses generated in the heart produce currents that can be detected by an **electrocardiogram (ECG)**. ☐

23 The **medulla** in the brain regulates the rate of the SAN through the **antagonistic** action of the **autonomic nervous system (ANS)**. ☐

24 **Sympathetic accelerator nerves** release **nor-adrenaline (nor-epinephrine)**, which increases the heart rate. ☐

25 The **parasympathetic nerves to the heart** release **acetylcholine**, which decreases the heart rate. ☐

26 Blood pressure changes in the aorta during the cardiac cycle. ☐

27 Measurement of blood pressure is performed using a **sphygmomanometer**. ☐

28 A typical reading for a young adult is 120/70 mmHg. ☐

29 **Hypertension** (high blood pressure) is a major risk factor for many diseases and conditions, including **coronary heart disease** and **strokes**. ☐

Summary notes

The structure of the heart

The heart is a muscular pump with four chambers, as shown in Figure 2.31.

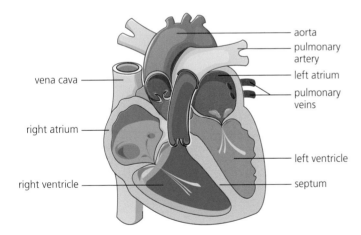

Figure 2.31 The structure of the heart

Circulation through the heart

The atria receive blood returning to the heart. The vena cava returns deoxygenated blood from the head and body to the right atrium. The left atrium receives oxygenated blood transported in the pulmonary vein from the lungs.

Blood is pumped into the ventricles, which contract to pump blood out of the heart. The right ventricle pumps deoxygenated blood through the pulmonary artery to the lungs. The left ventricle pumps oxygenated blood out of the heart through the aorta.

The heart is separated into two halves by the septum, which ensures that the deoxygenated blood in the right side of the heart is kept separate from the oxygenated blood in the left side of the heart.

Valves

Valves of the heart prevent the backflow of blood. The atrio-ventricular (AV) valves are found between the atria and the ventricles. The aortic valve is found between the ventricle and aorta leaving the left side of the heart. The pulmonary valve is found between the ventricle and the pulmonary artery leaving the right side of the heart.

Cardiac output

The cardiac output (CO) is the total volume of blood pumped out by a ventricle per minute. Cardiac output (CO) is determined by heart rate (HR) and stroke volume (SV):

$$CO = HR \times SV$$

where HR is the number of heartbeats in 1 minute and SV is the volume of blood pumped out by the left ventricle during contraction.

The cardiac cycle

The cardiac cycle is the pattern of contraction (systole) and relaxation (diastole) in one complete heartbeat. Relaxation of the heart muscles is called diastole and contraction is systole.

Diastole

During diastole heart muscle relaxes and the higher pressure in the arteries closes the SL valves. The atria fill with blood from the vena cava and pulmonary vein, and some of the blood flows into the ventricles.

Systole

Atrial systole is when both atria contract and transfer the remainder of the blood through the AV valves to the ventricles. Ventricular systole closes the AV valves and pumps the blood out through the semi-lunar (SL) valves to the aorta and pulmonary artery. Figure 2.32 shows one cardiac cycle. The average length of one cardiac cycle is 0.8 seconds (based on a heart rate of 75 beats per minute).

Hints & tips

In your exam, you could be asked to calculate a cardiac output from data that are given. Make sure you learn the formula:

$$CO = HR \times SV$$

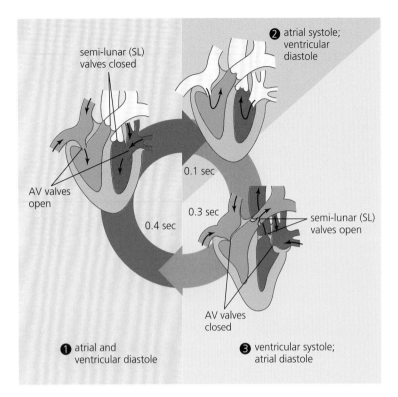

Figure 2.32 The cardiac cycle, showing the average duration of each stage

Stages in the cardiac cycle	
❶ Atrial and ventricular diastole	• Atria and ventricles are relaxed
	• Blood flows into the right atrium from the vena cava and into the left atrium from the pulmonary vein
	• Volume of blood increases and increased pressure opens AV valves
	• Blood flows down into the ventricles
	• The SL valves are closed
❷ Atrial systole (ventricular diastole)	• The atria contract, forcing the remaining blood through the AV valves into the ventricles
	• The ventricles fill and the SL valves remain closed
❸ Ventricular systole (atrial diastole)	• Ventricles contract, closing the AV valves
	• SL valves are pushed open and blood is pumped out of the heart through the pulmonary artery from the right ventricle and through the aorta from the left ventricle

Heart sounds

The opening and closing of valves is responsible for the main heart sounds heard with a stethoscope. The 'lubb' sound is caused by the shutting AV valves and the 'dup' by the shutting SL valves. Heart murmurs are caused by abnormal patterns of cardiac blood flow. They can be caused by valves that do not open or close fully. Figure 2.33 shows the positions of the heart sounds as pressures change in a normal cardiac cycle.

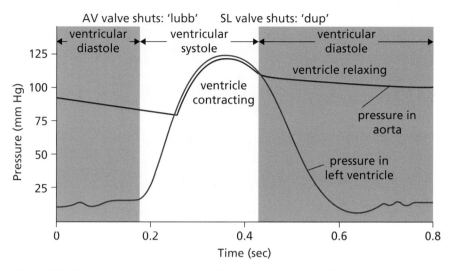

Figure 2.33 Pressure in the left ventricle and aorta during one cardiac cycle

The cardiac conducting system

The heartbeat originates in the heart itself. Heart muscle cells are self-contractile. This means they are able to contract and produce an electrochemical signal, which is passed on to other cardiac muscle cells, causing them to contract. The conducting system (nervous control) of the heart ensures that it beats in a coordinated manner.

The cells of the sino-atrial node (SAN) or pacemaker in the wall of the right atrium set the rate at which cardiac muscle cells contract.

The electrical impulse that is generated by cells in the SAN is passed through the atria and to the atrio-ventricular node (AVN) in the lower part of the right atrium wall. From the AVN, the electrical impulse is conducted to the muscle cells in the ventricles of the heart via conducting fibres down the septum between the atria and ventricles of the right and left sides of the heart. This results in the simultaneous contraction of the ventricles (ventricular systole). Figure 2.34 shows the cardiac conducting system.

Hints & tips

Remember, the conducting system is about the nervous control of the heartbeat – it's *not* about blood being conducted through the chambers of the heart.

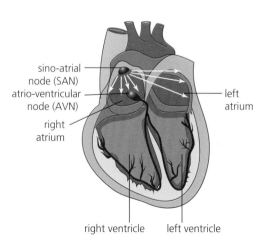

Figure 2.34 The cardiac conducting system

Electrocardiograms (ECGs)

Electrical impulses of the conducting system generate currents that can be shown on an electrocardiogram (ECG). An ECG is traced by placing electrodes on the surface of the body. These pick up the electrical impulses that are produced by the beating heart. The tracings can be used to identify problems with the heart such as myocardial infarction (heart attack). Figure 2.35 shows a normal ECG trace for one heartbeat.

An ECG can be labelled with the letters P, Q, R, S and T as reference points, as indicated in Figure 2.35 and described in the table below.

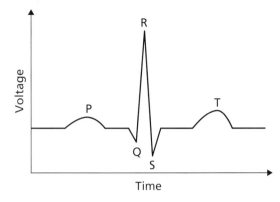

Figure 2.35 A normal ECG trace of one heartbeat

Part of ECG trace	Events recorded
P wave	Impulses spreading over the atria from the SAN
QRS complex	Impulses through the ventricles
T wave	Electrical recovery of the ventricles at the end of ventricular systole

Example

The patterns shown by ECGs of fast, slow and irregular heartbeats compared with a normal trace are shown in Figure 2.36.

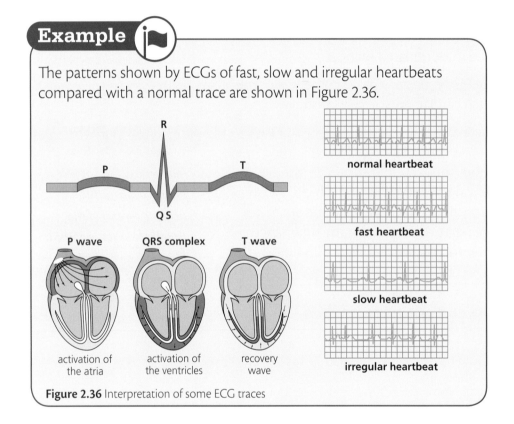

Figure 2.36 Interpretation of some ECG traces

Role of the medulla

The medulla regulates the rate of the SAN through the antagonistic action of the autonomic nervous system (ANS).

Sympathetic nerves accelerate the heart and strength of contractions, and release nor-adrenaline (nor-epinephrine). These fibres can be activated by stress and fear.

Parasympathetic nerves slow the heart and release acetylcholine. These fibres are activated during periods of rest.

Hints & tips

There is more about the ANS in Key Area 3.1 on pages 136–137. It is worth referring to this before reading on here.

The following table shows the control of the cardiac cycle by the autonomic nervous system.

Branch of autonomic nervous system	Chemical produced	Effect
Sympathetic nervous system (accelerator nerve)	Nor-adrenaline (nor-epinephrine)	Increases heart rate and cardiac output
Parasympathetic nervous system	Acetylcholine	Decreases heart rate and cardiac output

Figure 2.37 shows the effect of the autonomic nervous system on heart rate.

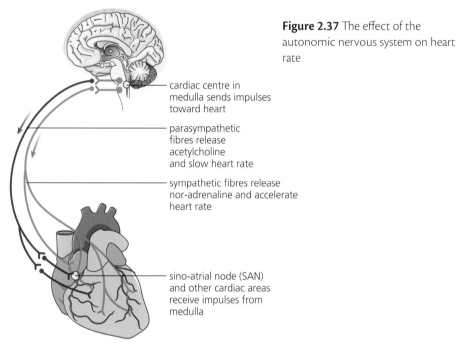

Figure 2.37 The effect of the autonomic nervous system on heart rate

cardiac centre in medulla sends impulses toward heart

parasympathetic fibres release acetylcholine and slow heart rate

sympathetic fibres release nor-adrenaline and accelerate heart rate

sino-atrial node (SAN) and other cardiac areas receive impulses from medulla

Blood pressure measurement

Blood pressure changes in the aorta during the cardiac cycle are shown in Figure 2.33.

Measurement of blood pressure is usually done using a sphygmomanometer attached to the arm. Two readings are taken. The first is the systolic pressure and the second the diastolic. A typical reading for a young adult is 120/70 mmHg (Figure 2.38).

Hints & tips

70 mmHg means that the pressure is enough to push a column of mercury (Hg) 70 mm up a tube against the force of gravity.

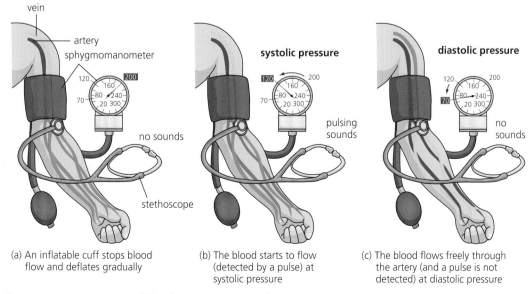

vein

artery

sphygmomanometer

no sounds

stethoscope

systolic pressure

pulsing sounds

diastolic pressure

no sounds

(a) An inflatable cuff stops blood flow and deflates gradually

(b) The blood starts to flow (detected by a pulse) at systolic pressure

(c) The blood flows freely through the artery (and a pulse is not detected) at diastolic pressure

Figure 2.38 Measurement of blood pressure using a sphygmomanometer

Hypertension (high blood pressure) is a major risk factor for many diseases and conditions, including coronary heart disease and strokes.

Key words

Acetylcholine – neurotransmitter released by parasympathetic nerve fibres

Antagonistic – opposing actions of the sympathetic and parasympathetic systems

Atrial diastole – part of the cardiac cycle in which the heart muscle of the atria relaxes

Atrial systole – part of the cardiac cycle in which the heart muscle of the atria contracts

Atrio-ventricular node (AVN) – nervous tissue found at the junction between the atria and the ventricles

Atrio-ventricular (AV) valve – heart valve found between the atria and the ventricles

Autonomic nervous system (ANS) – controls involuntary action of smooth and cardiac muscle and glands

Cardiac cycle – contraction and relaxation of the heart muscle in a heartbeat

Cardiac muscle – muscle that makes up the heart walls

Cardiac output – volume of blood expelled from one ventricle of the heart per minute

Coronary heart disease (CHD) – condition caused by blockage of coronary arteries

Deoxygenated blood – blood, usually in veins, that carries little oxygen

Diastole – part of the cardiac cycle during which cardiac muscle is relaxed

Electrocardiogram (ECG) – record of electrical activity in the heart; used to detect abnormalities

Hypertension – abnormally high blood pressure in arteries

Medulla – part of the brain with centres controlling breathing, heart rate and peristalsis

Nor-adrenaline (nor-epinephrine) – hormone and neurotransmitter

Oxygenated blood – blood containing a high level of oxygen

Parasympathetic nerves to the heart – nerve fibres which result in a decrease in heart rate; part of the autonomic nervous system (ANS)

Semi-lunar valves – valves leading into the main arteries leaving the heart

Sino-atrial node (SAN) – region of nervous tissue in the wall of the right atrium; receives impulses from the medulla

Sphygmomanometer – instrument used to measure blood pressure

Stroke – life threatening condition that occurs when blood supply to part of the brain is cut off

Stroke volume – volume of blood expelled from the left ventricle during one cardiac cycle

Sympathetic accelerator nerve – nerve fibre that stimulates an increase in heart rate; part of the autonomic nervous system (ANS)

Systole – part of the cardiac cycle in which cardiac muscle is contracted

Ventricular diastole – part of the cardiac cycle in which the cardiac muscle of the ventricles relaxes

Ventricular systole – part of the cardiac cycle in which the cardiac muscle of the ventricles contracts

Questions ?

Restricted response (structured in 1- or 2-mark parts)

1 Give the meaning of the term cardiac output. (1)
2 Describe how cardiac output is calculated. (1)
3 State the location of the sino-atrial node (SAN) in the heart. (1)
4 Describe the role of the sino-atrial node (SAN). (2)
5 Describe the role of the atrio-ventricular node (AVN). (2)
6 Describe the effect of impulses from the sympathetic nerves on the heart. (2)
7 Describe the effect of impulses from the parasympathetic nerves on the heart. (2)
8 Describe the state of the heart valves during ventricular systole. (2)
9 Describe the state of the atrial and ventricular muscles during the diastolic stage of the cardiac cycle. (1)
10 Describe the function of the semi-lunar valves. (1)
11 Name the stage of the cardiac cycle when the semi-lunar valves open. (1)
12 Name the instrument used to measure blood pressure. (1)
13 Give the meaning of the terms systolic blood pressure and diastolic blood pressure. (2)
14 Explain the change in blood pressure that occurs as blood flows through the circulatory system. (2)
15 Give the term used to describe the condition in which an individual has persistently high blood pressure and name **one** disease or condition associated with it. (2)
16 Electrocardiograms (ECGs) are used to show heart activity. Explain what allows an ECG to be produced and describe the appearance of a normal ECG trace. (2)
17 Explain what causes the three distinct waves obtained in a normal ECG trace. (2)

Extended response (4–9 marks each)

18 Describe the antagonistic action of the autonomic nervous system in the control of the cardiac cycle. (4)
19 Discuss the conducting system of the heart and how it is controlled. (9)

Answers are on page 122–123.

Pathology of cardiovascular disease (CVD)

Key points !

1 **Atherosclerosis** is the accumulation of fatty material (consisting mainly of **cholesterol**), fibrous material and calcium, forming an **atheroma** or plaque. ☐

2 An atheroma forms beneath the endothelium (inner lining) of the artery wall. ☐

3 As an atheroma grows, the artery thickens and loses its elasticity. ☐

4 An atheroma reduces the diameter of the lumen of an artery, which restricts blood flow and results in increased blood pressure. ☐

5 Atherosclerosis is the root cause of various **cardiovascular diseases (CVD)**, including **angina, heart attack**, stroke and **peripheral vascular disorders**. ☐

6 If an atheroma ruptures, the damage to the endothelium causes the release of clotting factors. ☐

7 Clotting factors cause the enzyme **prothrombin** to be converted into its active form **thrombin**. ☐

8 Thrombin causes molecules of the soluble plasma protein **fibrinogen** to form threads of insoluble **fibrin** protein. ☐

9 Fibrin threads form a meshwork that platelets adhere to, forming a blood clot, which seals a wound and provides a scaffold for the formation of scar tissue. ☐

10 **Thrombosis** is the formation of a blood clot (thrombus) in a vessel. ☐

11 If a thrombus breaks loose, it forms an **embolus** that travels through the bloodstream until it blocks a blood vessel. ☐

12 Thrombosis in a coronary artery can lead to a **myocardial infarction (MI)**. ☐

13 Thrombosis in an artery in the brain can lead to a stroke. ☐

14 Thrombosis normally results in the death of some of the tissue served by the blocked artery as the cells are deprived of oxygen. ☐

15 Peripheral vascular disorders include narrowing of arteries due to atherosclerosis of arteries other than those of the heart or brain. ☐

16 Blood clots can result in **deep vein thrombosis (DVT)** and **pulmonary embolism**. ☐

17 DVT is the formation of a blood clot in a deep vein, most commonly in the lower part of the leg. ☐

18 In DVT, pain is experienced in the leg muscles due to a limited supply of oxygen. ☐

19 A pulmonary embolism is caused by part of a thrombus breaking free and travelling through the bloodstream to the pulmonary artery, where it can cause a blockage, resulting in chest pain and breathing difficulties. ☐

20 Cholesterol is a component of cell membranes and a precursor for steroid synthesis. ☐

21 Most cholesterol is synthesised by the liver from saturated fats in the diet. ☐ ⇨

⇨

22 **Lipoproteins** contain lipid and protein. ☐

23 **High-density lipoprotein (HDL)** transports excess cholesterol from the body cells to the liver for elimination and so prevents the accumulation of cholesterol in the blood. ☐

24 **Low-density lipoprotein (LDL)** transports cholesterol to body cells. ☐

25 Most cells have **LDL receptors** that take LDL into the cell, where it releases cholesterol. ☐

26 Once a cell has sufficient cholesterol, a negative feedback system inhibits the synthesis of new LDL receptors and so LDL circulates in the blood where it may deposit the cholesterol in the arteries, forming atheromas. ☐

27 **Familial hypercholesterolaemia (FH)** is caused by an autosomal dominant allele that results in individuals developing high levels of cholesterol. ☐

28 The mutated gene involved in FH results in a decreased number or altered structure of LDL receptors on cell membranes, which stops the LDL from unloading its cholesterol into the cell. ☐

29 Genetic screening can be carried out to determine if the FH gene has been inherited. ☐

30 Treatment of FH involves lifestyle modification and drugs such as **statins**. ☐

31 A higher ratio of HDL to LDL results in lower blood cholesterol and a reduced chance of atherosclerosis. ☐

32 Regular physical activity tends to raise HDL levels. ☐

33 Dietary changes aim to reduce the levels of total fat in the diet and to replace saturated with unsaturated fats. ☐

34 Drugs such as statins reduce blood cholesterol by inhibiting the synthesis of cholesterol by liver cells. ☐

Summary notes

Process of atherosclerosis

Atherosclerosis is the fatty accumulation of substances, mainly of cholesterol, fibrous material and calcium salts, forming an atheroma beneath the endothelium of an artery wall. As an atheroma grows, the artery thickens and loses its elasticity. The lumen of the artery becomes narrowed and blood flow becomes restricted, resulting in increased blood pressure. Figure 2.39 shows the formation of an atheroma in the endothelium of an artery.

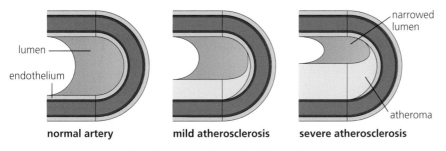

Figure 2.39 Formation of an atheroma in the endothelium of an artery

Atherosclerosis is the root cause of various cardiovascular diseases (CVD), including angina, heart attack, stroke and peripheral vascular disease. Factors that contribute to atheroma formation include diabetes mellitus, low HDL/LDL ratio, high blood pressure, a family history of CVD and smoking.

Hints & tips

There is more about arteries in Key Area 2.5 on pages 93–94.

Thrombosis

If an atheroma ruptures, the damage to the endothelium of the artery causes the release of clotting factors. These trigger a series of reactions, resulting in the conversion of the enzyme prothrombin to its active form thrombin. Thrombin then causes molecules of the soluble plasma protein fibrinogen to form threads of insoluble fibrin protein. The fibrin threads form a mesh, which traps platelets and blood cells, forming a thrombus (clot) (Figure 2.40).

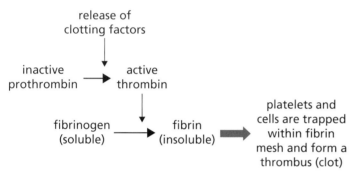

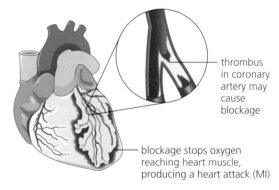

Figure 2.40 Series of events involved in the formation of a blood clot

Embolism

If a thrombus breaks loose, it forms an embolus, which travels through the bloodstream and could block a blood vessel resulting in cells being deprived of oxygen and leading to the death of tissues. A thrombus in a coronary artery can lead to a myocardial infarction (MI), as shown in Figure 2.41. A thrombus in an artery in the brain can lead to a stroke.

Figure 2.41 Myocardial infarction (MI)

Causes of peripheral vascular disorders

Peripheral vascular disease is narrowing of the arteries due to atherosclerosis in arteries other than those to the heart and brain. Deep vein thrombosis (DVT) is the formation of a thrombus in a deep vein, most commonly in the lower leg (Figure 2.42). Pain is experienced in the leg muscles due to a limited supply of oxygen. If a thrombus breaks loose, it forms an embolus that can travel through the bloodstream and block a blood vessel.

A pulmonary embolism is caused by part of a thrombus breaking free and travelling to the pulmonary artery, where it can cause a blockage, resulting in chest pain and breathing difficulties.

Hints & tips

There is more about veins in Key Area 2.5 on pages 93–94.

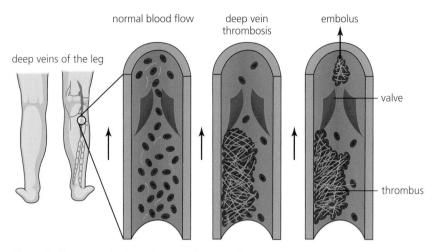

Figure 2.42 Deep vein thrombosis in the lower leg

Control of cholesterol levels and HDL to LDL ratios

Cholesterol is a component of cell membranes and a precursor for the synthesis of steroids such as sex hormones. Most cholesterol is synthesised by the liver from saturated fats in the diet.

High-density lipoprotein (HDL) transports excess cholesterol from the body cells to the liver for elimination, and so prevents the accumulation of cholesterol in the blood.

Low-density lipoprotein (LDL) transports cholesterol to body cells. Most cells have LDL receptors that take LDL into the cell, where it releases its cholesterol. Once a cell has sufficient cholesterol, a negative feedback system inhibits the synthesis of new LDL receptors and so LDLs continue to circulate in the blood, where they may deposit the cholesterol in the arteries, forming atheromas. A high ratio of HDL to LDL is therefore seen as better in the maintenance of healthy cholesterol levels in blood. Figure 2.43 shows the roles of HDL and LDL in the transport of cholesterol.

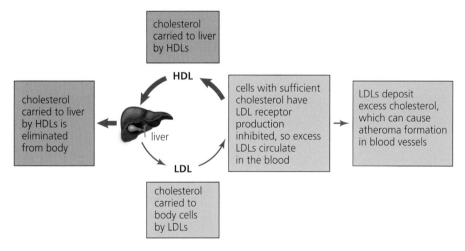

Figure 2.43 Roles of HDL and LDL in the transport of cholesterol

Familial hypercholesterolaemia (FH)

Familial hypercholesterolaemia (FH) is caused by an autosomal dominant allele that results in individuals developing high levels of cholesterol. The allele results in a decreased number or altered structure of LDL receptors on cell membranes, which stops the LDL from unloading its cholesterol into the cell. Genetic screening can be carried out to determine if the FH allele has been inherited. Treatment of FH involves lifestyle modification and drugs such as statins.

Hints & tips

There is more about autosomal dominant alleles in Key Area 2.4 on page 89.

Lifestyle choices and cholesterol level

A higher ratio of HDL to LDL will result in lower blood cholesterol and a reduced chance of atherosclerosis. Regular physical activity tends to raise HDL levels and so lowers the blood cholesterol. Reduced levels of total fat in the diet and the replacement of saturated fats with unsaturated fats also contribute to lower cholesterol levels. Prescribed medicines, such as statins, reduce blood cholesterol by inhibiting the synthesis of cholesterol by the liver cells.

Key words

Angina – chest pain occurring when blood supply to heart muscle is restricted

Atheroma – swelling on inner wall of artery made up of fatty material and connective tissue

Atherosclerosis – potentially serious condition in which atheromas clog the arteries

Cardiovascular diseases – diseases affecting the heart and circulation

Cholesterol – lipid molecule needed for cell membranes and in synthesising steroid hormones

Deep vein thrombosis (DVT) – blood clot in a deep vein, often in the leg

Embolus – any detached mass of material carried by the circulation

Familial hypercholesterolaemia (FH) – inherited condition in which LDLs are at a higher than normal level in the blood

Fibrin – protein that helps form a blood clot

Fibrinogen – blood protein that is converted to fibrin during the blood clotting process

Heart attack – serious medical emergency in which blood supply to the heart muscle is blocked

High-density lipoprotein (HDL) – carries excess cholesterol away from body cells and artery surfaces to the liver for elimination

LDL receptor – receptor that recognises LDLs and encourages their uptake

Lipoprotein – assembly of protein with lipid that enables movement of lipid in water and through membranes

Low-density lipoprotein (LDL) – carries cholesterol to body cells; if body cells have enough cholesterol, LDL may desposit cholesterol leading to atheroma in arteries

Myocardial infarction (MI) – medical term for a heart attack in which blood flow to the heart is reduced

Peripheral vascular disorder – condition caused by blockage to arteries other than coronary arteries, the aorta or those in the brain

Prothrombin – blood component important in clotting; it is converted to thrombin during clotting

Pulmonary embolism – an embolism (blood clot) in the pulmonary circulation

Statin – a medicine that helps lower LDLs in the blood

Thrombin – produced from prothrombin during blood clotting

Thrombosis – blood clot within a blood vessel

Questions ?

Restricted response (structured in 1- or 2-mark parts)

1   Describe the process of atherosclerosis. (2)
2   Give **two** effects that atherosclerosis has on the structure of an artery. (2)
3   Describe the events leading to a myocardial infarction (MI). (2)
4   Describe the events leading to a stroke. (2)
5   Give **two** examples of peripheral vascular disorders. (2)
6   Name the organ responsible for the synthesis of cholesterol. (1)
7   Give **two** functions of cholesterol in the body. (2)
8   Name the inherited condition that results in individuals developing high levels of cholesterol. (1)
9   Describe the role of high-density lipoprotein (HDL). (1)
10 Describe the role of low-density lipoprotein (LDL). (1)
11 Describe the function of LDL receptors. (1)
12 Name the type of control that causes the inhibition of LDL receptor synthesis once a cell has sufficient cholesterol. (1)
13 Name the procedure carried out to determine if familial hypercholesterolaemia (FH) has been inherited. (1)
14 Explain the benefit of a higher ratio of HDL to LDL in the blood plasma. (2)
15 Explain the benefit of regular exercise in reducing blood cholesterol levels. (2)
16 Name **one** group of drugs taken to reduce blood cholesterol. (1)

Extended response (4–9 marks each)

17 Describe the process of atherosclerosis and its effect on arteries and blood pressure. (5)
18 Describe events following the rupture of an atheroma, leading to the formation of a thrombus. (6)
19 Discuss how cardiovascular disease occurs. (9)
20 Give an account of the control of cholesterol levels in the blood. (9)

Answers are on pages 124–125.

Key points

1 Chronic elevated blood glucose levels lead to atherosclerosis and blood vessel damage. ☐

2 If levels of blood glucose become elevated due to untreated diabetes, the endothelium cells lining the blood vessels absorb far more glucose than normal, causing damage to the blood vessels. ☐

3 If atherosclerosis develops, this can lead to cardiovascular disease (CVD), stroke or peripheral vascular disease, which affects blood vessels leading to arms, hands, legs, feet and toes. ☐

4 Small blood vessels damaged by elevated glucose levels can result in haemorrhage of blood vessels in the retina, renal failure or peripheral nerve dysfunction. ☐

5 Blood glucose concentration is maintained within fine limits by negative feedback control involving the hormones **insulin**, **glucagon** and **adrenaline (epinephrine)**. ☐

6 Blood glucose concentration is monitored by receptors in the pancreas.

7 The pancreas controls blood glucose with the two hormones insulin and glucagon, which act antagonistically. ☐

8 The hormones are transported in the blood to the liver. ☐

9 When the blood glucose concentration increases above the norm, the pancreas secretes more insulin and less glucagon. ☐

10 Insulin makes the liver cells more permeable to glucose and activates the conversion of glucose to **glycogen**, decreasing the blood glucose concentration. ☐

11 When the blood glucose concentration decreases below the norm, the pancreas secretes more glucagon and less insulin. ☐

12 Glucagon activates the conversion of glycogen to glucose, increasing the blood glucose concentration. ☐

13 During exercise, and fight or flight responses, glucose levels are raised by adrenaline (epinephrine) released from the adrenal glands, stimulating glucagon secretion and inhibiting insulin secretion. ☐

14 Diabetics are unable to control their glucose concentration. ☐

15 Vascular disease can be a chronic complication of diabetes. ☐

16 Type-1 diabetes usually occurs in childhood. ☐

17 Individuals with type-1 diabetes are unable to produce insulin. ☐

18 Type-1 diabetes is treated with regular injections of insulin. ☐

19 Type-2 diabetes or adult-onset diabetes typically develops later in life. ☐

20 Type-2 diabetes occurs mainly in overweight individuals. ☐

21 Individuals with type-2 diabetes produce insulin, but their cells are less sensitive to it. ☐

22 Type-2 diabetes is linked to a decrease in the number of insulin receptors in the liver, leading to a failure to convert glucose to glycogen. ☐

23 Testing urine for the presence of glucose is often used as an indicator of diabetes. ☐

⇨

⇨

24 The glucose tolerance test is used to diagnose diabetes. ☐
25 Obesity is a major risk factor for cardiovascular disease and type-2 diabetes. ☐
26 Obesity is characterised by excess body fat in relation to lean body tissue (muscle). ☐
27 **Body mass index (BMI)** is a measurement of body fat based on height and weight. ☐
28 BMI can be used to indicate obesity, overweight, normal or underweight. ☐
29 A body mass index (weight divided by height squared) greater than $30\,kg\,m^{-2}$ indicates obesity. ☐
30 One disadvantage of the BMI measurement is that someone may be classified as overweight or obese when additional weight is not fat but muscle or bone mass. ☐
31 Accurate measurement of body fat requires the measurement of **body density**. ☐
32 Determining body composition using body density measurements depends on the fact that fat is less dense than lean tissue. ☐
33 Obesity is linked to high fat diets and a decrease in physical activity. ☐
34 Exercise increases energy expenditure and preserves lean tissue. ☐
35 Exercise can help to reduce risk factors for cardiovascular disease (CVD) by improving HDL to LDL blood lipid ratios. ☐

Summary notes

Blood glucose levels and vascular disease

Chronic elevated blood glucose levels lead to atherosclerosis and blood vessel damage.

If levels of blood glucose become elevated due to untreated diabetes, the endothelium cells lining the blood vessels absorb more glucose than normal, causing damage. Atherosclerosis may then develop, leading to cardiovascular disease, stroke or peripheral vascular disease.

Regulation of blood glucose levels

Blood glucose concentration is maintained within tolerable limits by negative feedback control involving the hormones insulin, glucagon and adrenaline (epinephrine). This is a part of **homeostasis**, which is the maintenance of steady conditions within the body.

Blood glucose concentration is monitored by receptors in the pancreas. The pancreas controls blood glucose with two hormones, insulin and glucagon, which act antagonistically. These hormones are transported in the blood to the liver.

Hints & tips ★

There is more about CVD, stroke and peripheral vascular disease in Key Area 2.7 on page 108.

Hints & tips ★

There is more about how adrenaline acts as a cell signal in Key Area 1.6 on pages 40–41.

When the blood glucose concentration increases above the norm, the pancreas secretes more insulin and less glucagon. Insulin makes the liver cells more permeable to glucose and activates the conversion of glucose to glycogen, decreasing the blood glucose concentration.

When the blood glucose concentration decreases below the norm, the pancreas secretes more glucagon and less insulin. Glucagon activates the conversion of glycogen to glucose, increasing the blood glucose concentration. Figure 2.44 provides a summary of the action of insulin and glucagon.

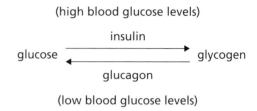

Figure 2.44 Action of insulin and glucagon

Figure 2.45 shows the control of blood glucose concentration by negative feedback.

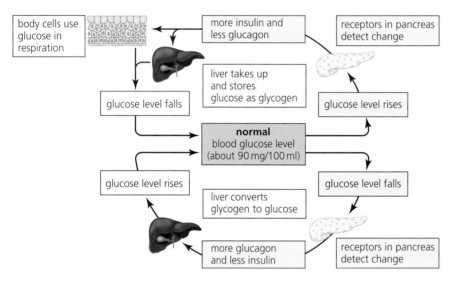

Figure 2.45 Control of blood glucose concentration by negative feedback

During exercise, and in fight or flight responses, glucose levels are raised by adrenaline (epinephrine) released from the adrenal glands, stimulating glucagon secretion and inhibiting insulin secretion.

Diagnosis, treatments and role of insulin in type-1 and type-2 diabetes

Vascular disease can be a chronic complication of diabetes. Type-1 diabetes usually occurs in childhood. A person with type-1 diabetes is unable to produce insulin and is treated with regular injections of insulin.

Type-2 diabetes or adult-onset diabetes typically develops later in life and occurs mainly in overweight individuals. Individuals with type-2 diabetes produce insulin but their cells are less sensitive to it. This is linked to a decrease in the number of insulin receptors on the liver cells, leading to a failure to convert glucose to glycogen. Type-2 diabetes is mainly treated by adjustments to diet and exercise.

In both types of diabetes, blood glucose concentrations rise rapidly after a meal and the kidneys are unable to reabsorb all the glucose, resulting in glucose being excreted in the urine. Testing urine for glucose is often used as an indicator of diabetes.

> ### Hints & tips ★
> *Learn this definition of negative feedback control: Any change away from the optimum is detected by receptors that switch on a corrective mechanism to restore the conditions back to normal. The corrective mechanism is then switched off.*

> ### Hints & tips ★
> ***GLU**ca**GON** is needed when **GLU**cose is **GON**e.*

> ### Hints & tips ★
> *A useful rhyme to remember:*
> *Low blood sugar – glucose gone,*
> *What you need is glucagon.*
> *To turn glucose into glycogen,*
> *What you need is insulin.*

Example

The glucose tolerance test can also be carried out to test for diabetes. The individual being tested has blood samples taken after fasting and after drinking a standard dose of glucose. Blood tests are done at intervals to determine how quickly the glucose is cleared from the blood. Figure 2.46 shows the glucose tolerance curves for normal and diabetic individuals.

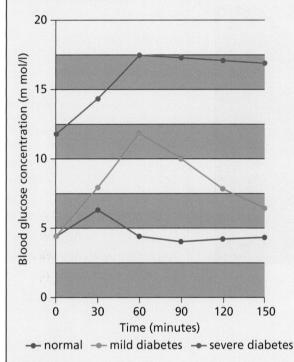

Figure 2.46 Glucose tolerance curves for normal and diabetic individuals

Obesity

Obesity is a major risk factor for cardiovascular disease and type-2 diabetes. It is characterised by excess body fat in relation to lean muscle. Body mass index (BMI) is a measurement of body fat based on height and weight:

$$BMI = \frac{\text{body weight (kg)}}{(\text{height (m)})^2}$$

It can be used to identify those who are overweight, obese, underweight or normal. A body mass index greater than 30 is used to indicate obesity. The following table shows the BMI measurements used to categorise individuals.

BMI range	Category
<18.5	Underweight
18.5–24.9	Normal
25–29.9	Overweight
30+	Obese

Example

Figure 2.47 shows how BMI can be related to obesity. Doctors can use charts like this to advise patients on their weight as it relates to health. Care is needed when using these charts since an individual may show up as obese if their body weight is increased due to the muscle or skeletal bulk that might be expected in a professional athlete.

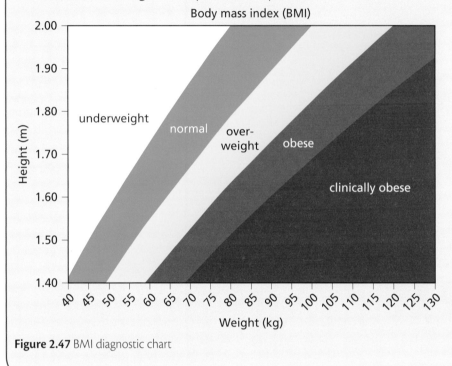

Figure 2.47 BMI diagnostic chart

One disadvantage of the BMI measurement is that someone may be classified as overweight or obese when additional weight is not fat but muscle or bone mass.

Accurate measurement of body fat requires the measurement of body density. Percentage body fat can be calculated from body density measurements using standardised tables. Determining body fat percentage by using body density measurements depends on the fact that fat is less dense that lean tissue.

Obesity is linked to high-fat diets and a decrease in physical activity. Exercise increases energy expenditure and preserves lean tissue. Exercise can also help to reduce risk factors for CVD by keeping weight under control, minimising stress, reducing hypertension and improving HDL blood lipid profiles.

Key words

Adrenaline (epinephrine) – hormone that stimulates the release of glucose from glycogen during stress or exercise

Body density – quantitative measure used to estimate body fat

Body mass index (BMI) – relative measurement based on height and weight

Glucagon – hormone produced by the pancreas that stimulates the conversion of glycogen into glucose in the liver

Glycogen – storage carbohydrate located in the liver and muscle tissues

Homeostasis – maintenance of a steady state in the cells of a living organism

Insulin – hormone produced by the pancreas that stimulates the conversion of glucose into glycogen in the liver

Questions ?

Restricted response (structured in 1- or 2-mark parts)

1 Describe **two** effects on the circulatory system that can result from chronic elevated blood glucose levels. (2)

2 Name the organ that contains the receptor cells that detect changes in the blood glucose concentration. (1)

3 Name three hormones involved in the control of blood glucose. (2)

4 Describe the role of the hormone insulin. (2)

5 Describe the role of the hormone glucagon. (2)

6 Name the organ in which excess glucose is stored and the storage carbohydrate involved. (2)

7 Explain the role of the hormone adrenaline (epinephrine) in the control of blood glucose concentration. (2)

8 Describe the difference between type-1 and type-2 diabetes. (2)

9 Name the test carried out to diagnose diabetes. (1)

10 Give the meaning of the term obesity. (1)

11 State the measurements taken to calculate the body mass index (BMI) of an individual. (1)

12 Give the minimum value of BMI that is generally used to indicate obesity in an individual. (1)

13 Give one disadvantage of the standard BMI measurement. (1)

Extended response (4–9 marks each)

14 Give an account of the principle of negative feedback with reference to the maintenance of blood sugar levels. (9)

Answers are on page 125–126.

Answers

Key Area 2.1

Restricted response

1 testes [1]
2 interstitial cells [1]
3 testosterone stimulates sperm production in the seminiferous tubules; it activates the prostate gland and seminal vesicles to produce their fluid/secretions [2]
4 location – seminiferous tubules; function – divide by mitosis then meiosis to produce sperm [2]
5 a) fluid is rich in the high-energy sugar fructose, providing the energy for the sperm to swim; contains hormone-like substances called prostaglandins that cause muscles in the female reproductive system to contract and move sperm along [2]
   b) fluid contains an enzyme that creates a thin consistency for the sperm to swim in through the oviduct [1]
6 corpus luteum [1]
7 oviduct [1]
8 a) oestrogen [1]
   b) progesterone [1]
9 structure that implants and becomes the embryo and placenta [1]

Extended response

10 male gametes/sperm are produced in the seminiferous tubules; gametes are produced from germline cells; germline cells are located in the seminiferous tubules of the testes; germline cells divide by mitosis then meiosis to produce the male gametes/sperm; testosterone stimulates sperm production in the seminiferous tubules [5]

Answers

Key Area 2.2

Restricted response

1 stimulates the interstitial cells in the testes to produce the male sex hormone testosterone [1]
2 releases FSH, promoting sperm production in the seminiferous tubules; releases ICSH, which stimulates the interstitial cells in the testes to produce testosterone [2]
3 testosterone stimulates sperm production in the seminiferous tubules [1]
4 overproduction of testosterone is prevented by a negative feedback mechanism; high testosterone levels inhibit the secretion of FSH and ICSH from the pituitary gland, resulting in a decrease in the production of testosterone by the interstitial cells [2]
5 secretes the sex hormone progesterone [1]
6 a) stimulates the development and maturation of a follicle surrounding the ovum; stimulates the production of oestrogen by the follicle [2]
   b) triggers ovulation; stimulates the development of the corpus luteum from the follicle [2]
7 oestrogen stimulates the repair of the endometrium; progesterone stimulates vascularisation of the endometrium, preparing it for implantation [2]
8 progesterone levels remain high; FSH levels drop [2]
9 high progesterone levels have a negative feedback effect on the pituitary gland, resulting in the inhibition of FSH and LH; the inhibition of FSH prevents further follicles from developing [2]

⇨

Extended response

10 FSH stimulates the maturation of a follicle surrounding the ovum and the production of oestrogen by the follicle; high levels of oestrogen stimulate the secretion of LH by the pituitary gland; LH stimulates the corpus luteum to secrete progesterone; high levels of oestrogen and progesterone inhibit the secretion of FSH and LH by the pituitary gland; this is an example of negative feedback control; if fertilisation does not occur, this results in a drop in LH levels; this causes the corpus luteum to break down; which in turn causes a decrease in progesterone and oestrogen levels [any 6 = 6]

11 pituitary gland produces FSH; FSH promotes sperm production; sperm are produced in the seminiferous tubules; pituitary gland produces ICSH; ICSH stimulates testosterone production; in the interstitial cells; testosterone stimulates sperm production; testosterone influences the production of semen/prostate gland/seminal vesicles; higher levels of testosterone inhibit ICSH/FSH; [any 8 = 8]

this is negative feedback; this ensures that levels of testosterone are kept within the normal range/constant [any 1 = 1]

12 cycle starts with menstruation; this involves the breakdown of the lining of uterus/endometrium; pituitary gland secretes FSH; FSH stimulates growth of a follicle; follicle/ovary produces oestrogen; oestrogen stimulates the repair of the endometrium/uterus lining; oestrogen also stimulates the production of LH; LH is produced by the pituitary gland; LH brings about ovulation; rising levels of oestrogen inhibit FSH production; this is negative feedback [any 9 = 9]

Answers

Key Area 2.3

Restricted response

1 males are continuously fertile and produce sperm throughout their lives; females' fertility is cyclical and usually restricted to approximately 5 days a month immediately before and after ovulation [2]

2 the time of ovulation can be estimated by the number of days after menstruation; a slight rise in body temperature on the day of ovulation; and the thinning of the cervical mucus [any 2 = 2]

3 surgery to open tubes/IVF [1]

4 ovulation-stimulating drugs/IVF with fertility drugs [1]

5 super ovulation that can result in multiple births; OHSS [any 1 = 1]

6 barrier methods; avoiding fertile periods; intra-uterine devices; sterilisation procedures [any 2 = 2]

7 contains synthetic progesterone and oestrogen; which inhibit secretion of FSH and LH by the pituitary gland [2]

8 contains synthetic progesterone, which can inhibit ovulation; causes thickening of cervical mucus, preventing the entry of sperm and fertilisation [2]

9 contains a high dose of synthetic progesterone and oestrogen; decreasing chances of ovulation/implantation; thickens cervical mucus to prevent entry of sperm [any 2 = 2]

10 semen is collected and inserted into the female reproductive tract; artificial insemination is useful if the male has a low sperm count, as several samples can be inserted at once [2]

11 ICSI involves a sperm being drawn into a needle; and injected directly into the egg [2]

12 if mature sperm are defective; or very low in number [2]

13 to identify single-gene disorders/chromosome abnormalities [1]

Extended response

14 ovulation stimulated by drugs preventing negative feedback control; these drugs prevent the negative feedback effect of oestrogen on FSH secretion; FSH continues to be released and ova are produced; some ovulatory drugs mimic FSH and LH; drugs that mimic FSH result in follicular development; drugs that mimic LH stimulate ovulation [any 5 = 5]

15 ovulatory drugs/hormone treatment to stimulate ovulation; surgical removal of eggs from ovaries; mixing sperm with eggs to achieve fertilisation; incubation of zygotes; fertilised eggs divide/form a ball of cells/form at least 8 cells/form a blastocyst; uterine implantation [any 4 = 4]

16 male infertility may be caused by defective sperm/low sperm count; fertility drugs may boost sperm production; other options include artificial insemination/intra-uterine insemination (IUI); several samples of semen are collected and combined over a period of time; injecting a sperm directly into the egg (ICSI); surgery to correct sperm tube blockage; sperm sample can be used with IVF procedure; if man is sterile then donor insemination may be an option; causes of sterility include genetics and disease [any 5 = 5]

17 failure to ovulate; cause – hormone imbalance/lack of hormones (FSH and LH); health reasons – anorexia/obesity/drug misuse/smoking/stress/poor diet; treatment – ovulatory (fertility) drugs/hormone treatment/improved lifestyle
blockage of uterine/fallopian tubes; cause – endometriosis/STD (sexually transmitted disease)/infection/cancer; treatment – surgery/laser treatment/IVF; IVF = fertilisation outside woman's body/in glass/Petri dish; failure of implantation; cause – hormone imbalance; treatment – ovulatory/fertility drugs [any 9 = 9]

18 a) multiple pregnancies/births; ovarian hyperstimulation syndrome (OHSS); others [any 2 = 2]
   b) high-cost treatments are out of financial reach for some couples; allocation of medical resources that could be used elsewhere; anti-abortion opposition to the destruction of embryos not transferred *in vivo*; religious leaders' opinions on fertility treatments; others [any 2 = 2]

Answers

Key Area 2.4

Restricted response

1 antenatal screening identifies the risk of a disorder before birth/involves testing for diseases or conditions in a fetus or embryo before it is born; so that further tests and a prenatal diagnosis can be offered [2]

2 ultrasound scanning; amniocentesis; chorionic villus sampling; rhesus antibody testing [any 2 = 2]

3 to produce a pregnancy or gestational dating scan; to produce an anomaly scan; to detect the presence of serious physical problems in the fetus [any 2 = 2]

4 karyotype [1]

5 screening identifies the risk/possible presence of a disorder/condition; diagnostic test confirms the presence of the condition [2]

6 to determine the rhesus status of the mother to ensure that they show no immune response to their fetus [1]

7 an autosomal recessive disorder is expressed relatively rarely in the offspring/affects males and females equally/may skip generations [1]

8 in sex-linked recessive disorders males are affected more often than females/male offspring receive the condition from their mother [1]

Extended response

9 sensitisation to rhesus antigens can occur; arises when the mother is rhesus negative and the fetus rhesus positive; red blood cells from the fetus cross the placenta and trigger the release of antibodies by the mother; these antibodies can cross back into the fetal blood circulation and cause the blood to clot; anti-rhesus antibodies are given so that the fetal rhesus positive red blood cells are destroyed before the mother's immune system can discover them [any 4 = 4]

10 amniocentesis and chorionic villus sampling (CVS) are procedures that confirm the presence of a condition such as Down syndrome; CVS can be carried out earlier in pregnancy than amniocentesis; both amniocentesis and CVS are invasive and carry a small element of risk of inducing a miscarriage; CVS has a slightly higher risk of inducing miscarriage than an amniocentesis; CVS cannot detect neural tube defects [any 4 = 4]

11 pedigree charts show the inheritance of a characteristic in families; they show how individuals are related and which show the characteristic; used to analyse patterns of inheritance in genetic screening and counselling; provide information and advice in situations where there is a chance of passing on a genetic disorder to potential offspring; used to analyse patterns of inheritance involving autosomal recessive/autosomal dominant/incomplete dominance and sex-linked, recessive, single-gene disorders [any 4 = 4]

12 a) caused by a gene mutation; it is an autosomal recessive genetic disorder; individuals with PKU cannot metabolise excess phenylalanine [3]

b) if PKU is not treated soon after birth the baby's mental development is affected; individuals with PKU are placed on a restricted diet that lacks the amino acid phenylalanine [2]

13 mother's blood pressure; blood type; blood tests; urine tests; general health check [any 2 = 2] ultrasound (imaging/scan); dating scan/scan at 8–14 weeks is used to determine stage of pregnancy/due date; anomaly scan/scan at 18–20 weeks for serious physical problems; biochemical/chemical tests detect (physiological) changes of pregnancy; marker chemicals/named chemical can indicate medical conditions/can give a false positive result; diagnostic/further testing can follow from routine testing/named test; amniocentesis/cells from amniotic fluid used to produce karyotype/to test for Down syndrome/chromosome abnormalities; chorionic villus sampling/CVS – cells from placenta/chorion used to produce karyotype/to test for Down syndrome/chromosome abnormalities; CVS carried out earlier in pregnancy than amniocentesis; allows immediate karyotyping; CVS has higher risk of miscarriage; rhesus antibody testing described (for sensitisation of Rh− mother by Rh+ antigens) [any 7 = 7]

Answers

Key Area 2.5

Restricted response

1 lumen [1]

2 endothelium [1]

3 a blood vessel that carries blood away from the heart [1]

4 a blood vessel that carries blood back to the heart [1]

⇨

5 valves prevent the backflow of blood; valves are needed as the blood is flowing back to the heart at low pressure (and generally against the force of gravity) [2]

6 veins have valves; relatively wide lumen; thinner muscular wall (or converse for arteries) [any 2 = 2]

7 wall one cell thick; capillaries allow exchange of substances with tissues [2]

8 blood in the arterioles is at a higher pressure than in capillary bed; pressure filtration causes the formation of tissue fluid [2]

9 tissue fluid is similar to blood plasma but does not contain plasma proteins [1]

10 tissue fluid contains glucose, oxygen and dissolved substances that supply the tissues with all their requirements [1]

11 re-enters capillaries by osmosis [1]

12 excess tissue fluid enters the lymph vessels and is returned to the circulatory system [1]

13 vasoconstriction/vasodilation allows the changing demands of the body's tissues to be met; during exercise, muscle arterioles vasodilate, increasing the blood flow to them; during exercise, the arterioles supplying the abdominal organs vasoconstrict, which reduces the blood flow to them [any 2 = 2]

Extended response

14 arteries carry blood away from the heart; blood is pumped through arteries at a high pressure; arteries have an outer layer of connective tissue containing elastic fibres; a thick middle layer containing smooth muscle with more elastic fibres; relatively narrow lumen; elastic walls of the arteries stretch and recoil to accommodate the surge of blood pressure after each contraction of the heart [any 4 = 4]
veins carry blood towards the heart; veins have an outer layer of connective tissue containing elastic fibres; thinner muscular wall than arteries; the lumen of a vein is wider than that of an artery; valves are present in veins to prevent the backflow of blood; valves needed as the blood is flowing back to the heart at low pressure [any 4 = 4]
capillaries are only one cell thick; allows quick/efficient exchange of materials/substances with tissues [any 1 = 1]

15 plasma is the liquid part of the blood [1]
named dissolved substances carried – oxygen, carbon dioxide, glucose, amino acids, urea, vitamins, minerals, etc. [any 2 = 1]
capillaries have a large surface area/thin walls; high pressure (at arterial end of the capillaries) forces fluid/plasma out; tissue fluid (bathes the cells); plasma proteins/blood cells do not pass through capillary walls/stay in blood; (dissolved) substances diffuse/move from tissue fluid into body cells; waste products/named example diffuse/move out of the cells; low pressure (at venous end of capillary network) allows return of fluid; liquid/water also returns by osmosis (into the plasma); (excess) tissue fluid enters lymph vessels/lymph; lymph/fluid is carried back to the blood (by lymphatic system) [any 7 = 7]

Answers

Key Area 2.6

Restricted response

1 the volume of blood pumped through each ventricle (out of the heart) per minute [1]

2 determined by heart rate and stroke volume (CO = HR × SV) [1]

3 situated in the wall at the top of the right atrium [1]

4 sets the rate at which cardiac muscle cells contract; generates an electrical impulse, which is passed through the (left and right) atria to the atrio-ventricular node (AVN) [2]

⇨

⇨

5 receives impulses from the SAN; sends impulses that result in the simultaneous contraction of the ventricles/ventricular systole [2]

6 sympathetic/accelerator nerves release nor-adrenaline/nor-epinephrine; increases/speeds up the heart rate [2]

7 the parasympathetic nerves release acetylcholine; decreases/slows the heart rate [2]

8 ventricular systole closes the AV valves; blood is pumped out through the open semi-lunar (SL) valves [2]

9 during diastole the muscles of the atria and ventricles are relaxed [1]

10 prevent the backflow of blood into the ventricles [1]

11 ventricular systole [1]

12 sphygmomanometer [1]

13 systolic blood pressure is the pressure that blood exerts on the arteries while the heart is contracting/beating; diastolic blood pressure is the pressure the blood exerts on the arteries while the heart is relaxed [2]

14 progressive decrease in blood pressure after leaving the heart; decrease in pressure due to arteries branching into arterioles/capillaries/smaller vessels and increase in surface area/friction *or* more space/combined internal diameter for blood flow [2]

15 hypertension; coronary heart disease (CHD)/stroke [2]

16 the electrical impulses generated in the heart produce currents that can be detected by an electrocardiogram (ECG)/an ECG is used to measure the electrical changes that take place in the heart; produces a PQRST wave [2]

17 P (wave) – the wave of electrical impulses spreading over the atria from the SAN; QRS (complex) – the electrical impulses through the ventricles; T (wave) – the electrical recovery of the ventricles at the end of ventricular systole [any 2 = 2]

Extended response

18 the medulla in the brain regulates the rate of the SAN through the antagonistic action of the autonomic nervous system (ANS); sympathetic accelerator nerves release nor-adrenaline/nor-epinephrine; which increases the heart rate; parasympathetic nerves release acetylcholine; which decreases the heart rate [any 4 = 4]

19 controlled by autonomic nervous system; medulla (oblongata) is control centre (in the brain); sympathetic nervous system/accelerator nerves release nor-adrenaline/nor-epinephrine which speeds up the heart; the parasympathetic nerves release acetylcholine which slows down the heart; sino-atrial node (SAN) in right atrium; SAN produces electrical impulses/starts contraction; impulses cause the atria to contract/atrial systole; reaches/stimulates the atrio-ventricular node (AVN); AVN found at junction of/between atria and ventricles; impulse (from AVN) carried by (conducting) nerves/fibres spread out over the ventricles; causes contraction of ventricles/ventricular systole; followed by relaxation/resting/diastolic phase [any 9 = 9]

Answers

Key Area 2.7

Restricted response

1 the accumulation of fatty material/cholesterol (and fibrous material and calcium) in an artery; forming an atheroma/plaque [2]

2 artery thickens/lumen diameter reduced; loses its elasticity [2]

3 a thrombus breaks loose/forms an embolus that travels through the bloodstream; thrombosis that blocks a coronary artery may lead to a myocardial infarction (MI) [2]

4 thrombus breaks loose/forms an embolus that travels through the bloodstream; thrombosis that blocks an artery in the brain may lead to a stroke [2]

5 deep vein thrombosis (DVT); pulmonary embolism [2]

6 liver [1]

7 component of cell membranes; (precursor for) steroid synthesis [2]

8 familial hypercholesterolaemia (FH) [1]

9 transports excess cholesterol from the body cells to the liver for elimination [1]

10 transports cholesterol to body cells [1]

11 LDL receptors take LDL into the cell where it releases the cholesterol [1]

12 negative feedback control [1]

13 genetic screening [1]

14 results in lower blood cholesterol; reduced chance of atherosclerosis [2]

15 regular physical activity tends to raise HDL levels; lowers blood cholesterol/chance of developing atherosclerosis [2]

16 statins [1]

Extended response

17 the accumulation of fatty material/cholesterol (and fibrous material and calcium) forming an atheroma/plaque; atheroma forms beneath the endothelium of the artery wall; artery thickens/lumen diameter reduced; artery loses its elasticity; blood flow is restricted and results in increased blood pressure; atherosclerosis is the cause of various cardiovascular diseases (CVD)/angina/myocardial infarction (MI)/stroke/peripheral vascular disorders [any 5 = 5]

18 endothelium is damaged; clotting factors are released; prothrombin (enzyme) is converted/activated/changed into thrombin; fibrinogen is converted into fibrin (by thrombin); fibrin/threads form a meshwork (that seals the wound); clot/thrombus formed may break loose, forming an embolus; clot/thrombus may lead to a heart attack/stroke [any 6 = 6]

19 results of cardiovascular disease (CVD) include: angina/stroke/myocardial infarction (MI)/heart attack/hypertension/high blood pressure/peripheral vascular disease [any 2 = 1] atherosclerosis is build-up of cholesterol/calcium/fatty/fibrous material in an artery; low-density lipoproteins/LDLs deposit cholesterol in the arteries; an atheroma/plaque forms beneath the endothelium/lining of artery; artery thickens/hardens/loses elasticity/narrows; blood pressure increases/hypertension develops; atheromas can rupture and clotting factors are released; formation of a clot/thrombus occurs or thrombosis occurs; clot/thrombus can break loose, forming an embolus; this can block arteries (causing a stroke/heart attack); cells are deprived of oxygen; deep vein thrombosis (can occur) or DVT is a clot in a vein; high blood glucose levels/diabetes can cause cardiovascular disease [any 8 = 8]

⇨

20 cholesterol is a component of cell membranes and a precursor for steroid synthesis; most cholesterol is synthesised by the liver (from saturated fats in the diet); high-density lipoprotein (HDL) transports excess cholesterol from the body cells to the liver for elimination; low-density lipoprotein (LDL) transports cholesterol to body cells; most cells have LDL receptors that take LDL into the cell where it releases cholesterol; negative feedback control inhibits the synthesis of new LDL receptors once a cell has sufficient cholesterol; familial hypercholesterolaemia (FH) results in individuals developing high levels of cholesterol; mutated gene results in a decreased number/altered structure of LDL receptors, which stops the LDL from unloading its cholesterol into the cell; higher ratio of HDL to LDL will result in lower blood cholesterol; regular physical activity tends to raise HDL levels; dietary changes aim to reduce the levels of total fat in the diet and to replace saturated with unsaturated fats; drugs such as statins reduce blood cholesterol by inhibiting the synthesis of cholesterol by liver cells [any 9 = 9]

Answers

Key Area 2.8

Restricted response

1 atherosclerosis; CVD; stroke; blood vessel damage; hypertension [any 2 = 2]
2 pancreas [1]
3 insulin; glucagon; adrenaline [all 3 = 2, 2/1 = 1]
4 insulin makes the liver cells more permeable to glucose/activates the conversion of glucose to glycogen; decreases the blood glucose concentration [2]
5 glucagon activates the conversion of glycogen to glucose; increases the blood glucose concentration [2]
6 liver; glycogen [2]
7 released during exercise/stress/fight or flight responses; stimulates glucagon secretion and inhibits insulin secretion [2]
8 individuals with type-1 diabetes are unable to produce insulin; individuals with type-2 diabetes produce insulin but their cells are less sensitive to it [2]
9 glucose tolerance test [1]
10 obesity is characterised by excess body fat in relation to lean body tissue/muscle [1]
11 body weight, height [1]
12 30 [1]
13 someone may be classified as overweight/obese when additional weight is not fat but muscle/bone mass [1]

Extended response

14 negative feedback maintains constant internal conditions in the body/homeostasis; a change from the normal level/set point is detected; corrective mechanism is switched on/activated; when condition returns to its normal level/set point, corrective mechanism is switched off [any 2 = 2]

⇨

blood sugar/glucose concentration/level detected by the pancreas/pancreatic receptors; if blood glucose concentration increases, (more) insulin is released; insulin increases permeability of cells to glucose *or* insulin increases uptake of glucose by cells; liver/muscle cells convert glucose to glycogen *or* glucose converted to glycogen and stored in liver/muscle; blood glucose concentration returns to its normal/set point; if blood glucose concentration decreases, (more) glucagon is released; glucagon causes conversion of glycogen to glucose; glucose released into blood; blood glucose concentration returns to normal/set point   [any 7 = 7]

Practice Course Assessment: Unit 2 (50 marks)

Section A (10 marks)

1 One function of the seminal vesicles is to
   A store sperm
   B supply nutrients to sperm
   C produce ICSH
   D produce sperm.

2 The diagram below represents part of the control mechanism for ovulation.

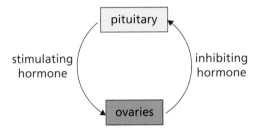

Which line in the table below identifies correctly the hormones shown in the diagram?

	Stimulating hormone	Inhibiting hormone
A	Luteinising hormone (LH)	Follicle stimulating hormone (FSH)
B	Progesterone	FSH
C	FSH	Oestrogen
D	Oestrogen	LH

3 Events that occur in the ovary during the menstrual cycle are listed below.

   1 Ovulation occurs
   2 Corpus luteum forms
   3 Progesterone is produced
   4 Follicle develops
   5 Corpus luteum degenerates
   In which order would these events occur in a normal menstrual cycle?
   A 1, 2, 3, 4, 5   C 2, 3, 1, 4, 5
   B 4, 1, 2, 3, 5   D 5, 3, 1, 4, 2

4 Fertility drugs may be used in the treatment of infertility to
   A stimulate meiosis in an ovum
   B prepare the oviduct for implantation
   C improve motility of sperm cells
   D correct hormone imbalances.

5 Which of the following fertility treatments would be appropriate for a woman with blocked oviducts?
   A *In vitro* fertilisation (IVF)
   B Artificial insemination
   C Ovulatory drugs
   D Calculation of the fertility period   ⇨

⇨

6 The procedures listed below can be used in the treatment of infertility.
   1 Artificial insemination (AI)
   2 Intracytoplasmic sperm injection (ICSI)
   3 Pre-implantation genetic diagnosis (PGD)
   For which of the procedures above is the surgical removal of eggs from ovaries required?

   A 1 and 2   C 1 and 3
   B 2 and 3   D 1, 2 and 3

7 The length of a fetus was monitored using an ultrasound scanner. The graph below shows the increase in length of the fetus over the 9 months of pregnancy.

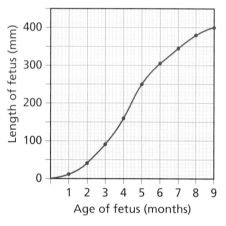

During which month was the greatest increase in the fetal length recorded?

   A 3rd   C 5th
   B 4th   D 6th

8 One form of muscular dystrophy is caused by a sex-linked recessive allele. Which line in the table below correctly predicts the effect on the sons and daughters of a mother who is a carrier for the condition and a father who is unaffected by it?

	Sons	Daughters
A	50% affected	50% carriers
B	50% affected	100% carriers
C	100% affected	50% carriers
D	100% affected	100% carriers

9 The diagram below represents part of a capillary bed involved in the exchange of materials with body cells.

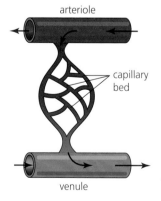

⇨

Which line in the table below correctly identifies changes in the concentration of glucose and carbon dioxide in the plasma as the blood flows through the capillary bed between the arteriole and the venule?

	CO_2 concentration	Glucose concentration
A	Decrease	Decrease
B	Increase	Increase
C	Decrease	Increase
D	Increase	Decrease

10 The graph below provides information about the population of the United Kingdom.

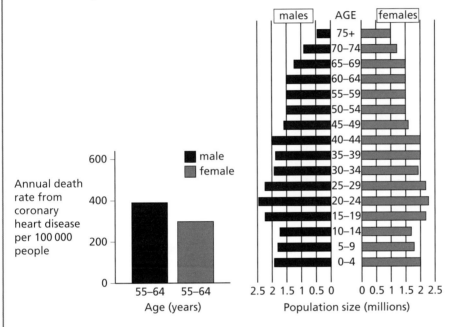

How many more males than females between the age of 55 and 64 die from coronary heart disease (CHD) annually?

A 100 **C** 3000

B 1500 **D** 6000

Section B (40 marks)

1 The graphs below show the changes in the plasma concentration of four hormones throughout the menstrual cycle. Graph 1 shows the concentration of FSH and LH. Graph 2 shows the concentration of two other hormones, X and Y.

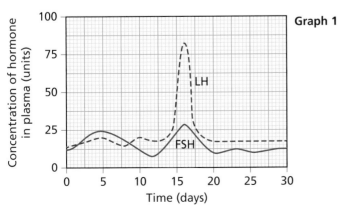

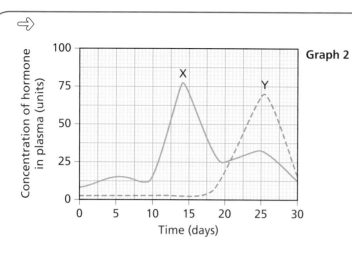

Graph 2

a) Name the site of production and release of FSH and LH. (1)
b) Name hormones X and Y. (1)
c) State the maximum concentration of hormone X. (1)
d) Predict the day of ovulation and give a reason to support your answer. (1)
e) Explain the differences that would occur in the concentrations of FSH and hormone Y after day 25 if pregnancy had occurred during this cycle. (2)

2 The graph below shows the sperm counts of 30 men taken between 1950 and 2010. A line of best fit has been drawn to indicate the trend over this period.

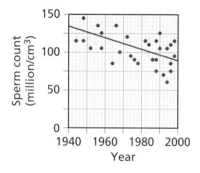

a) Use the line of best fit to calculate the percentage decrease in sperm count over the period of study. (1)
b) Give the minimum sperm count obtained from an individual recorded during this period. (1)
c) State why fertility is described as continuous in males and cyclical in females. (2)

3 Cystic fibrosis is a genetic disorder caused by the inheritance of two autosomal recessive alleles (**cc**).
a) Complete the following table for a man and a woman who do not have cystic fibrosis but are both carriers of the cystic fibrosis allele. (2)

Phenotype	Unaffected male	Unaffected female
Genotype		
Genotype(s) of gametes		

b) The couple plan to have a child. They consult a doctor who uses their pedigree chart to determine the chances of them having a child with cystic fibrosis.

   (i) Give the term applied to the type of advice given to the couple based on evidence gained from the construction and interpretation of a pedigree chart used to analyse patterns of inheritance. (1)

   (ii) Calculate the percentage chance of their child inheriting the cystic fibrosis condition. (1)

4 The graph below shows the change in pressure that occurs as blood flows through the circulatory system.

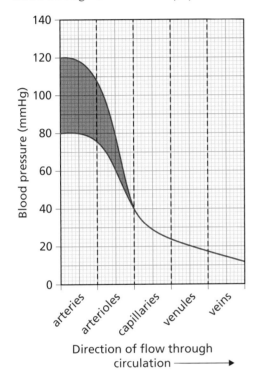

a) Calculate the percentage decrease in pressure that occurs in the capillaries. (1)

b) Identify the location in the circulatory system where the blood pressure is 25% of the highest value shown on the graph. (1)

c) Explain why there are maximum and minimum values for the blood pressure in the arteries and arterioles. (1)

d) Name the condition in which an individual has persistently high blood pressure. (1)

5 The diagram below represents a section through an artery.

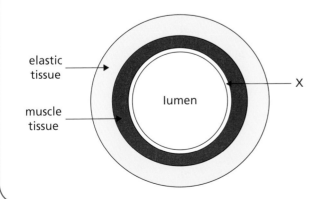

⇨

a) Name region X. (1)

b) Describe the process of atherosclerosis in an artery. (1)

c) Give **one** effect atherosclerosis has on the structure of an artery. (1)

d) Name **one** peripheral vascular disorder that can arise following atherosclerosis. (1)

6 The diagram below shows some stages in the control of blood glucose concentration.

Stage 1 Increase in blood glucose concentration above normal

is detected by receptors in **organ P**

⇩

Stage 2 Increased secretion of insulin;

decreased secretion of **hormone Q**

⇩

Stage 3 Liver converts glucose to storage carbohydrate

⇩

Stage 4 Blood glucose concentration returns to normal

⇩

Stage 5 Corrective mechanism switched off

a) Name organ P. (1)

b) Identify hormone Q. (1)

c) Name the carbohydrate stored in the liver. (1)

d) Explain how the mechanism of glucose control in the diagram demonstrates negative feedback. (2)

e) Name another hormone released during stress that results in a rapid increase in the blood glucose concentration. (1)

7 The formula for calculating body mass index (BMI) from the height and weight of an individual is:

$$BMI = \frac{body\ weight\ (kg)}{(height\ (m))^2}$$

The table below relates BMI to the degree of obesity in an individual.

BMI	Degree of obesity
Less than 25	None
25–29	Mild
30–34	Moderate
35–39	Severe
40 or above	Very severe

a) Use the information given to calculate the BMI and degree of obesity of an individual weighing 120 kilograms and measuring 1.8 metres in height. (1)

b) Apart from BMI, state one other method of estimating the degree of obesity of an individual. (1)

c) Give **one** disadvantage of using BMI to diagnose obesity in an individual. (1)

Question 8 contains a choice.

8 *Either* A Discuss the biological basis of contraception. (9)

Or B Discuss the screening and testing procedures that may be carried out as part of antenatal care. (9)

Answers to Practice Course Assessment: Unit 2

Section A

1 B, 2 C, 3 B, 4 D, 5 A, 6 B, 7 C, 8 A, 9 D, 10 C

Section B

1 a) pituitary gland   [1]
   b) X oestrogen, Y progesterone   [1]
   c) 77.5   [1]
   d) day 16/17 – the concentration of LH peaks/is at a maximum/is highest at this time   [1]
   e) FSH remains at a low concentration/stays low/remains the same or decreases/goes down;
      hormone Y/progesterone remains high or increases/rises   [2]
2 a) 33 *or* 33.3   [1]
   b) 60 million/cm^3 [1]
   c) males produce sperm from puberty throughout their lives; females' fertility is usually restricted
      to 4–5 days a month immediately before and following ovulation   [2]
3 a) Cc and Cc; C and c, C and c   [2]
   b) (i) genetic screening/counselling   [1]
      (ii) 25%   [1]
4 a) 40%   [1]
   b) capillaries   [1]
   c) maximum/upper value is the pressure due to systole/contraction of the heart muscles or when
      the heart is contracting *and* the minimum/lower value is the pressure when the heart
      is relaxing/in diastole   [1]
   d) hypertension   [1]
5 a) endothelium   [1]
   b) atherosclerosis is the accumulation of fatty material/cholesterol (and fibrous material and
      calcium), forming an atheroma/plaque   [1]
   c) artery thickens/lumen diameter reduced/loses its elasticity   [1]
   d) deep vein thrombosis/pulmonary embolism   [1]
6 a) pancreas   [1]
   b) glucagon   [1]
   c) glycogen   [1]
   d) change away from the norm is detected by receptors that switch on a corrective mechanism;
      once the condition returns to normal the corrective mechanism is switched off   [2]
   e) adrenaline   [1]
7 a) BMI = 37 *and* severe obesity   [1]
   b) densitometry   [1]
   c) an individual may have above average mass of muscle or bone   [1]
8 A contraception is the (intentional) prevention of fertilisation/pregnancy/conception; fertile
     period lasts for a few/4–5 days around day 14/mid-point of menstrual cycle/ovulation;
     fertile period can be detected by (slight) rise in body temperature on the day of ovulation;
     fertile period can be detected by changes in cervical mucus/mucus becomes thinner;
     chemical contraceptives can be pills/injections/implants; these contain synthetic oestrogen/
     progesterone; concentration of hormones (in blood) is increased; mimic negative feedback
     effect/inhibitory effect on pituitary gland; reduced production of FSH prevents maturation
     of ova/eggs; reduced production of LH prevents ovulation; physical method of   ⇨

contraception named; with correct explanation; examples – condom (prevents sperm being released into the female), diaphragm/cervical cap (prevents sperm entering the uterus), vasectomy (male sterilisation procedure preventing the release of sperm), tubal ligation (female sterilisation procedure preventing the release of eggs), intra-uterine device (IUD) (creates hostile environment for pregnancy to occur) [any 9 = 9]

B mother's blood pressure; blood type; blood tests; urine tests; general health check   [any 2 = 1]
ultrasound (imaging/scan) is used; dating scan/scan at 8–14 weeks is used to determine stage of pregnancy/due date; anomaly scan/scan at 18–20 weeks for serious physical problems; biochemical/chemical tests detect (physiological) changes of pregnancy; marker chemicals/ named chemical can indicate medical conditions/can give a false positive result; amniocentesis/ cells from amniotic fluid used to produce karyotype/to test for Down syndrome/chromosome abnormalities; chorionic villus sampling/CVS – cells from placenta/chorion used to produce karyotype/to test for Down syndrome/chromosome abnormalities; CVS carried out earlier in pregnancy than amniocentesis; allows immediate karyotyping; CVS has higher risk of miscarriage; rhesus antibody testing described (for sensitisation of Rh− mother by Rh+ antigens) [any 8 = 8]

Key Area 3.1

Divisions of the nervous system and parts of the brain

Key points !

1. The **central nervous system (CNS)** includes the brain and spinal cord. ☐
2. The **peripheral nervous system (PNS)** consists of the peripheral nerves and includes the **somatic nervous system (SNS)** and autonomic nervous system (ANS). ☐
3. The SNS controls voluntary actions by skeletal muscles. ☐
4. The ANS controls involuntary actions by glands, smooth muscle and cardiac muscle. ☐
5. The ANS consists of **sympathetic** and **parasympathetic nervous systems**, which have fibres that are antagonistic to each other. ☐
6. Sympathetic fibres speed the heart and breathing rates but slow digestive processes such as secretion of digestive juices, secretion of bile and **peristalsis.** ☐
7. Parasympathetic fibres slow the heart and breathing rates but speed up digestive processes such as secretion of digestive juices, secretion of bile and peristalsis. ☐
8. The **cerebellum** in the brain has centres that control balance and coordination. ☐
9. The medulla in the brain has centres that control heart rate, breathing rate and peristalsis. ☐
10. The **limbic system** has a role in **long-term memory (LTM)**, motivation, emotion and behaviour. ☐
11. The **cerebrum** is divided into the left and right **cerebral hemispheres.** ☐
12. The cerebral cortex is divided into localised regions including sensory, motor and association areas. ☐
13. The **cerebral cortex** receives sensory information, is involved with decision making in light of experience and coordinates voluntary movement. ☐
14. The sensory area receives impulses from the skin, organs and muscle. ☐
15. The motor area sends impulses to the skeletal muscles. ☐
16. There are association areas concerned with language, personality, imagination and intelligence. ☐
17. Information from one side of the body is processed by the cerebral hemisphere that is located on the opposite side. ☐
18. The **corpus callosum** transfers information between the two cerebral hemispheres. ☐

Summary notes

Structural division of the nervous system

The nervous system can be divided into the central nervous system (CNS) and the peripheral nervous system (PNS). The CNS is made up of the brain and spinal cord and the PNS consists of the peripheral nerves (Figure 3.1).

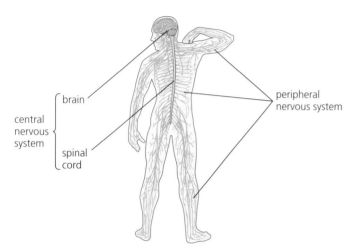

Figure 3.1 Parts of the nervous system

Functional division of the nervous system

The functions of the various parts of the nervous system are shown in the table below.

Part	Structure	Function
Central nervous system (CNS)	Brain	Processing of information
	Spinal cord	Connects brain with PNS
Peripheral nervous system (PNS)	Nerves	Carries information to and from all parts of the body

The overall functions of the peripheral nervous system (PNS) can be split:
- Those that are controlled in a voluntary way by the somatic nervous system (SNS) acting through skeletal muscle.
- Those that are controlled in an involuntary way by the autonomic nervous system (ANS) acting through smooth muscle, cardiac muscle and glands.

The ANS controls functions that bring about a steady internal state within the body. These functions include heartbeat, breathing rate and digestive processes. The ANS has sympathetic and parasympathetic fibres that work to regulate these processes, as shown in the following table.

Process		Sympathetic effects	Parasympathetic effects
Heart rate		Increases rate	Decreases rate
Breathing rate		Increases rate and depth	Decreases rate and depth
Digestive processes	Peristalsis	Decreases rate	Increases rate
	Secretion of digestive juices and bile	Decreases rate	Increases rate

Sympathetic and parasympathetic fibres are antagonistic. They exert opposing influences, which are usually in balance.

The sympathetic fibres act as accelerators and if they gain an upper hand the body is prepared for action by processes that ensure an increased supply of oxygen to the muscles. The parasympathetic fibres act as brakes on activity and when they gain the upper hand the body is able to rest and perform activities such as digestion of food.

The structure and function of the nervous system is summarised by Figure 3.2.

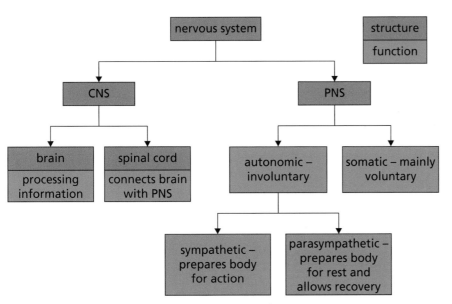

Figure 3.2 Summary of nervous system structure and function

Hints & tips ★

Autonomic is below the conscious level of thought — in a way these actions are automatic, but don't get the two words confused.

Hints & tips ★

Sympathetic nervous system actions are **sympathetic** to your needs when exercising or in times of stress, for example increasing your heart and breathing rates.

Hints & tips ★

Learn this **ASAP!**
ANS: **S**ympathetic is **A**ntagonistic to **P**arasympathetic

The brain

The brain is the complex central processing centre of the nervous system. It receives and assimilates incoming information from sense organs and responds by initiating appropriate actions. It can be divided into regions, as shown in Figure 3.3.

Brain functions

Cerebral cortex

The cerebral cortex receives sensory information and coordinates voluntary movements and decision making in light of experience. The

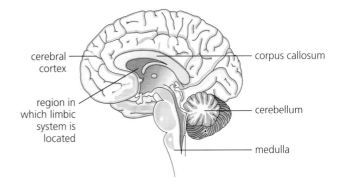

Figure 3.3 Vertical section of the human brain

association areas at the front of the brain seem to control many functions that could be related to intelligence. Intelligence might be defined in terms of an individual's capacity for logical and abstract thought, imagination, understanding, self-awareness, communication, ability to learn, planning, problem solving and many other aspects.

Brain functions are localised in the cerebral cortex, as shown in Figure 3.4.

Hints & tips ⭐

Remember:
MM – *Motor area to Muscles and glands*
SS – *Sensory area from Skin and other areas*

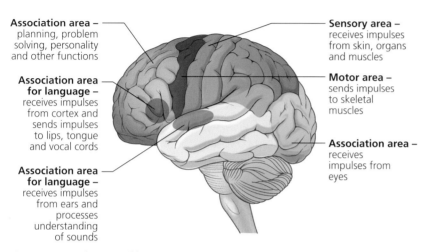

Association area – planning, problem solving, personality and other functions

Association area for language – receives impulses from cortex and sends impulses to lips, tongue and vocal cords

Association area for language – receives impulses from ears and processes understanding of sounds

Sensory area – receives impulses from skin, organs and muscles

Motor area – sends impulses to skeletal muscles

Association area – receives impulses from eyes

Figure 3.4 Localisation of function in the cerebral cortex

Limbic system

The limbic system is a collection of regions within the brain which supports a variety of functions, including long-term memory, emotion, behaviour and motivation.

Cerebellum

The cerebellum contains centres that control balance and are important in coordination of movement.

Medulla

The medulla contains centres that control aspects of the body's involuntary autonomic responses, such as heart and breathing rates, secretion of digestive juices and peristalsis.

Corpus callosum

The cerebral cortex is formed into two separate hemispheres, as shown in Figure 3.5. Information from one side of the body is processed in the cerebral cortex of the hemisphere on the opposite side of the brain. The corpus callosum is a bridge of tissue deep within the brain that connects the two cerebral hemispheres. Information is transferred between the hemispheres through the corpus callosum.

Hints & tips ⭐

There is more about memory in Key Area 3.2 on pages 144–146.

Hints & tips ⭐

Remember **LL** – *Limbic for Long-term memory.*

Hints & tips ⭐

Remember the four Cs: *Corpus Callosum from Cerebral hemisphere to Cerebral hemisphere*

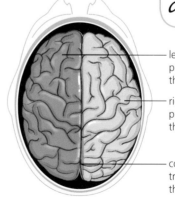

left cerebral hemisphere processes information from the right side of the body

right cerebral hemisphere processes information from the left side of the body

corpus callosum, deep in the brain, transfers information between the two hemispheres

Figure 3.5 Role of the cerebral hemispheres and the corpus callosum

Key words

Central nervous system (CNS) – brain and spinal cord

Cerebellum – area of the brain that contains the balance and coordination centres

Cerebral cortex – cells of the cerebrum

Cerebral hemispheres – two regions into which the cerebrum is divided

Cerebrum – region of the brain that has motor, sensory and association areas

Corpus callosum – band of tissue in the brain that connects the two cerebral hemispheres

Limbic system – area of the brain that contains LTM and other centres

Long-term memory (LTM) – apparently infinite capacity to store information over long periods

Parasympathetic nervous system – fibres of the autonomic nervous system that prepare body systems for rest

Peripheral nervous system (PNS) – all peripheral nerves

Peristalsis – involuntary muscular movements of food through the digestive system

Somatic nervous system (SNS) – controls the voluntary action of skeletal muscle

Sympathetic nervous system – fibres of the autonomic nervous system that prepare body systems for action

Questions

Restricted response (structured in 1- or 2-mark parts)

1 Describe the structure of the central nervous system (CNS). (2)
2 Give the difference between somatic and autonomic actions. (2)
3 Give the term that describes the relationship between sympathetic and parasympathetic fibres. (1)
4 Explain what is meant by the localisation of brain functions in the cerebral cortex. (1)
5 Give **two** examples of the functions of association areas in the cerebral cortex. (2)
6 State the role of the corpus callosum. (1)

Extended response (4–9 marks each)

7 Describe the structure and functions of the autonomic nervous system. (8)

Answers are on page 164.

Key points !

1 **Perception** is the process by which the brain analyses and makes sense out of incoming sensory information. ☐

2 The three areas of perception involve **segregation of objects**, perception of distance and recognition. ☐

3 Object segregation involves perception of figure (the object), ground (the background) and the organisation of stimuli into coherent patterns. ☐

4 Object segregation relies on visual cues such as relative size, superimposition and relative height in the field of view. ☐

5 Perception of distance is affected by **binocular disparity** and **perceptual constancy**. ☐

6 In recognition of objects, shape matched with a previous memory of the shape is more important than detail. ☐

7 **Inference** can help optimal perception of uncertain images. ☐

8 **Perceptual set** is a group of expectations based on past experiences and context, which affect how a stimulus is perceived. ☐

9 Memory involves the storage, retention and retrieval of information. ☐

10 Memories include past experiences, knowledge and thoughts. ☐

11 All information entering the brain passes through the **sensory memory** and enters the **short-term memory (STM)**. ☐

12 Items in the STM may be transferred to the **long-term memory (LTM)** or be discarded. ☐

13 Sensory memory lasts a few seconds and retains all of the visual or auditory input. ☐

14 **Memory span** is the number of discrete items, such as letters, words or numbers, that the STM can hold. ☐

15 The **serial position effect** is the tendency of a person to recall the first and last items in a series best, and the middle items worst. ☐

16 Items can be retained in the STM memory by **rehearsal** or lost by **displacement** or **decay**. ☐

17 STM can be improved by **chunking**, in which the items to be remembered are put in clusters based on the items' semantic relatedness or perceptual features. ☐

18 Information can be transferred to the LTM by rehearsal, **organisation** or **elaboration**. ☐

19 Information can be encoded by **shallow processing** or **deep (elaborative) processing**. ☐

20 Shallow processing occurs when only the appearance or sound of an item is involved, while deep processing involves elaborating the meaning of the item. ☐

21 **Retrieval** from LTM is aided by **contextual cues**. ☐

22 **Episodic** and **semantic memories** are stored in the cortex of the brain. ☐

23 **Procedural memories** are linked to the motor cortex of the brain. ☐

24 **Emotional memories** involve links between the cortex and the limbic system in the brain. ☐

25 **Spatial memories** are located in the limbic system. ☐

Summary notes

Perception

Perception is the process by which the brain analyses and makes sense out of incoming sensory information.

Visual perception

Segregation of objects

In perceiving a visual image, the brain segregates the image into the figure and the background, to make the image into a coherent pattern.

Example

Figure 3.6 shows an example in which the brain can perceive different figures and backgrounds from the same image. Is the figure a white vase on a black ground or two black face profiles on a white ground?

Figure 3.6 Example of figure and ground perception

Relative size

The brain uses visual cues such as relative size to make sense out of certain visual images. The further away an object is, the smaller it appears. This allows the perception of distance in some images.

Example

In Figure 3.7 there is a perception of railway lines going into the distance so that object A appears further away than object B. Although the bars are actually the same length, A appears bigger than B.

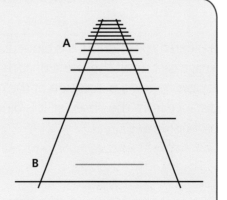

Figure 3.7 Example of visual perception – relative size

Superimposition

When the image of one object partially blocks the image of another by superimposition, the blocked object is perceived as further away.

In Figure 3.8 a blue disc appears to block a red disc, which therefore appears further away. Most people will perceive this as a red disc behind a blue disc and not as a red crescent beside a blue disc.

Figure 3.8 Example of visual perception – superimposition

Relative height in field

Where a group of objects have their bases below a visible horizon, the objects with lower bases appear closer to the viewer.

Example

In Figure 3.9 the fence post with the lowest base looks closer. Note that relative size also plays a part in the perception of this image.

visible horizon

this post appears furthest away from observer

this post appears closest to observer

Figure 3.9 Example of visual perception – relative height of a set of fence posts in a field of view

Distance perception

Binocular disparity

Each eye sees an object from a different position. This is binocular disparity and means that the image cast upon the retina of each eye is different. The brain fuses the images to give a perception of the overall object, which is related to its distance from the observer. It is binocular disparity that helps perception of distance.

In Figure 3.10 perception of the star's distance from the observer depends on binocular disparity.

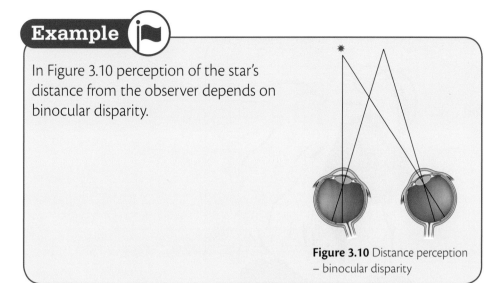

Figure 3.10 Distance perception – binocular disparity

Perceptual constancy

Our visual perceptions of our surroundings take into account sizes and shapes of well-known objects as we look at a changing scene. This prevents the perception of change in size and shape of objects, which would be unhelpful in an everyday situation.

Figure 3.11 shows three views of a door opening – although the image of the door changes shape and size, we accept that the door has not actually changed these dimensions.

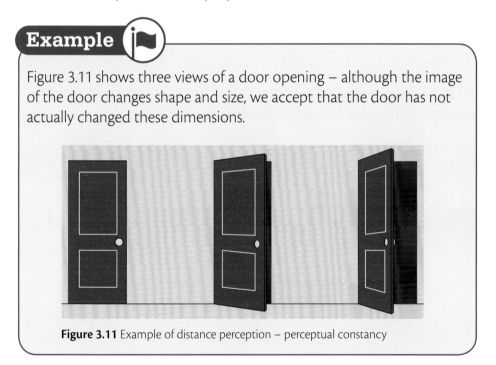

Figure 3.11 Example of distance perception – perceptual constancy

Recognition

In perception of objects, their shape is matched to images within memory and their identification can then be worked out. The overall shape of an object is more important than the detail. Recognition is affected by the perceptual set, which is a group of influences such as past experience, context and expectation. What a person sees is not easy to predict because of differences between individuals' perceptual sets.

Example 🚩

In Figure 3.12, some individuals see a young woman looking away while others see an older woman looking left. Which do you see?

Figure 3.12 Example of recognition

Memory

Memories include those generated by past experience, based on knowledge previously gained and thoughts had in the past. All information regarding environmental stimuli enters through a sensory memory, which lasts for a few seconds and retains all of the visual or auditory inputs. This then enters short-term memory (STM). The STM can be maintained by rehearsal, which then enables the information to be retrieved (Figure 3.13).

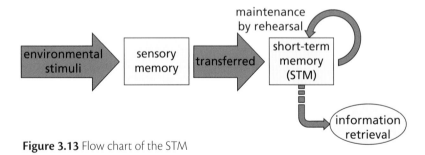

Figure 3.13 Flow chart of the STM

Items can be discarded from the STM by decay or by being displaced by new items entering. The STM has a limited span, which relates to its limited capacity.

Serial position effect

The serial position effect influences groups of items entering the short-term memory. Those items in the group that come first (primacy) and last (recency) are better recalled than the intermediate items. If individuals are presented with a sequence of words and then asked to recall words in the sequence, their performance is affected by the serial position effect, as shown in Figure 3.14.

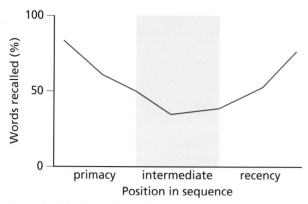

Figure 3.14 Serial position effect

Chunking

Chunking is a technique for the improvement of short-term memory (STM) span. It involves grouping items together to make a single item.

Example

Remembering telephone numbers can be improved if the sequence of numbers is reduced by chunking national and district codes together.

The url sqa.org.uk has 10 characters, too many for the STM. But chunking three items makes the url easy to remember, as shown in Figure 3.15.

Figure 3.15 Example of chunking

Long-term memory

The transfer of items to the long-term memory (LTM) can be brought about by rehearsal, organisation and elaboration.

Rehearsal involves simple repeats or practices of the information. Organisation involves placing the information into a framework and elaboration involves building more detail around the information. Retrieval is the recall of items from the long-term memory when required. An outline of long-term memory is shown in Figure 3.16.

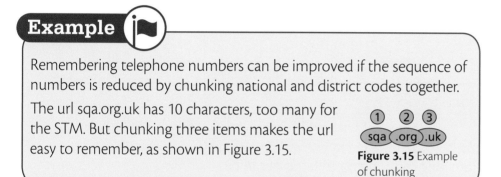

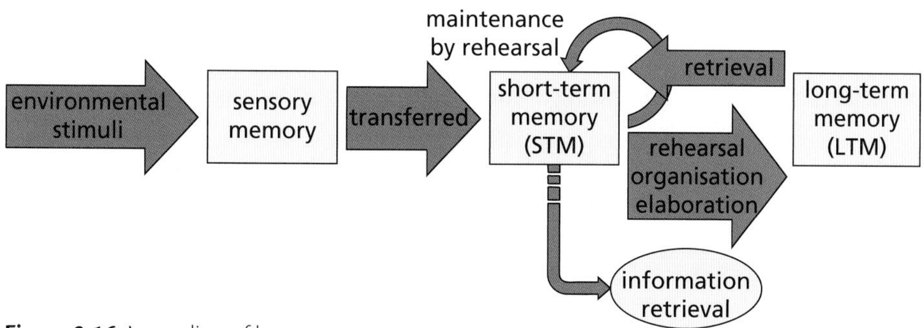

Hints & tips

Remember **ROE:**
Rehearsal
Organisation
Elaboration of meaning

Figure 3.16 An outline of long-term memory

Encoding

Information to be added to the memory has to be encoded. Encoding involves converting nerve signals into a form that can be received and interpreted by the brain. Methods of encoding can be shallow or elaborative (deeper). Encoding by rehearsal is an example of shallow encoding, whereas adding meaning to the information to be remembered is elaborative (deeper) encoding.

Example

Trying to remember an ingredients list for a dish by reading it over five times before going shopping is a shallow encoding technique. Focusing on what the dish is, say a cheese omelette, then imagining the recipe and the process of cooking the dish is a more elaborative technique and involves deeper coding. It is more likely to result in accurate memory of the ingredients.

Increasing the depth of encoding

Contextual cues

Information can be retrieved from long-term memory. Retrieval can be improved by contextual cues such as signals or reminders. These can be used by psychologists or psychiatrists to explore a person's previous experiences, for example by asking them to think back in time using photographs or significant objects as cues. Police investigators trying to help potential witnesses to recall crime details might set up reconstructions based on likely contextual cues to jog their memory.

Location of memory in the brain

The following table shows types of memory and where they are stored within the brain.

Type of memory encoded	Definition	Examples	Location of storage
Episodic	Recall of personal facts and experiences	Knowing birthday date Memories of a holiday	Various regions of the cortex
Semantic	Recall of general knowledge and non-personal facts	Knowing some capital cities Concept of gravity	Various regions of the cortex
Procedural	Motor and mental skills	Hitting tennis shots How to do arithmetic	Motor cortex
Emotional	Form when positive or negative associations are made with experiences	Liking going to the cinema Disliking going to the dentist	Links between the cortex and limbic system
Spatial	Recall of information about the environment and relative positions of objects	How to get to the airport Where things are in the kitchen	Limbic system

Key words

Binocular disparity – difference between the distance from an image to one eye and the other

Chunking – method for the expansion of the STM span

Contextual cues – aids to the retrieval of information from LTM

Decay – degradation of quality of STM

Deep (elaborative) processing – use of semantic methods of transfer of information to LTM

Displacement – loss of items from STM

Elaboration – method of encouraging transfer of information to LTM by adding meaning

Emotional memories – memories related to feelings

Episodic memory – memory of an event

Inference – process that can assist optimum perception in uncertain situations

Long-term memory – receives information from short-term memory and stores it permanently

Memory span – capacity of short-term memory for items

Organisation – method of encouraging transfer of information to LTM by adding structure

Perception – capacity to take in and make sense of sensory information

Perceptual constancy – capacity to appreciate the unchanging dimensions of an object as it moves

Perceptual set – factors influencing perception, including experience, context and expectation

Procedural memory – memory related to a skill

Rehearsal – practice by repetition of an item of information

Retrieval – recall of information from memory

Segregation of objects – capacity to distinguish between an object and its background

Semantic memory – memory of the meaning of something

Sensory memory – storage of sensory input that lasts a few seconds

Serial position effect – capacity to recall items presented in a sequence

Shallow processing – use of non-semantic methods of transfer of information to LTM

Short-term memory (STM) – receives information from sensory memory and has a limited span

Spatial memory – memory of where something is located

Questions ?

Restricted response (structured in 1- or 2-mark parts)

1   State what is meant by the term perception. (2)
2   Describe how the perception of objects can be affected by the segregation of objects into figures and background. (1)
3   Give the meanings of the following terms:
   a) binocular disparity (1)
   b) perceptual constancy. (1)
4   Explain how perceptual set can affect how a stimulus is perceived. (2)
5   Describe the serial position effect. (2)

Extended response (4–9 marks each)

6   Give an account of memory under the following headings:
   a) Sensory memory (2)
   b) Short-term memory (3)
   c) Long-term memory (4)
7   Give an account of memory under the following headings:
   a) Encoding (2)
   b) Transfer from short-term to long-term memory (4)
   c) Retrieval from long-term memory (2)

Answers are on page 164.

The cells of the nervous system and neurotransmitters at synapses

Key points ❗

1 **Neurons** are nerve cells. ☐
2 Neurons have a cell body and fibres called **dendrites** and **axons**. ☐
3 Three types of neuron are **sensory**, **inter** and **motor**. ☐
4 **Myelination** is the covering of neuron fibres with a **myelin sheath**, which insulates them, increasing the speed of nervous impulses. ☐
5 Myelination continues from birth to adolescence. ☐
6 **Glial cells** physically support neurons and produce the myelin sheaths. ☐
7 Glial cells maintain a homeostatic environment around neurons and remove debris by **phagocytosis**. ☐
8 **Synapses** are gaps between neurons. ☐
9 **Synaptic vesicles** containing chemical **neurotransmitters** are found in pre-synaptic neurons. ☐
10 Nervous transmission between neurons relies on neurotransmitters secreted into the **synaptic cleft**. ☐
11 **Receptors** in the **post-synaptic membrane** respond to neurotransmitters. ☐
12 Neurotransmitters must be removed from the synaptic cleft rapidly to maintain sensitivity. ☐
13 Neurotransmitters can be broken down by enzymes or reabsorbed into the **pre-synaptic membrane**. ☐
14 Receptors determine whether a signal is **excitatory** or **inhibitory**. ☐
15 Synapses can filter out weak stimuli resulting from insufficient secretion of neurotransmitter. ☐
16 Summation of a series of weak stimuli can trigger enough neurotransmitter to fire an impulse. ☐
17 Neural pathways are routes taken by impulses through the nervous system. ☐
18 In **converging neural pathways**, impulses from several neurons are passed to a single neuron. ☐
19 In **diverging neural pathways**, impulses from one neuron are passed to several others. ☐
20 In **reverberating neural pathways**, impulses are recycled round loop-like pathways. ☐
21 New neural pathways can be created to bypass areas of brain damage, to suppress reflexes or in response to sensory impulses. ☐
22 Creation of new neural pathways gives **plasticity** of response. ☐
23 **Endorphins** are neurotransmitters that stimulate neurons involved in reducing intensity of pain, creation of euphoria, appetite modulation and release of sex hormones. ☐
24 Endorphin production increases in response to severe injury, prolonged and continuous exercise, stress and certain foods. ☐

⇨

⇒

25 **Dopamine** induces the feeling of pleasure and reinforces particular behaviour in the **reward pathway**. ☐

26 **Agonist** drugs act like neurotransmitters and can enhance transmission. ☐

27 **Antagonistic** drugs bind to specific receptors, blocking the action of a neurotransmitter. ☐

28 Enzymes that degrade neurotransmitters or inhibit their reabsorption can be inhibited by certain drugs. ☐

29 **Recreational drugs** can mimic neurotransmitters, resulting in mood change, alteration of perception, and changes in cognition and behaviour. ☐

30 Many recreational drugs affect neurotransmission in the reward pathway. ☐

31 **Sensitisation** is an increase in the number and sensitivity of receptors as a result of exposure to antagonistic drugs – this can lead to drug addiction. ☐

32 **Desensitisation** is a decrease in the number and sensitivity of receptors as a result of exposure to agonistic drugs – this can lead to drug tolerance. ☐

Summary notes

Neurons

Most cells that make up the nervous system are called neurons. They have a nucleus, cytoplasm and a membrane like most cells but have other features specialised for their function. Neurons are adapted to carry electrical impulses and they have long fibres to carry these impulses through the nervous system. Figure 3.17 shows the three main types of neuron and their fibres.

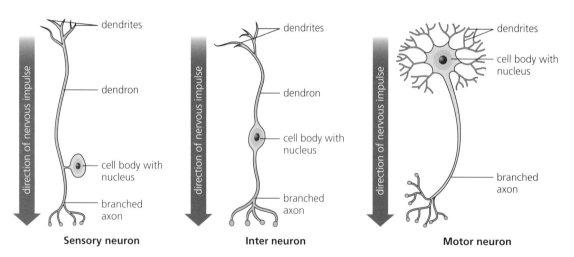

Figure 3.17 Types of neuron

Impulse conduction

Direction of flow

Impulses conducted along neuron fibres flow in one direction. Fibres that conduct impulses towards the cell body of the cell are dendrons and dendrites. Fibres that conduct impulses away from the cell body are axons, which usually branch at their ends.

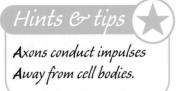

Hints & tips

Axons conduct impulses Away from cell bodies.

Myelination

The longest fibres have myelin sheaths around them, as shown in Figure 3.18. The sheath is made up of cells that lie around the fibre and contain a fatty material that insulates the fibre inside it. This increases the speed of the nervous impulse within the fibre. Myelination continues from birth to adolescence.

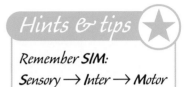

Hints & tips

Remember SIM:
Sensory → Inter → Motor

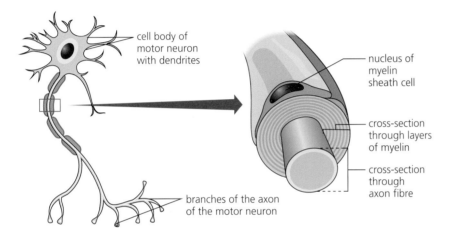

Figure 3.18 Motor neuron, showing the position and detail of the myelin sheath

Glial cells

Glial cells are associated with neurons. They have a variety of roles, including providing physical support for neurons and production of myelin sheaths. They maintain a homeostatic environment around neurons and remove debris from the area by phagocytosis. Figure 3.19 shows the position of some glial cells in relation to a motor neuron.

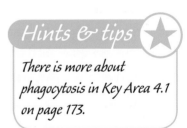

Hints & tips

There is more about phagocytosis in Key Area 4.1 on page 173.

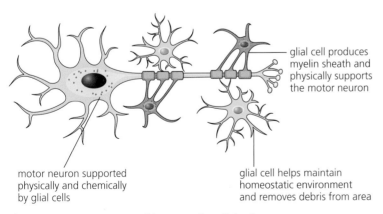

Figure 3.19 Motor neuron with supporting glial cells

Synapses

Neurons are separated from each other by tiny gaps called synapses. For a nervous impulse to cross the gap, chemicals called neurotransmitters have to enter the synapse. Figure 3.20 shows a synapse at the end of a motor neuron.

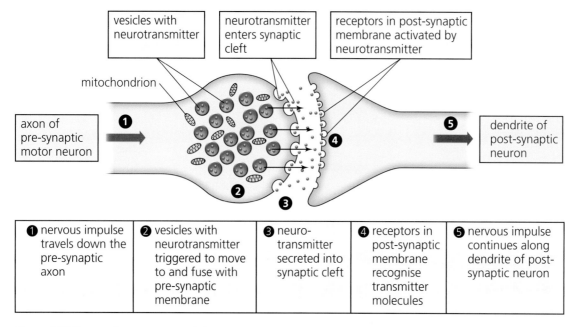

❶ nervous impulse travels down the pre-synaptic axon	❷ vesicles with neurotransmitter triggered to move to and fuse with pre-synaptic membrane	❸ neuro-transmitter secreted into synaptic cleft	❹ receptors in post-synaptic membrane recognise transmitter molecules	❺ nervous impulse continues along dendrite of post-synaptic neuron

Figure 3.20 Stages of nervous transmission at a synapse

Excitatory and inhibitory signals

Neurotransmitters bind with receptors. It is the type of receptor involved that determines whether a signal is excitatory or inhibitory. A neuron can have many synapses with other neurons. It is the sum of the excitatory and inhibitory signals that determines the overall effect and whether the signals pass on (Figure 3.21).

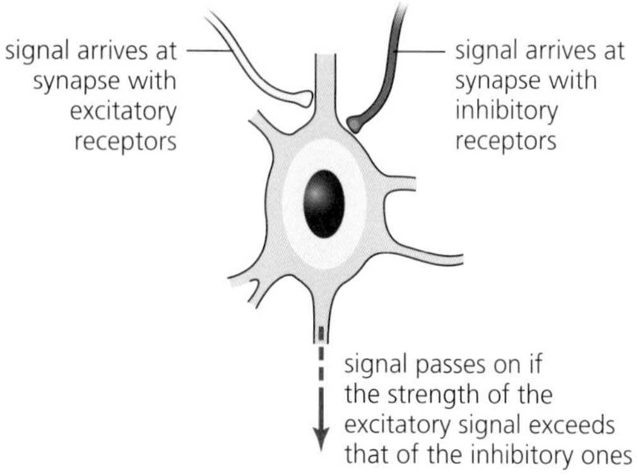

Removal of neurotransmitter

Neurotransmitter is removed from the synaptic cleft immediately following the passing on of any impulse. If the neurotransmitter was left in the synaptic cleft there would be continuous stimulation of the post-synaptic membrane and the system would not be able to respond to new signals, making precise control impossible. Removal is achieved in one of two ways:

signal arrives at synapse with excitatory receptors

signal arrives at synapse with inhibitory receptors

signal passes on if the strength of the excitatory signal exceeds that of the inhibitory ones

Figure 3.21 Effect of excitatory and inhibitory receptors on impulse transmission

- Enzyme degradation – some neurotransmitters, such as acetylcholine, are broken down by enzymes and the non-active products are reabsorbed by the pre-synaptic membrane.
- Re-uptake of neurotransmitter – other neurotransmitters, such as nor-adrenaline, are taken back up directly by the pre-synaptic membrane.

Energy for these processes is released from mitochondria, which are abundant in the pre-synaptic cytoplasm, as shown in Figure 3.20.

Weak stimuli

A nervous impulse can only pass a synapse if a certain minimum number of neurotransmitter molecules are released into the synaptic cleft. Weak stimuli fail to cause release of sufficient molecules and so the impulse fails to pass. This system prevents very weak stimuli, such as very quiet sounds, from bringing about responses.

Summation

If several weak stimuli reach a target neuron together then their effect can be summated and an impulse can be passed on, as shown in Figure 3.22.

Neural pathways

Neurons connected to each other through synapses form neural pathways through the nervous system.

Converging neural pathways

Figure 3.23 shows a converging neural pathway in which stimuli from several neurons converge on one neuron. An example of this system occurs in the retina of the eye. In very dim light impulses from rod cells would be insufficient to trigger the passing on of an impulse. Because several rods converge on the next neuron in the pathway, their effect can be summated and the impulse passes on. This allows some sensitivity of the eye in dim light conditions.

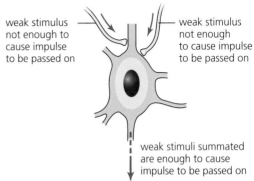

weak stimulus not enough to cause impulse to be passed on

weak stimulus not enough to cause impulse to be passed on

weak stimuli summated are enough to cause impulse to be passed on

Figure 3.22 Summation of weak stimuli

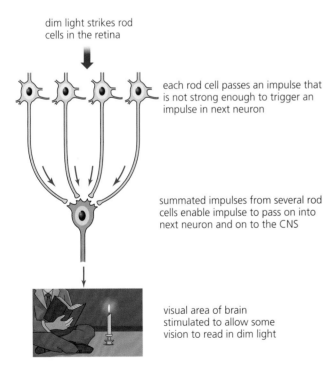

dim light strikes rod cells in the retina

each rod cell passes an impulse that is not strong enough to trigger an impulse in next neuron

summated impulses from several rod cells enable impulse to pass on into next neuron and on to the CNS

visual area of brain stimulated to allow some vision to read in dim light

Figure 3.23 Example of a converging neural pathway

Diverging neural pathways

Figure 3.24 shows a diverging neural pathway. In this example an impulse generated from a single neuron can be passed to several more and so, for example, it is possible for several muscles to be activated at once and bring about the coordinated fine-motor movement of the hand needed for writing.

Reverberating neural pathways

Figure 3.25 shows a reverberating neural pathway. In this system impulses can be recycled back through the pathway continuously to bring about repeated activities, such as breathing, which repeats for a lifetime.

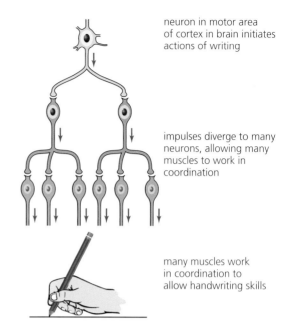

neuron in motor area of cortex in brain initiates actions of writing

impulses diverge to many neurons, allowing many muscles to work in coordination

many muscles work in coordination to allow handwriting skills

Figure 3.24 Example of a diverging neural pathway

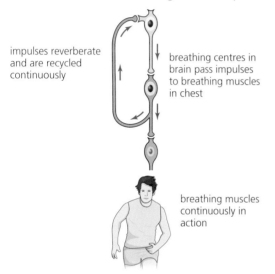

impulses reverberate and are recycled continuously

breathing centres in brain pass impulses to breathing muscles in chest

breathing muscles continuously in action

Figure 3.25 Example of a reverberating neural pathway

Plasticity of response

Plasticity of response refers to the creation of new neural pathways to allow new responses to be made. Examples are shown in the following table.

Reason to create new pathway	Example
Learning a new skill	A child learns to ride a bicycle
Recovery from brain damage	A stroke victim relearns speech
Suppressing reflex action	A mother resists dropping a bowl of hot water, which has spilled onto her skin, to protect her child crawling below
Suppressing responses to sensory impulses	A person resists answering a ringing telephone

Neurotransmitters

Many different neurotransmitter substances have been identified and drugs that affect their action have been discovered.

Endorphins

Endorphins are released from neurons involved in pathways related to the reduction of pain intensity, euphoric feelings, appetite modulation and the release of sex hormones. Production of endorphins increases following severe injury, prolonged continuous exercise, stress and eating certain foods.

Dopamine

Dopamine induces feelings of pleasure and reinforces behaviour in the reward pathway.

Medicinal drugs

Agonistic and antagonistic drugs

Some drugs affect the way in which neurotransmitters function and can be used medically to treat some conditions related to neurotransmitters.

- Agonistic drugs mimic natural neurotransmitters and can therefore enhance the action of these.
- Antagonistic drugs block the action of natural neurotransmitters and so prevent nerve impulses passing synapses (Figure 3.26).

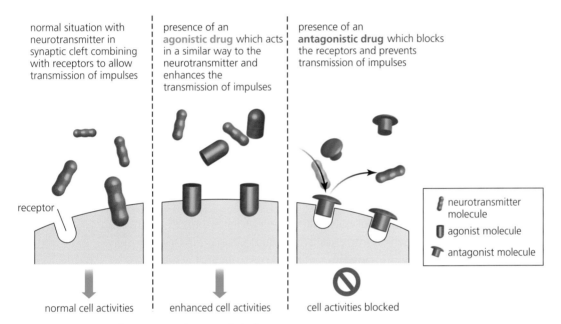

normal situation with neurotransmitter in synaptic cleft combining with receptors to allow transmission of impulses

presence of an **agonistic drug** which acts in a similar way to the neurotransmitter and enhances the transmission of impulses

presence of an **antagonistic drug** which blocks the receptors and prevents transmission of impulses

receptor

neurotransmitter molecule

agonist molecule

antagonist molecule

normal cell activities | enhanced cell activities | cell activities blocked

Figure 3.26 Action of agonistic and antagonistic drugs

Inhibitor drugs

Other drugs can inhibit certain parts of the normal neurotransmission process. Some can inhibit the enzymes that should remove the neurotransmitter from the synaptic cleft and others can inhibit reabsorption of neurotransmitter.

Recreational drugs

Recreational drugs affect neural transmission in the reward circuit of the brain. They can interact with neural transmission in different ways, altering aspects of consciousness, such as mood, perception, cognition and behaviour. Many recreational drugs, such as cannabis and cocaine, are illegal.

Drug addiction and tolerance

Sensitisation is an increase in the number and sensitivity of receptors, which results from exposure to antagonist drugs, and can lead to addiction.

Desensitisation is the decrease in number and sensitivity of receptors, which results from exposure to agonist drugs, and can lead to drug tolerance.

Hints & tips

There is more about enzyme inhibitors in Key Area 1.6 on pages 39–40.

Example

The following table shows examples of drugs and brief notes on their modes of action.

Drug	Brief note on mode of action
Cannabis	Contains substances that bind to receptors involved in the nerve transmission of muscular control and pain sensitivity
Cocaine	Inhibits dopamine re-uptake channels leading to higher level of dopamine in the reward circuit
MDMA (known as Ecstasy)	Inhibits the re-uptake of a neurotransmitter, which remains in synaptic clefts, increasing a feeling of well-being
Alcohol	Mimics a neurotransmitter that can act to reduce feelings of anxiety
Nicotine	Mimics the effect of acetylcholine on certain neural receptors leading to increased dopamine in the reward circuit

Key words

Agonist – chemical neurotransmitter or a drug that mimics one

Antagonist – drug that inhibits transmission of nerve impulses

Axon – neural fibre that conducts impulses away from the cell body

Converging neural pathway – pathway in which impulses from many neurons are passed to one neuron

Dendrite – neural fibre that conducts impulses towards the cell body

Desensitisation – decrease in number or sensitivity of synaptic receptors as a result of exposure to drugs

Diverging neural pathway – pathway in which impulses from one neuron are passed to many

Dopamine – neurotransmitter involved in inducing the feeling of pleasure and other actions

Endorphin – neurotransmitter involved in reducing intensity of pain and other actions

Excitatory signal – signal that affects a receptor and which can be passed on

Glial cell – cell in the nervous system that physically supports neurons and produces myelin sheaths

Inhibitory signal – signal that affects a synaptic receptor but is not passed on

Inter neuron – conducts impulses within the CNS, linking sensory and motor neurons

Motor neuron – carries impulses from the CNS to muscles or glands

Myelination – insulation of nerve fibres with myelin sheaths

Myelin sheath – layer of fatty insulation round a nerve fibre

Neuron – conducting nerve cell

Neurotransmitter – chemical released into a synaptic cleft to transmit impulses to the next cell

Phagocytosis – process by which phagocytes engulf and destroy foreign material

Plasticity – capacity to form new neural pathways

Post-synaptic membrane – membrane of the neuron that contains receptors for neurotransmitters

Pre-synaptic membrane – membrane of the neuron that releases neurotransmitters

Receptor – protein found in the post-synaptic membrane that binds neurotransmitter

Recreational drug – substance that changes neurochemistry; many are illegal

Reverberating neural pathway – pathway that recycles impulses round the same route

Reward pathway – neural pathway that produces pleasure

Sensitisation – increase in number or sensitivity of receptors as a result of exposure to drugs

Sensory neuron – neuron that carries impulses into the CNS from a sense organ

Synapse – junction between neurons

Synaptic cleft – gap between neurons at a synapse

Synaptic vesicle – tiny vacuole containing neurotransmitter; found in pre-synaptic neurons

Questions ?

Restricted response (structured in 1- or 2-mark parts)

1   Give the function of the myelin sheath found around some neurons. (1)
2   Describe the function of converging neural pathways. (1)
3   Give **two** examples of the plasticity of the nervous system. (2)
4   State the functions of each of the following neurotransmitters:
    a) endorphins (1)
    b) dopamine. (1)
5   Describe the function of agonist drugs. (2)
6   Give **two** ways in which neurotransmitters can be removed from the synaptic cleft. (2)
7   Explain the difference between drug addiction and drug tolerance in terms of neural receptors. (2)

Extended response (4–9 marks each)

8   Give an account of the transmission of a nervous impulse at a synapse. (4)
9   Give an account of the structure and function of cells in the nervous system under the following headings:
    a) Neurons (5)
    b) Glial cells (3)
10 Describe how recreational drugs can affect the brain. (8)
11 Give an account of the nervous system under the following headings:
    a) The role of neurotransmitters at the synapse (5)
    b) The structure and function of neural pathways (4)

Answers are on page 165–166.

Key points !

1. **Infant attachment** is important in laying the foundation for future stable relationships. ☐
2. Infant attachment can be secure or insecure, or there can be detachment. ☐
3. Insecure attachment can lead to responses of anger or inconsistent responses. ☐
4. Human offspring have a long period of dependency on adults, providing time for socialisation and learning to occur. ☐
5. Authoritative control by carers generally results in greater social competence in offspring than permissive control. ☐
6. **Non-verbal communication** is important in the formation of relationships between individuals. ☐
7. Non-verbal communication can signal attitude and emotion as well as acting as an aid to verbal communication. ☐
8. **Verbal communication** is used in the transmission of knowledge, development of culture and in social evolution. ☐
9. **Learning** is a change in behaviour as a result of **experience**. ☐
10. Repeated use of a **motor skill** results in a motor pathway being established. ☐
11. Human behaviour may be learned by **observation** and **imitation**. ☐
12. In **trial-and-error learning**, **reinforcement**, **shaping** and **extinction of behaviour** results in learning. ☐
13. **Generalisation** is the application of the outcome of a learning experience to all similar situations. ☐
14. **Discrimination** allows an individual to modify behaviour as a result of experiences in a diversity of similar situations. ☐
15. **Social facilitation** is increased performance in competitive or audience situations. ☐
16. **De-individuation** is the loss of personal identity in a group, leading to diminished restraints on behaviour. ☐
17. **Internalisation** is the changing of beliefs as a result of persuasion. ☐
18. **Identification** is the changing of beliefs to conform to a role model or admired individual. ☐

Summary notes

Infant attachment cycle

Humans live in social groups and it is important for survival that group members form relationships and communicate effectively with each other. Development of successful relationships starts as infants bond with their carers. The bond that connects infants to their carer is called infant attachment. Figure 3.27 shows the cycles of behaviour that are likely to lead to secure and insecure infant attachment.

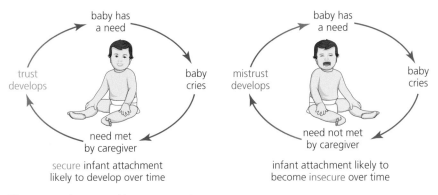

Figure 3.27 Secure and insecure attachment

The following table shows the results of an infant attachment study called 'The Strange Situation', in which a parent and infant enter a playroom and a stranger joins them a few minutes later. The parent then leaves the room and returns a short while later. The general behaviour shown by securely attached and two categories of non-securely attached infants is recorded.

Stage in The Strange Situation	Summary of general behaviour of infant		
Parent and child alone in room	Explores with orientation to parent	Explores with no orientation towards parent	Does not explore
Stranger enters	Comfortable with stranger when parent present	Comfortable with stranger	Uncomfortable with stranger
Parent leaves	Some discomfort	No discomfort	Distressed
Parent returns	Goes to parent for comfort	Ignores parent	Inconsistent behaviour towards parent; some anger may be shown
Conclusion about security of attachment	**Secure**	**Insecure (avoidant)**	**Insecure (resistant)**

It is thought that secure attachment is important in the formation of stable social relationships with others in future years.

Dependency period

Humans have a relatively long period during which the offspring depend on adults. This provides time for socialising and learning to occur. Parental control styles can affect the resulting social competence of the offspring. Figure 3.28 illustrates approaches to parenting, in which supportive and authoritative styles are more likely to result in a greater level of social competence in the offspring.

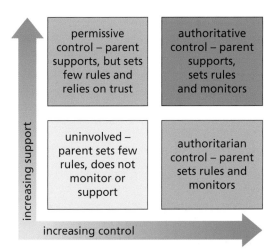

Figure 3.28 Parenting styles

Communication

Social relationships between members of groups rely on communication between them. Communication is a combination of non-verbal and verbal methods.

Non-verbal communication

Non-verbal communication is important in the formation of relationships between individuals and can signal attitude and emotion as well as acting as an aid to verbal communication. Categories of non-verbal communication are shown in Figure 3.29.

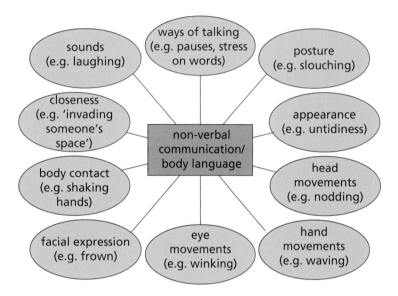

Figure 3.29 Categories of non-verbal communication

Verbal communication

Verbal communication is used in the transmission of knowledge, the development of culture and social evolution. The following table shows some categories of verbal communication.

Verbal communication	
Written	**Oral**
Letter	Face-to-face talk
Email	Team meeting or group discussion
Text on website or local intranet	Telephone call
Newspaper or magazine article or advert	Radio or TV advert
Book or journal	CD recording

Learning

Learning is a change in behaviour as a result of experience.

Learning through practice

Practice involves the repeated use of an activity in order to perfect it. This process is usually important in mastering a motor skill such as swimming.

The brain eventually establishes a motor memory for the activity so that it can be repeated without really thinking.

Learning by imitation

Much learning takes place by copying others. This is the basis of much of children's play. For many adults, copying an activity performed by others is a useful way of learning.

Trial-and-error learning

Humans learn many behaviours by trial and error. Shaping is a process used to produce desired behaviour from trial-and-error situations. Shaping is used by parents to pass on skills to their children. Reinforcement is used to ensure that desired behaviours are repeated and undesired behaviours become extinct. Positive reinforcement is often associated with rewarding performance of desired behaviour, as shown in Figure 3.30.

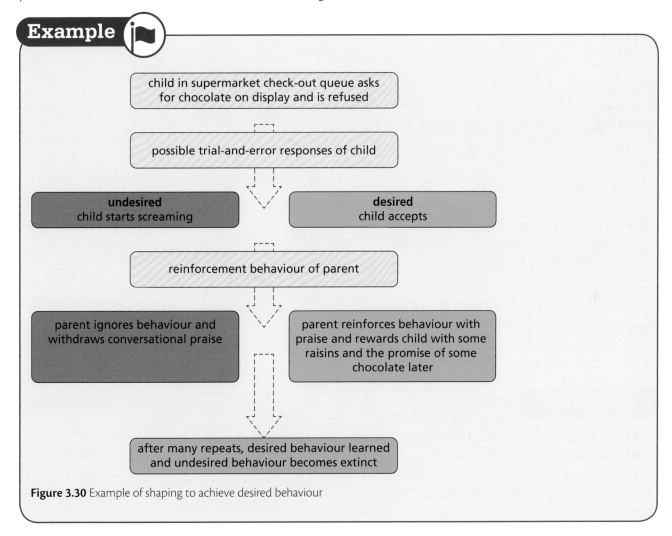

Example

child in supermarket check-out queue asks for chocolate on display and is refused

possible trial-and-error responses of child

undesired
child starts screaming

desired
child accepts

reinforcement behaviour of parent

parent ignores behaviour and withdraws conversational praise

parent reinforces behaviour with praise and rewards child with some raisins and the promise of some chocolate later

after many repeats, desired behaviour learned and undesired behaviour becomes extinct

Figure 3.30 Example of shaping to achieve desired behaviour

Generalisation and discrimination

Generalisation is responding in the same way to similar stimulations. For example, an individual who had learned that green fruit is unripe might reject a ripe but green apple or kiwi fruit for this reason. Discrimination is the ability to make different responses to similar stimulations. For example, an individual who could discriminate would behave differently with the pet dog they recognise compared with another unfamiliar and uncollared one met in the street.

Group behaviour and social influence

The social group itself can exert influence over behaviour in different ways.

Social facilitation

Competitive situations or situations in which an audience is involved can increase the performance of an individual.

De-individuation

This occurs when a behaviour is disowned by an individual and responsibility for it is given to a group. It can lead to a lowering of restraint on a behaviour, such as vandalism as part of a crowd.

Internalisation

This is the process by which individuals are persuaded to adopt a set of beliefs by an external influence. A political party might use broadcasts to persuade others to vote for their party.

Identification

In this process an individual purposely changes beliefs and behaviours to fall in line with those of an admired role model. For example an individual might try to be like a sporting hero. Advertising can influence this and be used to sell merchandise, which allows the individual to more closely copy their admired role model.

Key words

De-individuation – passing responsibility for an individual action to a group

Discrimination – application of different responses to a variety of closely related stimuli

Experience – events of the past that contribute to learning

Extinction of behaviour – removal of behaviour that has not been reinforced

Generalisation – application of a response to a variety of closely related stimuli

Identification – copying the behaviours or beliefs of a role model

Imitation – process of copying of a behaviour that has been observed

Infant attachment – result of the successful bonding process between infant and carer

Internalisation – changes in behaviour or beliefs as a result of persuasion

Learning – modification of behaviour in light of experiences

Motor skill – ability to carry out a task involving skeletal muscle

Non-verbal communication – communication by means other than by words and language

Observation – the process of seeing an event occurring
Reinforcement – the process by which behaviours are rewarded or not
Shaping – use of reinforcement in trial-and-error situations to produce desired behaviours
Social facilitation – enhanced performance in competitive or audience situations
Trial-and-error learning – type of learning that relies on reinforcement
Verbal communication – communication using words and language

Questions

Restricted response (structured in 1- or 2-mark parts)

1 Give the meaning of the term infant attachment and describe the importance of secure attachment. (2)
2 Describe **two** characteristics of responses of an insecurely attached infant. (2)
3 Explain why the long period of dependency is of advantage to human offspring. (2)
4 Describe the supposed advantage of authoritative control over permissive control in parenting behaviour. (1)
5 Explain how trial-and-error learning situations can be influenced by shaping. (2)
6 Give the meanings of the following terms:
   a) generalisation (1)
   b) discrimination. (1)

Extended response (4–9 marks each)

7 Give an account of communication between individuals under the following headings:
   a) Non-verbal (3)
   b) Verbal (4)
8 Give an account of group behaviour and social influence under the following headings:
   a) Social facilitation and identification (3)
   b) De-individuation and internalisation (3)

Answers are on page 166.

Answers

Key Area 3.1

Restricted response

1 consists of the brain; and the spinal cord [2]
2 somatic actions are voluntary *and* brought about by skeletal muscle; autonomic actions are involuntary *and* brought about by smooth muscle/cardiac muscle/glands [2]
3 antagonistic [1]
4 specific functions are located in discrete/specific regions of the cerebral cortex [1]
5 language area; personality; imagination; intelligence; (others) [any 2 = 2]
6 transfer of information between the left and right cerebral hemispheres [1]

Extended response

7 ANS works automatically/without conscious control *or* controls involuntary responses; impulses originate in the medulla (region of the brain); made up of sympathetic and parasympathetic systems/fibres; these two systems act antagonistically/description; sympathetic system prepares the body for fight or flight; parasympathetic system prepares the body for resting and digesting; correct description of the effect of the ANS in controlling heart rate; correct description of the effect of the ANS in controlling breathing rate; correct description of the effect of the ANS in controlling peristalsis; correct description of the effect of the ANS in controlling intestinal secretions [any 8 = 8]

Answers

Key Area 3.2

Restricted response

1 process by which the brain analyses sensory information; and makes sense out of sensory information [2]
2 brain segregates objects/figures from their ground/background then interprets which is which [1]
3 a) the difference in distance of an object from each of the two retinas [1]
   b) brain takes account of the constant shape of objects even though they appear to change shape in a moving scene [1]
4 past experience; context; expectation (affect the way an image is perceived) [any 2 = 2]
5 objects early in a sequence are recalled well/show primacy; objects at end of a sequence are recalled well/show recency [2]

Extended response

6 a) lasts a few seconds; all visual and auditory input retained; passed into STM [any 2 = 2]
   b) short span; affected by serial position effect; maintained by rehearsal; items displaced/undergo decay; improved by chunking [any 3 = 3]
   c) items transferred from STM; by rehearsal; by organisation; by elaboration; information encoded by shallow or elaborative means; retrieval aided by contextual cues [any 4 = 4]
7 a) encoding into a form that can be received by the brain; example of type of sensory input that can be encoded from visual/auditory/acoustic/olfactory [2]
   b) STM has a short span/time in STM very short; span can be improved by chunking; displaced by incoming information; rehearsal is repeating or practising to transfer to LTM; organising information assists transfer to LTM; elaboration means adding meaning/increasing the depth of encoding [any 4 = 4]
   c) retrieval means remembering/recalling information; assisted by contextual cues; example of a contextual cue [any 2 = 2]

Answers

Key Area 3.3

Restricted response

1 acts as insulation *and* increases the speed of impulse conduction [1]
2 allow low-level stimuli to be summated, to cause impulses to be passed on [1]
3 new responses/motor memory created; bypass damaged area of brain; suppress reflexes; suppress responses to sensory input [any 2 = 2]
4 a) reduction of pain intensity/euphoric feelings/appetite modulation/release of sex hormones [1]
   b) induces feeling of pleasure/reinforces behaviour in the reward pathway [1]
5 bind to and stimulate receptors; mimic neurotransmitters so impulse passed on [2]
6 by degradation by enzymes; by reabsorption/reuptake by pre-synaptic membrane [2]
7 sensitisation (increase in neural receptors) through exposure to antagonists can lead to addiction; desensitisation (decrease in neural receptors) through exposure to agonist drugs can lead to tolerance [2]

Extended response

8 impulse arrives at pre-synaptic membrane; vesicles release neurotransmitter into synaptic cleft; receptors in post-synaptic membrane bind neurotransmitters; receptors can be excitatory or inhibitory; impulse passes on through dendrite of post-synaptic neuron [any 4 = 4]
9 a) cell body with nucleus; fibres called axons carry impulses away from cell body; fibres called dendrites carry impulses to cell body; some fibres are myelinated; sensory neurons carry impulses from sense organs to CNS; inter neurons connect other neurons in CNS; motor neurons carry impulses from CNS to muscles or glands [any 5 = 5]
   b) support neurons; make myelin sheath; keep environment homeostatic; clear debris/phagocytosis [any 3 = 3]
10 many affect (neurotransmission in) the reward circuit of the brain; they alter mood/cognition/perception/behaviour [any 1 = 1]
   they may stimulate the release of neurotransmitters; they may act as agonists or antagonists (both); agonists imitate the actions of neurotransmitters; antagonists prevent the binding of neurotransmitters/bind to receptors; drugs may inhibit the reuptake/enzyme degradation of neurotransmitters (at a synapse); sensitisation may occur with an increase in the number/sensitivity of receptors; antagonists cause sensitisation leading to addiction; desensitisation may occur with a decrease in the number/sensitivity of receptors; agonists cause desensitisation, leading to drug tolerance; suitable example of a drug and how it affects the brain – (cocaine blocking dopamine reuptake (channels), cannabis binding to (cannabinoid) receptors, ecstasy/MDMA stimulating serotonin levels, alcohol binding to (GABA) receptors, increasing dopamine/serotonin/epinephrine levels, nicotine activating receptors, increasing dopamine/serotonin/epinephrine levels) [any 7 = 7]
11 a) synapse/synaptic cleft is the junction/gap between neurons/nerve cells *or* labelled diagram; neurotransmitters are stored in/released from vesicles; neurotransmitters are released on arrival of impulse; neurotransmitters diffuse across the gap; neurotransmitters bind with/reach receptors; threshold/minimum number of neurotransmitters is needed (for the impulse to continue); neurotransmitters are removed by enzymes and reuptake/reabsorption; neurotransmitters must be removed to prevent continuous stimulation; two named neurotransmitters – acetylcholine, nor-adrenaline, dopamine, endorphins [any 5 = 5]
   ⇨

b) converging pathway has several neurons linked to one neuron *or* labelled diagram but must show direction of impulse; this increases the neurotransmitter concentration/chances of impulse generation/sensitivity to excitatory or inhibitory signals; diverging pathway has one neuron linked to several neurons *or* labelled diagram but must show direction of impulse; this means that impulses are sent to/influence several destinations at the same time; reverberating pathways – neurons later in pathway synapse/link with neurons earlier in the pathway; new neural pathways can bypass areas of brain damage/create new responses/suppress reflexes/create plasticity [any 4 = 4]

Answers

Key Area 3.4

Restricted response

1 process of bonding between infant and carer; lays the foundation for future formation of stable relationships [2]
2 detached responses; inconsistent responses; angry responses [any 2 = 2]
3 (allows time for) socialisation; learning (to occur) [2]
4 results in greater social competence [1]
5 behaviour that is desired is rewarded; undesired behaviour is unrewarded *and* becomes extinct [2]
6 a) application of a learned response to many similar situations [1]
   b) modification of a learned response to suit slightly different situations [1]

Extended response

7 a) communication by body language/posture; facial expression/gestures; signals attitude and emotion; as well as supporting verbal communication [any 3 = 3]
   b) communication by written/spoken word; example; another example; (used to) transmit knowledge; (and) culture; (allows) social evolution [any 4 = 4]
8 a) social facilitation is increased performance; in presence of an audience/competitors; identification is the adoption of the behaviours/beliefs; of a role model/admired person [any 3 = 3]
   b) de-individuation is losing personal responsibility for actions; and passing it on to other members of a group; internalisation is the adoption of the behaviours/beliefs of others; through persuasion [any 3 = 3]

Practice Course Assessment: Unit 3 (25 marks)

Section A (5 marks)

1 The somatic nervous system (SNS) controls the action of
   A glands
   B smooth muscle
   C skeletal muscle
   D cardiac muscle.

2 Which line in the table below shows correctly a pair of antagonistic actions of the autonomic nervous system (ANS)?

	Parasympathetic action	Sympathetic action
A	Increased secretion of juices and bile	Decreased secretion of juices and bile
B	Decreased rate of peristalsis	Increased rate of peristalsis
C	Increased heart rate	Decreased heart rate
D	Increased breathing rate	Decreased breathing rate

3 During a set of trials to investigate the serial position effect, a group of participants was read a list of 12 letters. Ten seconds later they were asked to recall the list in its original order. Their responses were analysed and the results shown in the graph below.

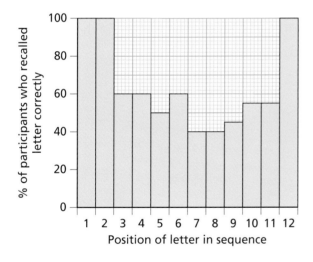

What percentage of the letters were correctly recalled in their correct positions by more than 60% of the participants?
   A 6
   B 25
   C 50
   D 60

4 The diagram right shows a neural pathway in the nervous system.

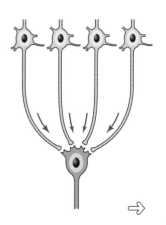

Which line in the table below correctly identifies the type of pathway and an example of an action that is supported by this type of system?

	Type of pathway	Example of action supported
A	Diverging	Seeing in dim light
B	Converging	Using a screwdriver
C	Diverging	Using a screwdriver
D	Converging	Seeing in dim light

5 Rewarding young children for behaving in the way their parent desires is part of a process called
   A identification
   B shaping
   C social facilitation
   D generalisation.

Section B (20 marks)

1 The diagram below shows a section through the brain.

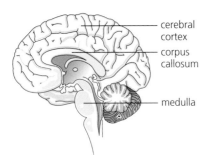

a) Name an area of the cerebral cortex in which a specific brain function is localised and describe its action. (2)
b) State the function of the corpus callosum. (1)
c) Name the division of the nervous system that has its main centres in the medulla. (1)

2 The diagram below shows part of a motor neuron, with arrows showing the direction of the nervous impulse in fibres A and B.

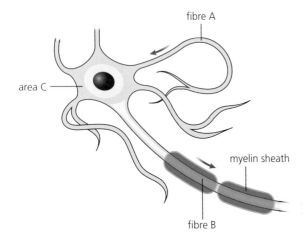

a) Name fibres A and B and identify area C. (3)
b) Describe the function of the myelin sheath around fibre B. (2)

3 Describe how a nervous impulse can be transmitted at a synapse. (4)

4 Recreational drugs alter the neurochemistry of the user's brain and use of these drugs can lead to addiction.
   a) Describe how drug use can lead to addiction. (2)
   b) Describe how the appearance of a celebrity figure in an anti-drugs TV broadcast might be used to influence young adults. (1)

5 The diagram below shows a well-known optical illusion.

a) Describe how perceptual organisation forms the basis for this illusion. (2)

b) The perception of a stimulus can be influenced by perceptual set. Give **two** factors that make up perceptual set. (2)

Answers to Practice Course Assessment: Unit 3

Section A

1 C, 2 A, 3 B, 4 D, 5 B

Section B

1 a) motor area *or* sensory area *or* association area; sends impulses to muscles/effectors *or* receives impulses from sense organs *or* language/personality/imagination/intelligence (must match)   [2]
   b) transfers information between the cerebral hemispheres   [1]
   c) autonomic nervous system   [1]
2 a) A, dendrite; B, axon; C, cell body   [3]
   b) insulates fibre; so speeds up rate of transmission   [2]
3 nervous impulse reaches the pre-synaptic membrane; vesicles release neurotransmitter; neurotransmitter in synaptic cleft; neurotransmitter binds to receptors; receptors excite an impulse in the dendrite of the next neuron   [any 4 = 4]
4 a) drugs can act as antagonists and cause sensitisation; an increase in number and sensitivity of receptors can result in addiction   [2]
   b) young person might adopt the celebrity as a role model *and* copy the anti-drugs behaviour of the celebrity in the advert   [1]
5 a) white vase seen as the figure with a black background; two black faces seen as figures with a white background   [2]
   b) past experience; context; expectation   [any 2 = 2]

Key Area 4.1
Non-specific defences

Key points !

1 **Non-specific defences** can be physical and chemical. ☐
2 Epithelial cells form a physical barrier. ☐
3 Specialised epithelial cells produce chemical secretions, such as acid and mucus, that help prevent infection. ☐
4 The **inflammatory response** to damage includes release of **histamine** by **mast cells**, which causes vasodilation and increased capillary permeability. ☐
5 Increased blood flow and release of **cytokines** leads to accumulation of phagocytes and delivery of antimicrobial proteins and clotting elements to the site of infection. ☐
6 Phagocytes and **natural killer (NK) cells** are white blood cells that release cytokines, which stimulate the specific immune response. ☐
7 Phagocytes recognise surface antigen molecules on pathogens and destroy them by phagocytosis. ☐
8 **Apoptosis** is the advantageous self-destruction of infected cells. ☐
9 NK cells induce cells infected by viruses to produce self-destruct enzymes during apoptosis. ☐

Summary notes

The non-specific immune system

The non-specific immune system comprises the cells and mechanisms that defend humans against infection by other organisms. The system recognises and responds to pathogens immediately, but it does not give long-lasting or protective immunity. The major functions of the non-specific immune system are shown in the following table.

Function	Notes
Action as a physical barrier	Undamaged skin; epithelium lining respiratory, digestive and urinary systems; protects against entry of pathogens
Production of secretions	Epithelium releases substances such as mucus and acids to help fight infection
Inflammatory response	Complex response by host cells, blood vessels and proteins to eliminate the cause of damage and to start repair
Production of cytokines	Cytokines secreted by white blood cells act as signal molecules to other defence cells
Phagocytosis	Phagocytic cells recognise surface antigens on pathogens and then engulf and destroy them
Action of NK cells	NK cells induce virus-infected cells to produce self-destruct enzymes during apoptosis

Epithelium

Epithelium can form a simple protective covering for underlying tissue, as shown in Figure 4.1.

Some types of epithelium are more complex. Ciliated epithelium, which lines breathing tubes, secretes mucus, which traps infective particles. The cilia beat to sweep mucus and trapped particles away from the lungs (Figure 4.2).

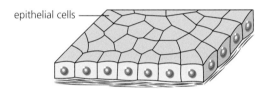

Figure 4.1 Simple epithelium from lining of the bladder

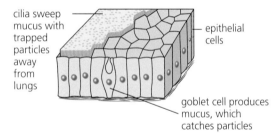

Figure 4.2 Ciliated epithelium from lining of breathing tubes

Secretion

Some types of epithelium line glands such as the gastric glands in the stomach (Figure 4.3). These cells secrete mucus and acid. The mucus protects the epithelium from the acid, digestive enzymes and bacteria.

Hints & tips

There is more about epithelium in Key Area 1.1 on pages 4–5.

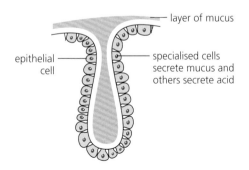

Figure 4.3 Gastric gland in stomach epithelium

Cytokines

Cytokines are a category of small proteins important in cell signalling. They are secreted by a range of immune system cells and affect the behaviour of other cells in response to infection. Cytokine signalling can result in accumulation of phagocytes and the delivery of antimicrobial proteins and clotting elements to infection sites.

Hints & tips ★

There is more about cell signalling in Key Area 1.6 on pages 40–41.

Phagocytosis

In phagocytosis, pathogens are engulfed and destroyed, as shown in Figure 4.4.

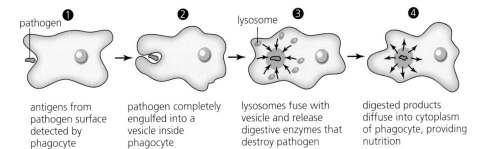

❶	❷	❸	❹
antigens from pathogen surface detected by phagocyte	pathogen completely engulfed into a vesicle inside phagocyte	lysosomes fuse with vesicle and release digestive enzymes that destroy pathogen	digested products diffuse into cytoplasm of phagocyte, providing nutrition

Figure 4.4 Stages in phagocytosis

Hints & tips ★

There is more about the specific immune response, antigens and cytokines in Key Area 4.2 on pages 176–179.

Inflammation

Inflammation involves changes to protect the tissues that have become infected. Figure 4.5 shows what happens during an inflammatory response to an infected needle breaking the skin.

events of damage, inflammation and repair processes occurring through time →

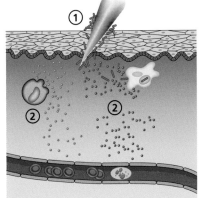
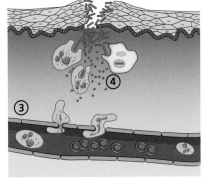
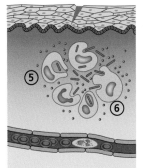

❶ needle carrying bacteria breaks skin

❷ mast cells release histamine and other immune system cells release cell signalling molecules – cytokines

❸ histamine causes blood capillary to dilate and become more permeable

❹ cytokines cause antimicrobial proteins, clotting elements and phagocytes to be delivered to and accumulate at site of infection

❺ phagocytes accumulate and engulf pathogens

❻ phagocytes release more cytokines, which stimulate specific immune response

Figure 4.5 Inflammatory events at an infection site

Hints & tips ★

Remember: inflAMMAtory response – histAMine is released from MAst cells.

173

Natural killer (NK) cells and apoptosis

Natural killer (NK) cells are white blood cells that can induce cells that have been invaded by viruses to produce self-destruct enzymes in a process called apoptosis. This prevents viral reproduction and assists recovery from viral infections.

Hints & tips

There is more about apoptosis in Key Area 4.2 on pages 177–178.

Key words

Apoptosis – advantageous death of infected cells

Cytokines – category of defence proteins secreted from cells; involved in signalling to other cells

Histamine – substance released by mast cells that causes the inflammatory response

Inflammatory response – response to damage or infection involving vasodilation and cytokine release

Mast cells – cells that produce histamine in response to tissue damage

Natural killer (NK) cell – cell that releases cytokines and can cause apoptosis in infected cells

Non-specific defence – general response to infection, including phagocytosis

Questions

Restricted response (structured in 1- or 2-mark parts)

1 Describe what is meant by the term 'non-specific defence' as applied to cells. (1)
2 Explain how tissues can provide a physical defence against infection. (1)
3 Give **two** examples of secretions from epithelial cells that provide defence against infection. (2)
4 Name the molecules present on the surfaces of pathogens that phagocytes recognise. (1)
5 Define the term apoptosis. (1)

Extended response (4–9 marks each)

6 Describe non-specific defences that the body uses to protect itself from pathogens. (8)
7 Give an account of inflammation under the following headings:
 a) The role of mast cells (3)
 b) Phagocytosis (4)
8 Describe the action of natural killer (NK) cells. (4)

Answers are on page 190.

Specific cellular defences

1 Body tissues are monitored by a range of white blood cells that constantly circulate and provide **immune surveillance**. ☐

2 If tissues are damaged or invaded, certain cells release cytokines, which increase blood flow to the site of damage or invasion. ☐

3 Increased blood flow leads to the accumulation of specific white blood cells at the site of damage or infection. ☐

4 Each lymphocyte has a single type of membrane receptor specific to one type of **antigen**. ☐

5 A lymphocyte responds to antigens on pathogen cells, infected cells or toxins released by pathogens. ☐

6 When a lymphocyte binds to an antigen, repeated lymphocyte division produces a **clone** of identical lymphocyte cells. ☐

7 There are two broad categories of lymphocyte, called **T lymphocytes** and **B lymphocytes**. ☐

8 **Clonal selection theory** refers to the selection of lymphocytes by antigens and their response in producing a clone. ☐

9 T lymphocytes have specific surface proteins that allow them to distinguish between the surface molecules of the body's own cells (self antigens) and cells with foreign molecules on their surfaces (non-self antigens). ☐

10 In **autoimmunity**, T lymphocytes respond to the body's own cell surface antigens and produce auto-immune disease. ☐

11 One group of T lymphocytes destroys infected cells by inducing apoptosis. ☐

12 One group of T lymphocytes releases cytokines, which activate B lymphocytes and phagocytes. ☐

13 Phagocytes that engulf pathogens display fragments of the pathogens' antigens on their surfaces. ☐

14 **Antigen-presenting cells** activate T lymphocytes, which move to the site of infection guided by the presence of cytokines in the area. ☐

15 Each B lymphocyte clone produces specific antibody molecules, which recognise specific antigens on the surface of a pathogen or a toxin. ☐

16 Antibody–antigen complexes may inactivate a pathogen, render it more susceptible to phagocytosis or cause an infected cell to undergo **lysis**. ☐

17 B lymphocytes activated by antigen-presenting cells and stimulated by T lymphocytes produce a clone of B lymphocytes, which secrete antibodies into the blood and lymph to transport them to infection sites. ☐

18 In **allergy**, B lymphocytes respond to an antigen that is normally harmless. ☐

19 Some T and B lymphocytes produced by clonal selection survive as **memory cells** over a long-term period. ☐

20 A **secondary exposure** to the same antigen gives rise to a clone of new lymphocytes, producing a more rapid and greater immunological response than to the primary exposure. ☐

Summary notes

Antigens and the immune response

Antigens are proteins that are able to trigger an immune response by the body. It is the presence of antigens associated with specific pathogens that triggers the specific response to the individual pathogen types.

Immune surveillance

The body tissues are constantly monitored by a range of white blood cells providing immune surveillance. If tissues are damaged or infected, certain white blood cells release cytokines, which trigger an increase in blood flow to the damaged area. This allows more white blood cells to accumulate in the area. Some of the white blood cells leave through the thin blood capillary walls and move in between the cells of infected tissue (Figure 4.6).

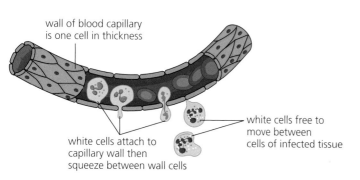

wall of blood capillary is one cell in thickness

white cells free to move between cells of infected tissue

white cells attach to capillary wall then squeeze between wall cells

Figure 4.6 White blood cells leaving a blood capillary

White blood cells that accumulate in the damaged tissue include phagocytes involved in the non-specific response and lymphocytes involved in the specific response.

Action of lymphocytes

There are several different types of lymphocyte in two main groups – T lymphocytes and B lymphocytes.

Clonal selection theory

Lymphocytes have surface proteins that allow them to distinguish between foreign or non-self antigens and self antigens. This is vital in preventing lymphocytes attacking the body's own cells. Lymphocytes with surface proteins that recognise an individual's own antigens normally die during embryonic development.

An individual lymphocyte also has membrane receptors specific for one type of foreign antigen. When a lymphocyte with membrane receptors that match an invading antigen arrives in the damaged area, it is selected by binding with the antigen. The lymphocyte then undergoes repeated cell divisions to make many identical copies of itself, known as a clone. Most of the clonal population fight the infection but some remain in the body for years as memory cells (Figure 4.7).

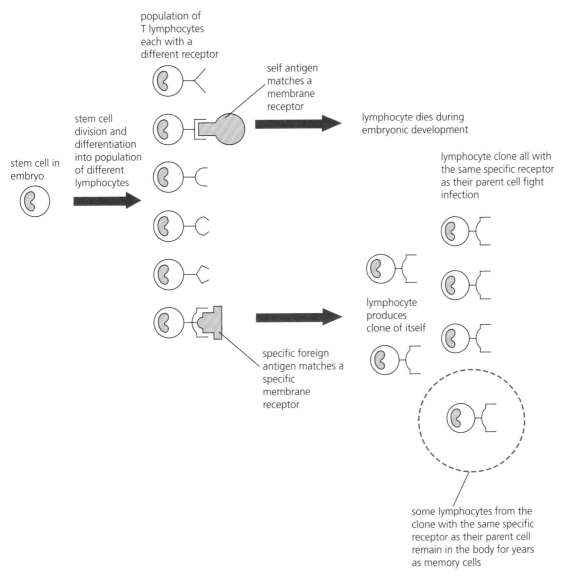

Figure 4.7 Clonal selection of lymphocytes

T lymphocytes

Two different types of T lymphocyte are described below:

- **T lymphocytes that induce apoptosis** When phagocytes engulf and destroy pathogens, antigenic fragments of the pathogen are often presented at the cell surface of the phagocyte. Some T cells recognise these antigen-presenting cells and are activated by binding to them. The activated T cell then produces a clone. Some of the clone cells move to the site of the originally infected cells, which present the same specific antigenic fragments, and cause them to undergo a form of cell suicide called apoptosis. Figure 4.8 summarises the action of these T cells.

- **T cells that secrete cytokines** These helper T cells are activated by the presence of specific antigens. They secrete cytokines that stimulate specific B lymphocytes to divide to form clones, as shown in Figure 4.9.

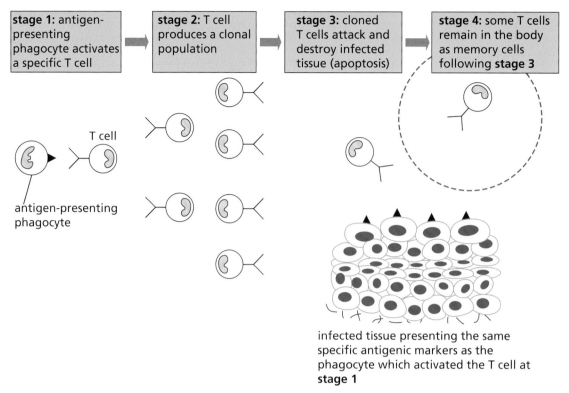

Figure 4.8 Summary of the stages of action of apoptosis-inducing T cells

B lymphocytes

The cytokines released by helper T cells stimulate specific B cells to clone themselves. A clone of B cells secretes copies of molecules called antibodies, which are released in huge quantities into the blood and lymph and carried to infected tissue. Antibodies act by recognising and binding to antigens to inactivate pathogens or make them more easily targeted by phagocytes (Figure 4.9).

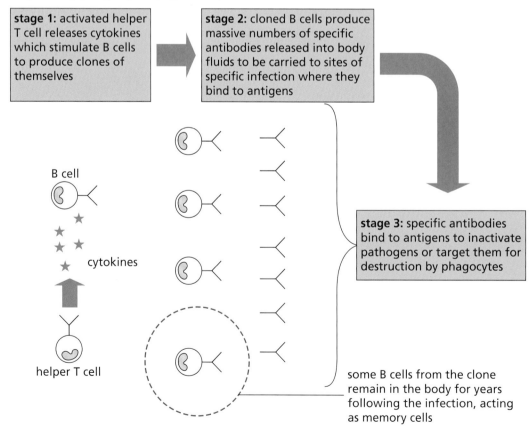

Figure 4.9 Action of B lymphocytes

Autoimmune disease

Immune system failure can cause an immune response by T lymphocytes to self antigens present in the body. The attack on the body tissues by the lymphocytes causes the symptoms of autoimmune diseases such as multiple sclerosis and rheumatoid arthritis.

Allergy

In allergy, B lymphocytes become hypersensitive to certain normally harmless antigens such as those on pollen and nuts. The subsequent immune response produces the allergic symptoms of conditions such as hay fever and peanut allergy.

Immunological memory

As outlined in Figures 4.8 and 4.9, some T and B lymphocytes produced in response to the first exposure to antigens in clonal selection survive as memory cells in the long term. A second exposure to the same antigen gives rise to a new clone of lymphocytes, producing a faster and greater response than occurred during the first exposure, as shown in Figure 4.10. The individual is immune to the disease caused by the pathogen carrying this antigen and may not even be aware that the second exposure has occurred.

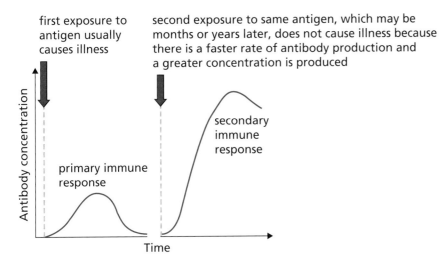

Figure 4.10 Primary and secondary immune responses

Hints & tips

If you are asked to compare the primary and secondary responses, make sure you refer to both a faster rate of antibody production and to a greater concentration of antibodies produced.

Key words

Allergy – immune response to a normally harmless antigen
Antigen – molecule that can produce an immune response in the body
Antigen-presenting cell – cell that has been infected by pathogens and displays their antigens on its surface
Autoimmunity – abnormal immune response to self antigens, which leads to autoimmune disease
B lymphocyte – white blood cell with specific cell surface receptors; secretes antibodies into blood and lymph
Clonal selection theory – selection of lymphocytes to produce clones when exposed to specific antigens
Clone – group of genetically identical cells produced from one parent cell
Immune surveillance – monitoring of the tissue for infection by white blood cells
Lysis – breakdown of cells
Memory cell – lymphocyte remaining in the body for many years after recovery from an infection
Secondary exposure – a second exposure to the same infective agent
T lymphocyte – type of white blood cell; some kill infected cells while others stimulate the immune response

Questions ?

Restricted response (structured in 1- or 2-mark parts)

1 State what is meant by the phrase immune surveillance. (1)
2 Describe the role of cytokines in defence. (2)
3 Describe what happens to a lymphocyte immediately after it binds with an antigen. (1)
4 Give an account of the following responses:
   a) allergic response (2)
   b) autoimmune response. (2)
5 State what is meant by the phrase immunological memory. (2)

Extended response (4–9 marks each)

6 Write notes on specific cellular defence against infection under the following headings:
   a) action of B lymphocytes (4)
   b) action of T lymphocytes (3)
7 Describe how immunity is naturally acquired. (7)

Answers are on page 190–191.

The transmission and control of infectious disease

Key points ❗

1 Infectious diseases are caused by **pathogens**. ☐
2 Disease-causing pathogens can be transmitted from person to person by physical contact, in water, in body fluids, in inhaled air or by **vector organisms**. ☐
3 Disease-causing pathogens can be controlled by **quarantine** and **antisepsis**. ☐
4 Individuals have responsibility for the control of disease pathogens through observing good hygiene, taking care with sexual health and appropriate handling and storage of food. ☐
5 Communities have responsibility for the control of disease pathogens through the quality control of drinking water, use of safe food webs, appropriate waste disposal systems and the control of vector organisms. ☐
6 **Epidemiology** is the science that studies the causes, patterns and effects of health and disease in populations. ☐
7 Spread of disease can be **sporadic**, in which there is occasional occurrence of a disease. ☐
8 **Endemic** disease involves regular occurrence of a disease in a particular area. ☐
9 An **epidemic** is an unusually high number of cases of a disease in a given area. ☐
10 A **pandemic** is a global epidemic. ☐
11 Disease control measures include prevention of transmission, drug therapy, immunisation or a combination of these. ☐

Summary notes

Infectious diseases

Infectious diseases are caused by pathogens of different types. The following table gives some examples.

Pathogen type	Examples of diseases caused
Bacterium	Tuberculosis (TB)
Protozoan	Malaria, trypanosomiasis
Fungus	Athlete's foot, tinea
Virus	Influenza, HIV infection and AIDS

Hints & tips ⭐

There is more about some of these diseases in Key Area 4.4 on pages 187–188.

Infectious disease can be passed from one person to another by different methods of transmission, as shown in the following table.

Method of transmission	Description	Example
Direct physical contact	Touching	Shaking hands
Indirect physical contact	Sharing	A syringe needle
Inhaled air	Breathing in	Contaminated air, droplets or dust
Body fluids	Exchanging fluids	Saliva, seminal fluid or blood
Contaminated food or drink	Consuming food or drink	Sewage-contaminated food or water
Vector organisms	Being bitten	Infected mosquito

Disease control measures

Various methods are used to control infectious disease. Some of these are the responsibility of individuals and communities, while others require medical intervention. In practice, it is a combination of all these methods that allows society to control infectious disease.

Control of transmission

- **Quarantine** Quarantine is enforced isolation of individuals at risk of transmitting an infectious disease, so that they cannot come into contact with others. Periods of quarantine vary with the time taken for different diseases to show symptoms. Different countries have different regulations on quarantine.
- **Antisepsis** Antisepsis refers to practices that destroy or inhibit growth of the microorganisms that cause disease. Common antiseptic practices include sensible hygiene, sterilisation of equipment, use of antiseptic chemicals and soaps, dressing of wounds, and wearing of masks and rubber gloves.
- **Social responsibilities** In our societies, we allocate responsibilities to individuals to follow practices that reduce the risk of transmission of infectious disease. These include the expectation that people will have good personal hygiene, take due care in the handling and preparation of foods and adopt safe sexual practices. We allocate responsibility to whole communities to maintain high-quality water supplies, ensure that the food webs that supply human food are safe and have appropriate methods of waste disposal and vector control.
- **Drug therapies** Various antibiotic drugs can be used to speed up recovery from an infection and so reduce the likelihood of an infected individual passing it on.
- **Immunisation** Vaccination is a method of artificially immunising individuals against certain diseases. Vaccinated individuals are unlikely to become infected and so therefore do not pass infections on to others.
- **Epidemiology** Epidemiology is the study of the causes, patterns of occurrence and spread of infectious disease. The spread patterns of infectious disease are broadly classified as shown in the following table.

Hints & tips

There is more about vaccination in Key Area 4.4 on pages 185–188.

Spread pattern	Notes
Sporadic	Occasional occurrence in an area
Endemic	Regular occurrence in an area
Epidemic	Unusually high number of cases in an area
Pandemic	An epidemic on a global scale

Key words

Antisepsis – methods aimed at preventing growth of infectious agents such as bacteria

Endemic – infectious disease that occurs regularly in a particular area

Epidemic – infectious disease that affects individuals in unusually high numbers

Epidemiology – study of the transmission of infectious disease

Pandemic – worldwide epidemic

Pathogen – biological agent of disease, such as a bacterium, virus, protozoan or fungus

Quarantine – enforced isolation of an infected individual to prevent further infection

Sporadic – referring to an infectious disease that occurs occasionally and unpredictably

Vector organism – organism that can carry or transfer a stage of a disease parasite into the body

Questions ?

Restricted response (structured in 1- or 2-mark parts)

1 Give **two** examples of groups of microorganisms that can act as pathogens. (2)
2 Give **two** examples of how pathogens can be transmitted from person to person. (2)
3 Give the meaning of the following terms:
   a) quarantine (1)
   b) antisepsis. (1)
4 Describe the responsibility of individuals to control the spread of infection. (2)
5 Describe the responsibility of communities to control the spread of infection. (2)

Extended response (4–9 marks each)

6 Write notes on the epidemiological terms used to describe patterns of disease occurrence and their meanings. (6)
7 Give an account of infectious diseases under the following headings:
   a) Methods of transmission (3)
   b) Control of disease transmission (3)
Answers are on page 191.

Active immunisation and vaccination, and the evasion of specific immune responses by pathogens

Key points !

1 Active immunity can be developed by **vaccination** with antigens from infectious pathogens to create an **immunological memory**. ☐

2 **Adjuvants** can be mixed with antigens from infectious pathogens to enhance the immune response generated by a vaccine. ☐

3 Sources of antigens for vaccines include inactivated pathogen toxins, dead pathogens, parts of pathogens and weakened pathogens. ☐

4 Vaccines undergo clinical trials to establish their safety and effectiveness. ☐

5 Designs of **clinical trial** include **randomised, double-blind** and **placebo-controlled protocols**. ☐

6 Group size and **replicates** are important when carrying out a clinical trial because they can affect reliability of results and the significance of any statistics collected. ☐

7 **Herd immunity** occurs when a large percentage of a population is immunised. ☐

8 In herd immunity, non-immune individuals are protected as there is a lower probability that they will come into contact with infected individuals. ☐

9 The herd immunity threshold depends on the disease, the effectiveness of the vaccine and the contact parameters for the population. ☐

10 In the UK, a number of diseases are immunised against as part of public health programmes. ☐

11 Public health immunisation programmes aim to establish herd immunity to a number of diseases. ☐

12 Widespread vaccination is not possible when populations are malnourished, the population is in poverty or a percentage of the population rejects the vaccine for some reason. ☐

13 Many pathogens have evolved mechanisms to evade specific immune responses. ☐

14 Immune response evasion has consequences for vaccination strategies. ☐

15 Some pathogens can change their antigens and so evade the immunological memory. ☐

16 **Influenza** is a viral disease that is widely vaccinated against using annually developed vaccines. ☐

17 **Malaria** and **trypanosomiasis** are diseases caused by **protozoa**, which are carried by vectors and which are difficult to vaccinate against because they change their antigenic nature frequently. ☐

18 **HIV** and **tuberculosis (TB)** are examples of pathogens involved in direct attack on the immune system. ☐ ⇨

19 HIV is a virus that attacks lymphocytes and is the major cause of AIDS. ☐

20 Tuberculosis (TB) is caused by a bacterium that survives within phagocytes and avoids immune detection. ☐

Summary notes

Vaccination

It has been possible to develop vaccines against many diseases. A vaccine contains a form of the antigen carried by the infective pathogen.

The vaccine starts an immune response in the same way as the real antigen would but without the illness. This leaves behind immunological memory cells, which protect the body through a greater and more rapid response if it becomes exposed to the real antigen in the future. The following table shows the sources of antigen in vaccines for some diseases.

> **Hints & tips** ⭐
>
> There is more about memory cells in Key Area 4.2 on pages 176–179.

Source of antigen in vaccine	Example of disease vaccinated against in this way
Dead pathogens	Polio
Weakened pathogens	Measles
Parts of pathogens	Hepatitis B
Inactivated toxin from pathogen	Diphtheria

Adjuvants

Adjuvants are substances such as aluminium hydroxide that can be mixed with antigens from infectious pathogens to enhance the immune response. This results in a higher concentration of antibodies being produced and provides longer-lasting protection. By boosting the immune response it minimises the amount of foreign material that needs to be injected to trigger the immune response.

Clinical trial of vaccines

In most countries new drugs, including vaccines, are licensed before general use. To become licensed, clinical trials are carried out to test that the new product is safe and produces the intended benefit for those who are vaccinated.

Once a new vaccine is thought to be safe for trials on humans, volunteers are divided into a test group and a control group. To increase reliability, it is important that selection of groups is randomised and that replicates are carried out where possible.

The test group receive the vaccine and the control group do not. The control group receive a placebo instead of the vaccine. The placebo is administered in the same way as the vaccine but does not contain the antigenic material of the vaccine. Members of the groups are usually unaware if they are receiving the vaccine or the placebo. A trial in which the doctors involved are also unaware of which group an individual is in is called a double-blind trial.

Herd immunity

The principle of herd immunity is that if enough people are immune to a disease that is spread from person to person, then that protects those who are not. The immune individuals act as a barrier, preventing spread of infection, as shown in Figure 4.11.

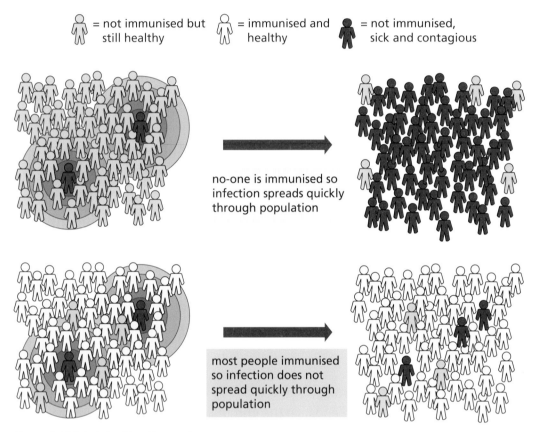

= not immunised but still healthy   = immunised and healthy   = not immunised, sick and contagious

no-one is immunised so infection spreads quickly through population

most people immunised so infection does not spread quickly through population

Figure 4.11 Principle of herd immunity

The threshold percentage of immune people needed for effective herd immunity to occur depends on various factors, as shown in the following table.

Factor	Notes
Type of disease	How easily spread the disease is – is the disease very contagious and how long is it before an infected individual can spread the disease on?
Effectiveness of the vaccine	How well the vaccine protects individuals – what percentage of people are successfully immunised following vaccination?
Contact parameters in the population	How well mixed the population is – can any member of the population pass the disease to any other member?

Public health immunisation

Many countries in the world have programmes aimed at establishing herd immunity to certain diseases through mass vaccination of the population. This is true in the UK, where the NHS aims to make a programme of vaccinations available to each child born. The programme starts when babies are 2 months old and continues through childhood to age 14 years and older. Examples of diseases included in the programme are measles, mumps, rubella, polio, whooping cough, tetanus, diphtheria and meningitis.

Problems in achieving herd immunity

In some areas of the world, mass immunisation is not possible because of poverty levels or lack of nourishment among the population, which makes receiving vaccines dangerous.

In developed countries access to the vaccination programmes is generally voluntary. In some cases parents may reject vaccinations for their children because of worries about the safety of the vaccines involved. This damages the herd immunity principles and instances of disease among the non-vaccinated rise.

Example

Malaria and trypanosomiasis

Malaria is one of the world's most significant public health problems. At least 300 million people are ill with it each year and well over a million die.

The disease is caused by several species of a single-celled organism called *Plasmodium*. The organism is passed into human blood during bites from certain mosquito species. Malaria has the potential to infect 40% of the world's population, who live in zones where the disease occurs.

Trypanosomiasis (sleeping sickness) occurs in Africa. Like malaria, it is caused by a single-celled organism. It is passed into human blood during bites from tsetse flies.

Developing effective vaccines against malaria and trypanosomiasis has not been possible because the organisms change their antigenic characters very rapidly as they evolve. A vaccination based on one set of antigens would not be effective if the antigens changed.

Influenza

Influenza (flu) is caused by viruses that spread around the world in seasonal epidemics, causing around 3–5 million cases of severe illness and 250 000 to 500 000 deaths each year. Mortality can rise to millions of deaths in some pandemic years. A vaccine formulated for one year may be ineffective in the following year, since the influenza virus evolves rapidly and new strains with changed antigens quickly replace the older ones. New vaccines are developed and administered each year.

Human immunodeficiency virus (HIV)

HIV mutates very rapidly, presenting the immune system with constantly changing arrays of antigens. Memory cells that developed during a vaccination are unlikely to bind to the changed antigens $\Rightarrow$

that are present during a subsequent infection. Currently, no effective vaccine against HIV has been developed.

HIV infects and kills certain T lymphocytes and phagocytes. Because these cells are involved in the immune response, affected individuals are unable to fight other infections. Eventually they develop AIDS and often die from illnesses that those with healthy immune systems would fight off easily.

Tuberculosis (TB)

Tuberculosis is caused by a bacterium that can survive attack by phagocytes. When the phagocyte engulfs the bacterium, the pathogen prevents lysosomes fusing with the vesicle that engulfs it. This prevents the bacterium from being digested and destroyed. Also, the bacterium is enclosed in a thick waxy coat, which resists attack by digestive enzymes from the phagocyte.

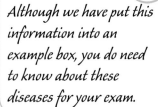

Hints & tips

Although we have put this information into an example box, you do need to know about these diseases for your exam.

Key words

Adjuvant – substance added to a vaccine to enhance the immune response

Clinical trials – methods of obtaining data about new drugs or treatments

Double-blind protocol – method in which neither trial participant nor experimenter knows the treatment given

Herd immunity – principle by which many vaccinated individuals protect those unvaccinated

HIV – virus that attacks lymphocytes, often leading to AIDS

Immunological memory – existence of memory lymphocytes, allowing rapid response to re-infection

Influenza – viral infection that can become pandemic

Malaria – globally important disease caused by a protozoan infection

Placebo-controlled protocol – procedure that involves giving certain participants a blank instead of the drug under trial

Protozoan – a single-celled organism; some protozoans can cause disease

Randomised – describing protocols in clinical trials that are the result of chance selection

Replicate – repeat experiment in an investigation or clinical trial

Trypanosomiasis – disease caused by a protozoan

Tuberculosis (TB) – disease caused by a bacterium that can survive within phagocytes

Vaccination – using an antigen that has been made harmless to produce an immune response and memory cells

Questions

Restricted response (structured in 1- or 2-mark parts)

1 Describe what is meant by a vaccine. (1)
2 Explain the role of adjuvants in immunisation. (1)
3 Define the following protocols as they are used in carrying out clinical trial procedures:
   a) double blind (1)
   b) placebo controlled. (1)
4 Explain why it is important to work with a large group of participants in a clinical trial. (2)
5 Give **two** methods by which pathogens can evade the human immunological memory system. (2)

Extended response (4–9 marks each)

6 Give an account of immunisation under the following headings:
   a) Vaccination (5)
   b) Difficulties encountered in achieving widespread vaccination (2)
7 Give an account of the principle of herd immunity. (4)
8 Write notes on the following human diseases:
   a) malaria (3)
   b) influenza (3)
   c) AIDS. (3)

Answers are on page 192.

Answers

Key Area 4.1

Restricted response

1 defences are general to any/all invading pathogens [1]
2 epithelium can form a barrier, which prevents entry of pathogens [1]
3 acid secreted by cells in stomach epithelium; enzymes secreted by cells in stomach epithelium; mucus secreted from cells in stomach/breathing tube epithelium [any 2 = 2]
4 antigens [1]
5 self-induced cell death/suicide [1]

Extended response

6 skin prevents the entry of pathogens/is a physical barrier; epithelial cells (in cavity linings) produce (protective chemical) secretions; mucus produced by windpipe; stomach produces acid; lysozyme/anti-bacterial substances in tears; coughing/sneezing; blood clotting; inflammatory response; action of phagocytes; action of NK cells [any 8 = 8]
7 a) mast cells release histamine; histamine causes capillary vasodilation; histamine causes increased permeability of capillaries; increased delivery of phagocytes/antimicrobial proteins to infection site [any 3 = 3]
   b) phagocytes recognise pathogens; engulfing of pathogen by phagocyte; release of digestive enzymes into vesicle; from lysosomes; pathogen destroyed [any 4 = 4]
8 NK cells release cytokines; cytokines trigger specific immune response; NK cells induce virus-infected cells to produce degrading enzymes; enzymes cause cells to die *or* apoptosis occurs [4]

Answers

Key Area 4.2

Restricted response

1 a range of white blood cells circulate, constantly monitoring the tissues [1]
2 cytokines are signal molecules; they increase blood flow to infection sites; they activate white blood cells [any 2 = 2]
3 divides repeatedly to produce a clone [1]
4 a) hypersensitive B lymphocyte response; to a normally harmless antigen [2]
   b) immune system regulation failure; leads to response of T lymphocytes to self antigens [2]
5 long-term existence of memory cells following a primary exposure to antigen; allows rapid, greater immune response to secondary exposure to same antigen [2]

Extended response

6 a) respond to specific antigens by producing a clone; B lymphocytes activated by antigen-presenting cells/T cells; B lymphocytes produce antibodies; antibodies released into blood or lymph and bind to specific antigens; antigens rendered harmless [any 4 = 4]
   b) respond to specific antigens by producing a clone; have surface proteins that allow them to distinguish between self and foreign antigens; one group induces apoptosis in infected cells; one group secretes cytokines to activate B cells and phagocytes [any 3 = 3]
⇨

7 immunity is when the body makes antibodies in response to an infection/pathogen/disease; invading pathogens have antigens (on their surface); lymphocytes recognise foreign/non-self antigens (on the invading pathogen); B lymphocytes produce antibodies; antibodies are specific/ have receptor sites that bind/attach to foreign antigens; T lymphocytes kill the infected cell/ produce chemicals that destroy microbes; following an infection memory cells are produced/ remain in the body; these detect a reinvading microbe and destroy it (before it can cause infection); this (secondary) response is faster/stronger (than the primary response)   [any 7 = 7]

Answers

Key Area 4.3

Restricted response

1 bacteria; viruses; protozoa; fungi   [any 2 = 2]
2 touching; sharing objects like cups; breathing in droplets; exchanging fluids   [any 2 = 2]
3 a) enforced isolation of infected individuals   [1]
   b) practices that destroy pathogens or inhibit their growth   [1]
4 personal hygiene; safe sexual practices   [2]
5 high-quality water supply; safe food webs; safe sewage disposal   [any 2 = 2]

Extended response

6 sporadic; occasional occurrence in an area; endemic; regular occurrence in an area; epidemic; unusually high number of cases in an area; pandemic; an epidemic on a global scale   [any 6 = 6, must match]

7 a) transmitted by direct physical contact; by body fluids; in inhaled air/air droplets; by infected food/water; by animal vectors; one example of a named disease and how it is spread [any 3 = 3]
   b) vaccination/immunisation; drug therapy/antibiotic use/antiviral drugs; antiseptics/ disinfectants; maintaining clean water/sanitation (separating sewage and drinking water); quarantine *or* description; good (personal) hygiene/care in sexual health/education about hygiene; safe storage/handling of food; control of vectors e.g. use of pesticides   [any 3 = 3]

Answers

Key Area 4.4

Restricted response

1 pharmaceuticals that produce an immune response without symptoms of the disease [1]
2 added to vaccines to enhance the immune response [1]
3 a) neither the participant nor the administrator know if the participant is receiving the vaccine or the placebo [1]
   b) placebos are given to some participants instead of the vaccine under trial [1]
4 reduces experimental error; gives statistically more significant results [2]
5 constantly changing antigens; surviving within host cells [2]

Extended response

6 a) immunisation can be given through vaccination; vaccines are based on antigens that have been rendered harmless; dead/weakened/inactivated/parts of antigens used; adjuvants added to enhance the immune response; memory cells produced during the immune response/ immunological memory created; remain in the body for many years after the vaccination; produce more rapid/greater immune response following exposure to antigen [any 5 = 5]
   b) poverty prevents widespread vaccination; parental resistance to allowing their children to be vaccinated; malnutrition may make vaccination unsafe [any 2 = 2]
7 large number of individuals in a population are immunised; non-immune individuals are protected; there is a lower probability that they will contact an infected individual; threshold percentage of population varies with the disease; threshold varies with the effectiveness of the vaccine; threshold varies with the contact parameters in the population [any 4 = 4]
8 a) malaria caused by a protozoan; malaria transmitted by a vector/mosquitoes; malaria very common worldwide/is endemic in some areas; malaria parasite can change its antigens making immunisation difficult [any 3 = 3]
   b) influenza caused by a virus; influenza transmitted by contact/droplets in air; influenza can occur in global pandemics; influenza changes its antigens, meaning new vaccines need to be developed regularly [any 3 = 3]
   c) HIV is a major cause of AIDS; HIV is a virus; transmitted by exchange of body fluids/blood/ seminal fluid; HIV changes its antigens, making vaccine development difficult [any 3 = 3]

Practice Course Assessment: Unit 4 (25 marks)

Section A (5 marks)

1 Which of the following cells release histamine during the inflammatory response?
   A phagocytes
   B B lymphocytes
   C mast cells
   D natural killer (NK) cells

2 During recovery from a bacterial liver infection apoptosis occurs within the liver. Which cells are most likely to undergo apoptosis in this situation?
   A liver cells
   B phagocytic cells
   C natural killer (NK) cells
   D bacterial pathogen cells

3 Which term, used in epidemiology, describes a disease that occurs regularly in a given area of the world?
   A sporadic
   B endemic
   C pandemic
   D epidemic

4 The table below contains information about the number of cases of tuberculosis (TB) reported to public health services in a European country over a 5-year period.

Year	Cases of TB reported per 100 000 population	
	Rural areas	Urban areas
2002	4	7
2003	5	7
2004	6	11
2005	6	9
2006	7	10

Which of the following conclusions **cannot** be drawn from the data in the table?
Over the 5-year period

   A there are always more cases reported in urban areas than in rural areas
   B the percentage increase in cases over the period is greater in the urban areas
   C the total number of cases in the rural areas is lower than in the urban areas
   D the incidence of TB is rising in rural areas.

5 Which of the following best describes the cause of autoimmune disease?
   A attack on lymphocytes by pathogens
   B hypersensitivity to a harmless antigen
   C evasion of the immune system by a pathogen
   D recognition of self antigens by the immune system

⇨

Section B (20 marks)

1 The diagram below shows a phagocyte engulfing a bacterial cell.

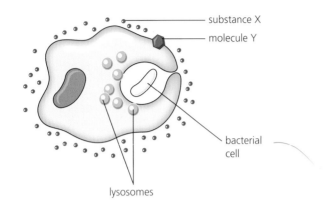

a) Explain why this type of cellular defence is described as non-specific. (1)

b) (i) Name substance X released by the phagocyte, which stimulates a specific immune response. (1)

(ii) Describe the role of the lysosomes in the destruction of the bacterium. (2)

(iii) Name molecule Y, which was derived from the invading bacterium. (1)

2 The diagram below shows the simplified structure of a virus from a strain that can cause influenza.

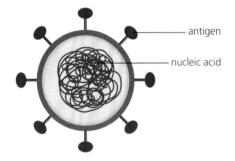

a) These viruses are used in the production of a vaccine against this strain of influenza. Explain why each of the following is included in the vaccine:

(i) viral antigens (1)

(ii) adjuvants. (1)

b) New vaccines against influenza are developed each year. Explain why new vaccines against influenza are needed so regularly. (1)

c) In setting up clinical trials to test the new vaccines, double-blind protocols are often used. Describe what is meant by a double-blind protocol. (1)

Question 3 contains a choice.

3 *Either* A Give an account of the action of B lymphocytes in response to a specific pathogen entering the body for the first time. (5)

Or B Give an account of the establishment of herd immunity to a range of diseases in a human population. ⇨ (5)

⇒

4 The table below shows estimates of the death rate from malaria worldwide in various years from 2000.

Year	Estimated worldwide death rate from malaria (per 100 000 population)
2000	45
2005	40
2006	36
2009	30
2010	28
2012	25

a) On a piece of graph paper, draw a line graph to show the worldwide death rate from malaria against the year. (2)

b) Describe how the trend in death rate decrease between 2000 and 2006 compares with the trend in decrease between 2006 and 2012. (1)

c) Calculate the percentage reduction in death rate from malaria worldwide between 2000 and 2009. (1)

d) (i) Calculate the actual number of deaths from malaria worldwide in 2012, assuming a global population of 7 billion. (1)

   (ii) Explain why the death rate is expressed as number per 100 000 rather than the actual numbers involved. (1)

Answers to Practice Course Assessment: Unit 4

Section A

1 C, **2** A, **3** B, **4** B, **5** D

Section B

1 a) any pathogen/antigen attacked [1]
  b) (i) cytokines [1]
    (ii) lysosomes fuse with vesicle; digestive enzymes added to vesicle [2]
    (iii) antigen [1]
2 a) (i) to trigger immune response *or* to be recognised by white blood cells [1]
    (ii) to enhance the immune response [1]
  b) strain mutates/changes antigens regularly [1]
  c) neither participants nor experimenters know which individuals get vaccine or placebo [1]
3 A B lymphocytes produce specific antibodies, which recognise a specific antigen; B lymphocytes are activated by T cells/antigen-presenting cells; B lymphocytes produce a clone of cells in response; clone secretes antibodies; antibodies released to bloodstream and lymph; antibodies bind to antigens and render them harmless [any 5 = 5]
  B herd immunity occurs when a large percentage of a population is immune to a certain disease; non-immune individuals are protected because there is a lowered probability they will come into contact with the disease; threshold for herd immunity depends on the disease; effectiveness of the vaccine; contact parameters in the population; public health immunisation programmes aim to produce herd immunity; public health immunisation programmes are aimed at a number/range of diseases [any 5 = 5]
4 a) axes scaled *and* labelled; points plotted *and* connected with straight lines [2]
  b) the decrease between 2000 and 2006 was less than the decrease between 2006 and 2012 *or* converse [1]
  c) 33.33% [1]
  d) (i) 1.75 million [1]
    (ii) to allow valid comparison between years/take account of changing population size [1]

The questions within the Key Areas of this book all test knowledge. This section covers the skills of scientific inquiry and includes questions to test these. We have given three different approaches to working with these science skills and recommend that you use all three.

- The first approach simply provides sets of hints and tips on answering science skills questions.
- The second approach goes through the skills one by one and gives you some exam-style questions to try. There is a grid on page 203 that shows which skills are tested in the parts of each question. The answers are given on pages 212–213.
- The third approach gives an example of a scientific investigation and breaks it down into its component skills. There are questions on each skill area. The answers are on page 213.

The context of scientific skills questions will usually be unfamiliar to you but the approaches we have covered should apply to most situations. This means extra marks and improved grades.

Approach 1: hints and tips

Tips on selecting information

Note that you can be asked to deal with information that is more complex than that which you could be asked to present or process.

- Some questions might be based on passages of *text* – you could be asked to pick out information, identify evidence, explain relationships, draw conclusions and show biological knowledge. Try using a highlighter to pick out important points in the text.
- Data might be presented as a *table* – again, a highlighter is helpful.
- The main types of chart you could see are **bar charts** and **pie charts**.
- You could be presented with **line graphs** or **graphs of best fit**. A line graph is used when data points are simply connected by straight lines. If data are scattered on a graph, lines can be fitted using the results of calculations on the data.
- On graphs, the variable being investigated (independent variable) is usually on the *x*-axis and what is being measured (dependent variable) is on the *y*-axis.

- You might be asked to identify variables that should be controlled – use **CID**:
  - **C**ontrolled variables should be kept **C**onstant.
  - **I**ndependent variables are being **I**nvestigated.
  - **D**ependent variables give the **D**ata that form the results.
- Time intervals are often graphed on the *x*-axis but are not true variables. Watch out for this if you are asked to identify a variable.
- Watch out for graphs with a double *y*-axis – these are tricky! The two *y*-axes often have different scales to increase the difficulty. You must take care to read the question and then the graph carefully to ensure that you are reading the correct *y*-axis – there will usually be a key, which is critical.
- On bar charts and line graphs, work out the value of the smallest square on either scale before trying to read actual values.
- You might see a graph with a **semi-logarithmic scale**. These are often used when the numbers involved in a graph scale range from low to very high, such as those dealing with numbers of bacteria present in a growing culture.
- You could see bar charts or line graphs with **error bars**. These are used to show the extent of variability of data, the level of confidence that exists regarding the data or if two sets of data differ from each other significantly. You would not be asked to draw error bars. An example is shown on page 207.
- If you are asked to calculate an increase or decrease between points on a graph, you should use a ruler to help accuracy – draw pencil lines on the actual graph if this helps.
- When you are asked to describe a trend it is essential that you quote the values of the appropriate points and use the exact labels given on the axes in your answer. You must use the correct units in your description.
- Sometimes there will be two sources of data, for example a graph and a table. Make sure you study the two sources carefully – there will be something that links them and it is this link that you will be asked to use.
- You could be asked to deal with statistical measures such as **mean**, **range** and **standard deviation**. The mean is an arithmetic average of the data and the range describes the difference between the highest and lowest values in a group. The standard deviation is a measure of how varied the data are. You would not be expected to calculate standard deviation values.
- **Box plots** are used to show differences between groups of data – they are graphical ways to display the data so that groups can be compared visually. You could see box plots in a question but you would not be asked to draw one. An example is shown on page 207.
- **Keys** are used to identify and, usually, name an organism or substance using features and characteristics as clues.

Tips on presenting information

- The most common question in this area requires you to present information that has been provided in a table as a graph – usually a line graph or sometimes a chart (usually a bar chart), although it is possible that you could be asked for a simple diagram or to draw a key.

- Check the question to see if it is a line graph or a bar chart that is required – the question will usually tell you.
- Marks are given for providing scales, labelling the axes correctly and plotting the data points. Line graphs require points to be joined with straight lines using a ruler. Bar charts need to have the bars drawn precisely, using a ruler.
- Ensure that you can identify the dependent and independent variables.
- The graph labels should be identical to the table headings and units. Copy them exactly, leaving nothing out.
- You need to decide which variable is to be plotted on each axis. The data for the variable under investigation (independent variable) is placed in a left column of a data table and should be scaled on the x-axis. The right column in a data table provides the label and data for the y-axis – the dependent variable. You will lose a mark if these are reversed.
- You must select suitable scales. Choose scales that use at least half of the graph grid provided, otherwise a mark will be deducted. The values of the divisions on the scales you choose should allow you to plot all points accurately.
- Make sure that your scales include zero if appropriate and extend beyond the highest data points.
- The scales must rise in regular steps. At Higher level the examiners will often test you on this by deliberately skipping one of the values that they have given you to plot in the table.
- Be careful to include one or both zeros on the origin if appropriate. It is acceptable for a scale to start with another value other than zero if this suits the data.
- Take great care to plot the points accurately using crosses or dots and then connect them exactly using a ruler.
- Do not plot zero or connect the points back to the origin unless zero is actually included in the data table. If 0 is there, you must plot it.
- When drawing a bar graph, ensure that the bars are the same width. Remember to include a key if the data require it.
- If you make a mistake in a graph, a spare piece of graph paper is provided at the end of your exam paper.

Tips on processing information

General points

- You can be asked to do calculations involving whole numbers, decimals or fractions. Answers might be whole numbers or decimals.
- Decimal answers should be rounded to the appropriate degree of accuracy, which will generally be to the nearest two decimal places or to three significant figures.

- You can be asked to convert between units, such as those for mass (µg, mg, g and kg) or for distance (µm, mm, m and km).
- You might be asked to do calculations involving negative numbers or using scientific notation.
- You might be asked to put values into a given equation and calculate an unknown.

Tackling the common calculations

Percentages: expressing a number as a %

The number required as a percentage is divided by the total and then multiplied by 100, as shown:

$$\frac{\text{number wanted as a \%}}{\text{total}} \times 100$$

Percentage change: increase or decrease

First, calculate the increase or decrease. Then, express this value as a percentage:

$$\frac{\text{change}}{\text{original starting value}} \times 100$$

Ratios

These questions usually require you to express the values given or being compared as a simple whole number ratio.

First you need to obtain the values for the ratio from the data provided in the table or graph. Take care that you present the ratio values in the order they are stated in the question. Then simplify them, first by dividing the larger number by the smaller one then dividing the smaller one by itself. However, if this does not give a whole number then you need to find another number that will divide into both of them. For example, 21:14 cannot be simplified by dividing 21 by 14 since this would not give a whole number. You must then look for another number to divide into both, in this case 7. This would simplify the ratio to 3:2, which cannot be simplified any further.

Mean

This is one type of average – the others are the median (used in box plots) and the mode.

Add up the values provided and then divide the total by the number of values given. Make sure you include all values even if one or more is actually a zero value – they still count.

You might be asked to calculate the mean increase per unit time in a value over a period. If so, calculate the total increase, then divide by the number of units of time in the period given.

Range

This refers to the difference between the lowest and the highest values in a set of data. Find the lowest and the highest – give the range from one to the other and the arithmetic difference between them.

Tips on experimental skills of planning, designing and evaluating

Questions designed to test your skills in this area require you to deal with aspects such as those that appear in the questions below.

Experimental aims

The aim of an experiment or investigation is usually stated at the start of a question – make sure you read the stem carefully because you cannot give a conclusion without knowing the aim.

Hypothesis formation

When an observation is made, the suggested scientific explanation for it is called a hypothesis. You may be given an observation and asked to construct a hypothesis.

Variables

You should be able to identify the independent and dependent variables in an investigation or experiment.

- The **i**ndependent variable is the **i**nput variable – it usually appears in the first column of a data table and is plotted on the *x*-axis of a graph.
- The **d**ependent variable refers to the **d**ata (results) produced – it usually appears in the second column of a **d**ata table and is plotted on the *y*-axis of a graph.

Validity

To improve validity, only the independent variable should be altered while the other variables should be kept constant. Examples of the variables that might need to be controlled and kept constant to ensure results are valid include temperature, pH, concentration, mass, volume, length, number, surface area and type of tissue, depending on the experiment.

The control should be identical to the original experiment apart from the one factor being investigated. If you are asked to describe a suitable control, make sure that you describe it in full. A control experiment allows a comparison to be made and allows you to relate the dependent variable to the independent one.

Experimental procedure

- If the effect of temperature on enzyme activity is being investigated, it is good practice to allow solutions of enzyme and substrate to reach the required temperature before mixing them, to ensure that the reaction starts at the experimental temperature.
- It is good experimental practice to use percentage change when you are comparing results. A percentage change allows a fair comparison to be made when the starting values in an investigation are different.
- Precautions to minimise errors include washing apparatus such as beakers or syringes or using different ones if the experiment involves different chemicals or different concentrations. This prevents cross contamination.
- Questions regarding procedures that ask why the experiment was left for a certain time require you to state that this is to allow enough time for particular events to occur. These events could include the following:
  - diffusion or absorption of substances into tissue
  - growth taking place
  - the effect of substances being visible
  - a reaction occurring.

Observations and measurements

When observing and measuring you need to ensure reliable results. To improve the reliability of experiments and the results obtained, the experiment should be repeated.

Remember **ROAR**: **r**epeat and **o**btain an **a**verage, which increases **r**eliability.

Modifications needed in light of experience

You will probably be asked to suggest a modification to an experimental procedure to test different variables. If you are asked about this, think about how to alter the different variables while keeping the original variable constant. For example, when investigating enzyme action, temperature is often varied. If temperature were kept constant then pH level could be investigated as long as all other variables were kept the same.

Concluding, predicting and generalising

When **concluding**, you must provide a reference to the experimental aim, which is likely to be stated in the stem of the question. You could be asked to:

- summarise experimental results, including describing patterns, trends or rates of change
- look at supplied information and **predict** results or outcomes of experiments
- make **generalisations** about, state relationships between, or suggest rules about biological processes.

Approach 2: skill by skill

The basic skills that can be tested in your exam are listed in the table below. We have provided four practice questions (1–4), one from each Unit, which cover all the skill areas between them. The table shows the parts of the practice questions where you can find each skill tested. It is probably better to try the whole of each question in turn. If you find particular difficulty with any part of a question, you can use the table to identify the skill area that needs further work. Use the other material in this chapter to work on each skill, either in turn or as you come across difficulties.

Skill area	Category within skill area	Practice questions			
		1: Unit 1 data	2: Unit 2 practical	3: Unit 3 data	4: Unit 4 data
1 Selecting information...	...from a line graph, bar chart or box plot	e	–	e, f	ai
	...from a table	–	–	a	–
2 Presenting information...	...as a line graph	–	b	–	–
3 Processing information...	...as a ratio	–	–	–	biii
	...as an average	–	g	–	bii
	...as a percentage	–	–	–	bi
	...by general calculation (addition, subtraction, multiplying, dividing)	c	–	–	–
4 Planning and designing	Planning: aim, hypothesis, dependent and independent variables	–	c	g	–
	Designing: apparatus, replicates, other variables, controls	–	a, d, f	–	–
5 Predicting and generalising	Predicting	–	i	–	–
	Generalising	d	–	–	–
6 Concluding and explaining	Concluding	a, b	h	d	aii, ci
	Explaining	–	–	h	cii 1 and 2
7 Evaluating	Identifying source(s) of error	–	–	c	–
	Suggesting improvement(s)	–	e	b	–

Unit 1 Human cells

Question 1   Data question

Chemical analysis of the nucleotide base ratios of DNA samples from various sources was carried out. The molecular ratios of the nucleotide bases were obtained by dividing the number of adenine bases by the number of each of the other bases present in the sample.

The results are shown in Table 1.

Table 1

Source of sample	Molecular ratios of nucleotide bases in sample		
	Adenine to thymine	Adenine to guanine	Adenine to cytosine
Human	1.00	1.50	1.50
Cattle	1.00	1.30	1.30
Domestic hen	1.00	1.45	1.45
Wheat plants	1.01	1.42	1.41
Yeast	1.00	1.67	1.67

a) Describe the evidence in Table 1 that suggests the following conclusions:
   (i) Adenine pairs with thymine in DNA. (1)
   (ii) There may have been experimental error in the analysis of the sample from wheat plants. (1)
b) Explain why the ratios of adenine to guanine and adenine to cytosine in Table 1 are almost identical. (1)
c) Copy the table below and complete it using information from Table 1 to show the numbers of guanine, cytosine and thymine bases in the human DNA sample. (3)

Base name	Number of molecules present in sample
Adenine	2800
Guanine	
Cytosine	
Thymine	

d) Explain why the ratios of adenine to guanine are different in different groups of living organisms. (2)
e) DNA strands are separated by melting. The melting temperature (T_m) is proportional to the percentage of guanine to cytosine bonds (% G–C) present in the molecule, as shown in the graph below.

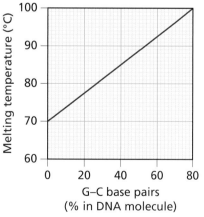

   (i)   Give the percentage of G–C base pairs in a molecule of DNA that has a T_m of 80°C. (1)
   (ii) Give the T_m for a DNA sample in which 25% of the bases are guanine. (1)
   (iii) Use information in Table 1 to predict the T_m for the human DNA sample. (1)
Answers are on page 212.

Unit 2 Physiology and health

Question 2   Practical question

Hydrogen peroxide is a toxic substance produced during human metabolism.

Catalase is an enzyme that breaks down hydrogen peroxide, as shown below:

$$\text{hydrogen peroxide} \xrightarrow{\text{catalase}} \text{water} + \text{oxygen}$$

An experiment was carried out to investigate the effect of a competitive inhibitor on the action of catalase.

Raw liver containing catalase was chopped finely and added to 5 cm³ of 5% hydrogen peroxide solution in a tube. The tube was kept at 20°C and the volume of oxygen released was measured every minute over a period of 6 minutes, as shown in the diagram below.

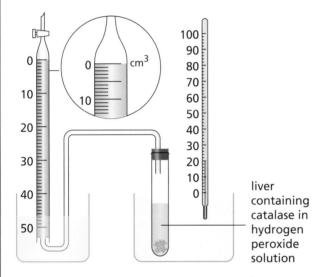

The experiment was repeated with the competitive inhibitor hydroxylamine hydrochloride added to the tube. The results are shown in the table below.

Time (minutes)	Volume of oxygen produced (cm³)	
	Without inhibitor	With inhibitor
0	0.0	0.0
1	7.8	3.4
2	8.6	5.8
3	9.0	6.6
4	9.3	8.6
5	9.5	9.3
6	9.6	9.6

a) Suggest why the liver was chopped finely before being added to the hydrogen peroxide.   (1)

b) On a sheet of graph paper, draw a line graph of time against volume of oxygen produced when the inhibitor was absent.   (2)

c) Identify the independent variable in this investigation.   (1)

d) Identify **two** variables not already described that should be kept constant to ensure the validity of the results.   (2)

e) Describe how the reliability of the experiment could be increased.   (1)

f) Explain how the tube with no inhibitor acted as a control in this experiment.   (1)

⇨

g) Calculate the average volume of oxygen produced per minute over the first 3 minutes in the tube without the inhibitor. (1)

h) State the effect of the inhibitor on the activity of catalase. (1)

i) Predict the volume of oxygen that would have been produced after 7 minutes in the tube without the inhibitor. (1)

Answers are on page 212.

Unit 3 Neurobiology and communication

Question 3   Data question

An investigation was carried out that aimed to show how age affected boys' ability to carry out a finger maze test. A group of 15 boys aged 8 was given the test and their individual times to complete the maze were recorded. The tests were repeated using a group of 15 boys aged 7, as shown in the table below. The mean values were plotted on the chart below and error bars added. The data were processed and box plots drawn, as shown on page 207.

Table

Boy in sample	Time taken for an individual boy to complete a standard finger maze (s)	
	8-year-old boys	7-year-old boys
1	7	7
2	7	9
3	7	10
4	8	11
5	8	11
6	8	11
7	8	11
8	9	11
9	9	12
10	10	13
11	10	14
12	11	14
13	11	15
14	12	15
15	12	16
Mean	9	12

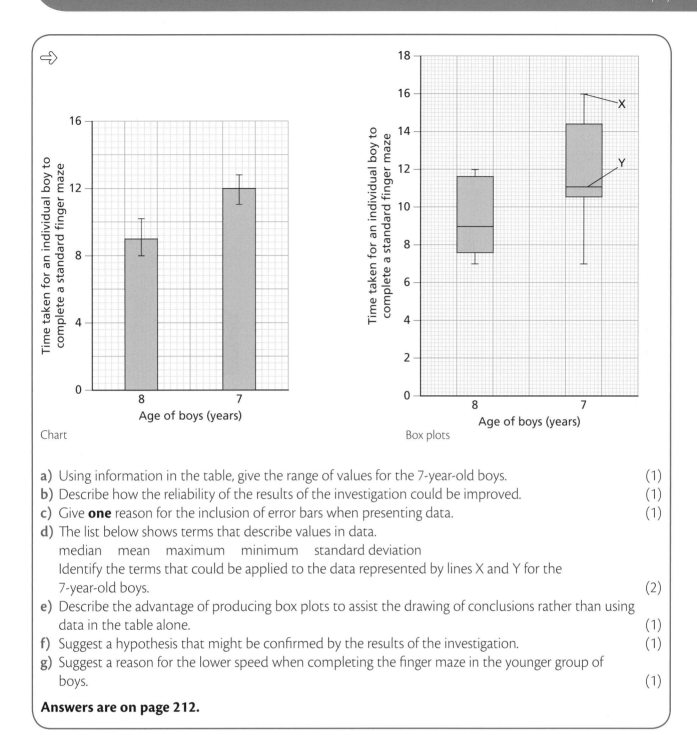

Chart

Box plots

a) Using information in the table, give the range of values for the 7-year-old boys. (1)

b) Describe how the reliability of the results of the investigation could be improved. (1)

c) Give **one** reason for the inclusion of error bars when presenting data. (1)

d) The list below shows terms that describe values in data.

median   mean   maximum   minimum   standard deviation

Identify the terms that could be applied to the data represented by lines X and Y for the 7-year-old boys. (2)

e) Describe the advantage of producing box plots to assist the drawing of conclusions rather than using data in the table alone. (1)

f) Suggest a hypothesis that might be confirmed by the results of the investigation. (1)

g) Suggest a reason for the lower speed when completing the finger maze in the younger group of boys. (1)

Answers are on page 212.

Unit 4 Immunology and public health

Question 4   Data question ❓

The graph below shows information relating to the incidence of tuberculosis (TB) in the UK between 2004 and 2013, and compares UK-born and non-UK-born individuals.

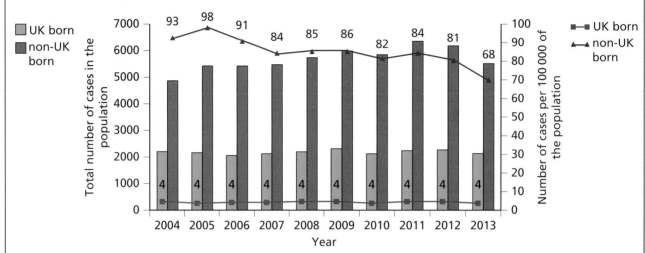

a) (i)   Describe the trend in the total number of cases of TB among those in the population not born in the UK throughout the period. (2)

   (ii) Suggest why the total number of cases among those born in the UK has changed over the period while the number of cases per 100 000 has remained the same. (1)

b) (i)   Calculate the percentage decrease in the number of cases per 100 000 among those non-UK-born between 2008 and 2013. (1)

   (ii) Calculate the average number of cases per 100 000 per year in the non-UK-born population in the period 2010 to 2013. (1)

   (iii) Calculate the ratio of number of cases per 100 000 in the UK-born population to the number of cases in the non-UK-born population in 2011. (1)

c) TB is a disease that has been vaccinated against in the UK throughout most of the period covered by the graph.

   (i)   Describe how the figures given support the statement that the vaccination programme has been successful. (1)

   (ii) 1 What evidence is there that some individuals choose not to be vaccinated? (1)

        2 Describe how herd immunity gives a degree of protection to these individuals. (2)

d) The bacterium that causes TB can avoid detection by the body's immune system. Describe how it can do this. (1)

Answers are on pages 212–213.

Investigating the effects of different antibiotic concentrations on the growth of *E. coli*

Read through the information about the experiment below and then work through the skill areas listed, commenting on the questions in each category.

Introduction

Bacteria can grow into colonies on nutrient agar. Multidiscs are blotting papers that have circular areas that have been soaked in antibiotic. Colonies are not able to grow in areas of agar into which antibiotic substances to which they are sensitive have diffused and so clear areas are created, as shown in the diagram below.

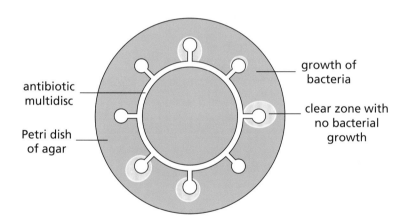

In an experiment that aimed to investigate the effects of increasing the concentration of an antibiotic on the growth of the bacterium *Escherichia coli* (*E. coli*), the following method was used.

Method

1. Five Petri dishes were set up, each containing 10 ml of sterile nutrient agar.
2. An antibiotic multidisc with different concentrations of an antibiotic was added to the surface of the agar in each, pressed down and left for 24 hours.
3. Using a sterile pipette, 0.5 ml of broth containing a suspension of 10^5 *E. coli* per ml was removed from a culture bottle and squeezed onto the surface of each agar plate.
4. The culture was carefully spread across the agar surfaces using a glass spreader, which was sterilised between uses.
5. The dishes were kept in an oven at 30°C for 48 hours, then removed, and the diameters of any clear zones that were visible around the antibiotic measured using a ruler.

Results

The mean diameters of the clear zones that developed around each antibiotic concentration are shown in the table below.

Antibiotic concentration (%)	Mean diameter (mm)
Control	0.0
0.5	0.1
1.0	3.3
1.5	4.1
2.0	4.6
2.5	6.1
3.0	6.6
3.5	6.7

Planning experiments and designing experiments

This is about confirming the aim of an experiment and suggesting a likely hypothesis, choosing apparatus, thinking about the dependent variable and deciding what to measure. Designing is closely related to planning but involves details of how often to measure, which variables need to be controlled and how to do this. It also involves anticipating possible errors and trouble-shooting these.

Q1 Suggest what the aim of the experiment was.

Q2 Suggest a hypothesis that would go with this aim.

Q3 Why is *E. coli* used?

Q4 What should be done to minimise the risks linked to using *E. coli* in the experiment?

Q5 What is the purpose of the control arm on each multidisc?

Q6 Why is nutrient agar used? (Hint: think about the conditions for bacterial growth.)

Q7 Why is the multidisc pressed into the agar and left for 24 hours?

Q8 Why is sterility important in this investigation? (Hint: many species of bacteria and fungi are present in air and on surfaces.)

Q9 Why is the plate left in the oven at 30°C for 48 hours?

Q10 Why is the *E. coli* culture spread evenly on the agar?

Q11 Which variables have been controlled in this procedure?

Q12 Which is the dependent variable and which the independent variable?

Q13 Why was the experiment repeated five times?

Selecting information

This is about using a source such as a table or line graph to extract particular pieces of information. This can be simply reading off a value. The skill requires knowledge about labels, scales and units.

Q14 How could the results be expressed in a different numerical form?

Q15 Which concentration of antibiotic had the most effect on the *E. coli*?

Presenting information

This is about taking some information and presenting it in a different and more useful form. A common type of presentation might be to take information from a table and present it as a line graph. The skill requires knowledge of labels, scales and units, as well as careful drawing using a ruler and accurate plotting.

Q16 On a sheet of graph paper, draw a line graph to show the effect of antibiotic concentration on the growth of *E. coli*.

Processing information

This is often about working with numerical data and using calculations to convert a lot of data into a simple form.

Q17 What is the ratio of the diameter of the clear zone produced by antibiotic at 1% compared with that produced by antibiotic at 3%?

Q18 What is the mean diameter of the clear zones around the different antibiotic concentrations?

Q19 What is the percentage increase in the diameter of the clear zone as the percentage of antibiotic is increased from 0.5% to 2.5%?

Q20 What is the range of diameters of clear zones in the investigation?

Q21 How many bacterial cells were in 0.5 ml of the culture liquid?

Q22 How could a culture with only 50% of this number be obtained?

Predicting and generalising

Predicting is about taking an experimental result and imagining what would happen if a variable changed. Generalising is about looking at experimental results and trying to find a rule that would hold true in all situations.

Q23 Predict the effect on the diameter of the clear zone produced if a concentration of the antibiotic at 4% was used.

Q24 How would you expect the results to compare if a different species of bacterium was used?

Q25 How could the diameters of the clear zones be increased without changing the concentration of antibiotic in the disc?

Q26 How could the diameters of the clear zones be decreased without changing the concentration of antibiotic in the disc?

Concluding and explaining

Concluding involves making a statement about the relationship between variables in an experiment. Explaining is about using knowledge to understand why a result has been obtained.

Q27 What is causing the clear zones?

Q28 What is the general conclusion that can be drawn from the results? (Hint: remember to look at the aim of the experiment.)

Evaluating

Evaluating is looking critically at an experiment and deciding if it is likely to be valid and if its result can be relied on; it is about looking for potential sources of error. Evaluating also involves suggesting improvements to an experiment that might remove sources of error in future experimental repeats.

Q29   What sources of error might be present?

Q30   How reliable are the results obtained?

Q31   How could this experiment be improved?

Q32   Which other factors that might affect bacterial growth could be investigated using multidisc apparatus? How could you adapt the experimental set-up to investigate one of these?

Answers are on page 213.

Scientific inquiry skills answers

Skill by skill

1 a) (i)   number of adenine molecules divided by number of thymine molecules equals 1.0   [1]

   (ii) the answer/value obtained for adenine divided by thymine is very slightly more than 1.0 *or* ratio of adenine to guanine very slightly different from ratio of adenine to cytosine   [1]

   b) number of cytosine should equal the number of guanine (because they pair) [1]

   c) guanine 4200; cytosine 4200; thymine 2800   [3]

   d) different groups have different proteins; and so different genetic codes in their DNA   [2]

   e) (i)   26/27%   [1]
      (ii) 89°C   [1]
      (iii) 92.5°C   [1]

2 a) to increase surface area/to maximise/improve the release of catalase into the solution   [1]

   b) scales and labels with units; plotted correctly and connected with straight lines   [2]

   c) presence of inhibitor/hydroxylamine hydrochloride   [1]

   d) mass of liver; pH   [any 2 = 2]

   e) repeat the investigation with and without the inhibitor   [1]

f) allows comparison to show that it was the inhibitor that was causing the effect   [1]

g) $3.0\,cm^3$ [1]

h) slows down the rate of enzyme reaction over the first 5 minutes of the experiment   [1]

i) $9.6–9.7\,cm^3$ [1]

3 a) 9   [1]

   b) use more trial participants   [1]

   c) to give information about the spread of the data *or* to show the confidence level linked to the data *or* to indicate significant differences between sets of data   [1]

   d) X – maximum   [1]
      Y – median   [1]

   e) show the distribution/spread/variability of the data more clearly *or* allow sets of data to be compared more easily   [1]

   f) brain development/myelination/memory/dexterity progresses as boys get older   [1]

   g) less well developed brains/myelination/learning/dexterity   [1]

4 a) (i)   increased from 2004 to 2011; then decreased from 2011 to 2013   [2]

      (ii) the total UK-born population has varied slightly during the period   [1]

   b) (i)   20%   [1]
      (ii) 78.75   [1]
      (iii) 1:21   [1]

⇨

⇨

c) (i) the incidence of TB is decreasing over the period *or* the number of cases has remained small throughout the period [1]

(ii) 1 there are still cases reported annually [1]

2 herd immunity means that there is a decreased probability of an unvaccinated individual coming into contact with an infected individual; because most people are vaccinated and so remain uninfected [2]

d) TB bacteria can remain undetected within phagocytic cells [1]

Through an example

Q1 To show the effects of increasing antibiotic concentration on the growth of *E. coli*

Q2 That increasing the concentration of antibiotic would increase the inhibition of growth of *E. coli*

Q3 Easily obtained bacterium which grows rapidly in culture

Q4 A risk assessment should be carried out to identify and minimise the impact of hazards

Q5 To show that any effect recorded is due to presence of antibiotic

Q6 Provides food and other requirements for the culture of *E. coli*

Q7 To allow the substance to diffuse into the agar

Q8 To prevent entry of other microorganisms that might compete with *E. coli* and affect results or that are hazardous

Q9 To provide optimum conditions for enzymes involved in growth of *E. coli*

Q10 So that any colonies develop evenly on the agar and are easier to see

Q11 Volume of nutrient agar; volume of *E. coli* culture; concentration of *E. coli* culture; temperature

Q12 Dependent – diameter of clear zones independent – concentration of antibiotic

Q13 To increase the reliability of the results

Q14 Area/radius of clear zones

Q15 3.5%

Q16 Scales, labels and units *and* points plotted accurately and joined with straight lines

Q17 1:2

Q18 4.5 mm

Q19 6000%

Q20 6.6 mm

Q21 50 000 *or* 5×10^4

Q22 Mix a volume of culture with an equal volume of distilled water

Q23 6.7–6.8 mm

Q24 Might be expected to have similar effects

Q25 Leave dishes longer at start to allow more antibiotic to diffuse into agar

Q26 Do not leave dishes for 24 hours at the start of the experiment

Q27 Antibiotic prevents growth of bacteria, so no colonies develop

Q28 That increasing the concentration of antibiotic increases inhibition of the growth of *E. coli*

Q29 Potential for contamination; failure to have multidisc evenly pressed down; failure to spread bacteria evenly; errors in measuring diameters of clear areas

Q30 Reliability has been increased by repeating five times but could be improved further by even more repeats

Q31 More dishes; more accurate measurement of clear zones

Q32 Different types of antibiotic; nutrient requirements; precursor requirements; inducer requirements; effects of hormones/pesticides/other; repeat experiment with discs containing appropriate substances but keeping all other variables constant

Your assignment

The assignment is an open-book task, which is based on a research investigation that you have carried out, mainly in class time. *You choose the topic* to be studied and then investigate or research the underlying biology and any impact it may have on society or the environment.

The assignment will assess the application of skills of scientific inquiry and related biology knowledge and understanding that you have developed throughout the course. Your report must be completed independently.

The investigation is supervised by teachers, who will supply you with the *Instructions for Candidates* document, published by SQA. You will have to write up the work in the form of a report of 800–1200 words, or equivalent, under *controlled assessment conditions* at a later stage. During your write up you will have access to your investigation notes.

The report will be *marked out of 20 marks* with 15 of the marks being for scientific inquiry skills and 5 marks for the application of knowledge. It is marked by the SQA and contributes 17% to the overall grade for your course.

Outline of the stages in the assignment

Research stage

1 Selection of a topic

The topic must relate to a key area of the Higher Human Biology course. Once you have chosen your topic, you need to decide on the specific aspect that you want to research. This will become the aim of your assignment. The aim might change during the research stage of your assignment, depending on the information you find.

Your teacher will probably give you some ideas to choose from. Make sure you choose something you are interested in and that you understand. The lists below show some suggested topics from the four Units – don't feel you need to use any of these.

Unit 1 Human cells

- Case study on use of stem cells in repair of diseased or damaged organs (e.g. skin grafts, bone marrow transplantation and cornea repair).
- Case study on ethics of stem cell research and sources of stem cells.
- Case study on phage experiments of Hershey and Chase.

- Case study examining the experimental evidence of the bacterial transformation experiments of Griffiths.
- Case study on Meselson and Stahl experiments on DNA replication.
- Single gene mutation case studies.
- Chromosome mutation case studies.
- Genome determination case studies, including the Human Genome Project and the comparison of individual genomes using single nucleotide polymorphisms (SNPs).
- Bioinformatics case studies.
- Case study on use of personalised medicine in cancer treatment.
- Case study on evolution of primates and bears using Geneious software.
- Case study on the use and application of PCR (e.g. identification of suspects from crime scenes, prenatal diagnosis of genetic disorders, identification of viruses).
- Case studies on the medical uses of DNA probes in: detecting single-gene mutations, genotype microarrays and gene expression microarrays manufactured from RNA transcripts.
- DNA profiling.
- Researching different uses of substrates during exercise and starvation.
- Case study on the effects of creatine supplements on fitness and sporting performance.
- Case study on comparison of the ratios of slow-twitch muscle fibres to fast-twitch muscle fibres among elite athletes in different sports.

Unit 2 Physiology and health

- Case studies on infertility, its causes and treatments, to include overcoming problems in sperm production and ovulation, predicting fertile periods, and surgical approaches.
- Examining data on the success rate for *in vitro* fertilisation (IVF) and its effect on long-term health.
- Case studies on the biological basis of physical and chemical contraceptives.
- Case study on antenatal care, to include the use of ultrasound images and biochemical tests.
- Examining data on the risks associated with testing for Down syndrome.
- Blood test for alpha-fetoprotein (AFP) and subsequent test for the 'marker' nuchal translucency by ultrasound.
- Examining case studies of inherited conditions, including single-gene disorders, chromosome abnormalities and conditions influenced by multiple genes.
- Case study on disorders of the lymphatic system. Suitable examples include the effect of kwashiorkor on fluid balance and elephantiasis.
- Investigate the use of thrombolytic medications such as streptokinase and tissue plasminogen activator.
- Comparing and contrasting the use of antiplatelet and anticoagulant therapies.

215

- Investigating examples of bleeding disorders, such as Von Willebrand disease and haemophilia A, B and C.
- Researching data on the action of cholesterol-reducing drugs.
- Investigating current views on the use of statins in treatment of patients at risk of CVD.
- Genetic screening of familial hypercholesterolaemia (FH) and its treatments.
- Investigating the symptoms associated with 'microvascular' and 'macrovascular' disease.
- Researching the role of exercise and diet in reducing obesity and CVD.
- Examining risk factors and remedial measures in treating CVD.

Unit 3 Neurobiology and communication

- Case studies investigating the role of the limbic system in regulating fear, anger, aggression, pleasure, pain, addiction, sexual behaviour, thirst or hunger.
- Case study on a memory disorder (e.g. Alzheimer's, stroke/brain injury, aphasia, amnesia, Wernicke-Korsakoff syndrome).
- Analysing data on the mode of action of memory-enhancing drugs (smart drugs).
- Analysing causes, symptoms and treatments of polio, multiple sclerosis and Tay-Sachs disease.
- Researching neurotransmitter-related disorders and their treatment.
- Researching the mode of action of recreational drugs.
- Examining drug rehabilitation programmes that combat physical tolerance (e.g. methadone and buprenorphine) and psychological dependency (e.g. counselling and cognitive-behavioural approaches).
- Case studies of rewarded behaviour, unrewarded behaviour and shaping in learning.

Unit 4 Immunology and public health

- Case studies on rheumatoid arthritis (cells in the joints produce cytokines that promote an immune response), type 1 diabetes (T cells attack insulin-producing cells), multiple sclerosis (T cells attack antigens on the myelin sheath).
- Case studies on hay fever, anaphylactic shock and allergic asthma.
- Case study on the comparison of the transmission methods of different pathogens, e.g. measles (airborne), HIV (body fluids) and cholera (water or food).
- Case study on mass vaccination programmes (TB, polio, smallpox) and the eradication of diseases.
- Case study on HIV, including the public health measures and drug therapies for its control.
- Case study on measles epidemiology and vaccination.

2 Planning the investigation

Think carefully about your task – what do you already know? Where can you find out more? Focus on any applications and on the impact the content of your chosen topic has on society or the environment.

Ensure that you have a clear aim for the assignment and are sure of the reason you chose your topic. Be clear about the process you will adopt and how you might finally present your findings, including any data or results that you collect.

3 Identifying resources

You can use books, magazines, journals, monographs, the internet, resource packs, personal interviews, visits to appropriate facilities or any other suitable approach that your teacher agrees with. Choose media that you have easy access to. Your school library and librarian might be able to help.

4 Carrying out the investigation

As you work through various sources and extract relevant information, you will want to record anything of potential value. How will you record this material?

Downloads directly from the internet or copying directly from books might suggest that you have not understood the biology involved. This can be considered as plagiarism unless you acknowledge the sources carefully. It is always best to put things in your own words to make sure you really understand them.

Be aware of the need to provide a balanced evaluation in terms of the impact the topic you have studied might have on society or the environment.

You must select sufficient sources of information/data that are relevant, reliable and useful for your topic. These could include raw data from an experiment/practical activity, as well as extracted tables, graphs, diagrams and text. They can have similar or different perspectives and they can agree or disagree with each other.

If you are working in a group to gather data/information, you must take an active part in this and choose your own sources of data/information.

If you use an experiment/practical activity as one of the sources of information/data, your assessor will give you instructions for this. The experiment/practical activity will not be assessed and you may carry it out as part of a group.

Record the sources you have used with enough detail to allow someone else to find them again. If one of the sources is an experiment/practical activity, then you need to record the title and the aim.

This stage should be carried out mainly in class time and you will be allowed to take some of the material produced during this stage for use in the controlled assessment stage – *make sure you know what you will be taking in!*

Checkpoint

This is the point at which you inform your teacher that you have finished the research stage.

5 Selecting and gathering relevant information

You will go through a process of selecting the most relevant and appropriate material from the research stage to include in your final report. How will you organise your report?

Communication stage

6 Writing up your assignment report

You will have to write up your assignment under controlled, supervised conditions, with access to your notes (which cannot include a prepared draft report). As a guide, your report should be 800–1200 words, excluding tables, charts and diagrams.

It is also expected that your work will show literacy and numeracy skills. Here is a short checklist:

- Topic and aim clear
- Spelling and grammar correct
- Word count appropriate
- Explanation of how the underlying biology relates to the topic
- Divided up into coherent sections
- Relevant material only
- Graphs and tables neatly presented with labels, headings and units
- Statistical calculations (averages, percentages and ratios) accurate and clear
- Conclusion(s) justified
- Impact on society or environment clearly stated
- References with sources given

The table below shows how many marks are available for each aspect of your report.

Skills, knowledge and understanding	Mark allocation
Aim	1
Applying knowledge and understanding of biology	5
Selecting information	2
Processing and presenting data/information	4
Analysing data/information	2
Conclusion	1
Evaluation	3
Presentation	2

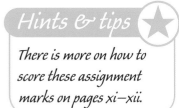

Hints & tips

There is more on how to score these assignment marks on pages xi–xii.

Before submitting your assignment report, check that you have included everything that is required – there is a grid on pages xi–xii to help with this.

General exam revision: 20 top tips

These are very general tips and would apply to all your exams.

1 Start revising in good time.

Don't leave it until the last minute – this will make you panic and it will be impossible to learn. Make a revision timetable that counts down the weeks to go.

2 Work to a study plan.

Set up sessions of work spread through the weeks ahead. Make sure each session has a focus and a clear purpose. What will you study, when and why?

3 Make sure you know exactly when your exams are.

Get your exam dates from the SQA website and use the timetable builder tool to make up your own exam timetable. You will also get a personalised timetable from your school but this might not be until close to the exam period.

4 Make sure that you know the topics that make up each course.

Studying is easier if material is in chunks – why not use the SQA chunks? Ask your teacher for help on this if you are not sure.

5 Break the chunks up into even smaller bits.

The small chunks should be easier to cope with. Remember that they fit together to make larger ideas. Even the process of chunking down will help!

6 Ask yourself these key questions for each course.

Are all topics compulsory or are there choices? Which topics seem to come up time and time again? Which topics are your strongest and which are your weakest?

7 Make sure you know what to expect in the exam.

How is the paper structured? How much time is there for each question? What types of question are involved – multiple choice, restricted response, extended response?

8 There is no substitute for past papers – they are simply essential!

The last four years' papers for all courses are on the SQA website – look for the past paper finder and download as PDF files. There are answers and mark schemes too.

9 Use study methods that work well for you.

People study and learn in different ways. Reading and looking at diagrams suits some people. Others prefer to listen and hear material – what about reading out loud or getting a friend or family member to do this for you? You could also record and play back material.

10 There are only three ways to put material into your long-term memory:

- practice – e.g. rehearsal, repeating
- organisation – e.g. making drawings, lists, diagrams, tables, memory aids
- elaborating – e.g. winding the material into a story or an imagined journey.

11 Learn actively.

Most people prefer to learn actively – for example, making notes, highlighting, redrawing and redrafting, making up memory aids, writing past paper answers.

12 Be an expert.

Be sure to have a few areas in which you feel you are an expert. This often works because at least some of them will come up, which can boost confidence.

13 Try some visual methods.

Use symbols, diagrams, charts, flash cards, post-it notes etc. The brain takes in chunked images more easily than loads of text.

14 Remember – practice makes perfect.

Work on difficult areas again and again. Look and read – then test yourself. You cannot do this too much.

15 Try past papers against the clock.

Practise writing answers in a set time. As a rough guide, you should be able to score a mark per minute.

16 Collaborate with friends.

Test each other and talk about the material – this can really help. Two brains are better than one! It is amazing how talking about a problem can help you solve it.

17 Know your weaknesses.

Ask your teacher for help to identify what you don't know. If you are having trouble, it is probably with a difficult topic so your teacher will already be aware of this – most students will find it tough.

18 Have your materials organised and ready.

Know what is needed for each exam. Do you need a calculator or a ruler? Should you have pencils as well as pens? Will you need water or paper tissues?

19 Make full use of school resources.

Are there study classes available? Is the library open? When is the best time to ask for extra help? Can you borrow textbooks, study guides, past papers etc.? Is school open for Easter revision?

20 Keep fit and healthy!

Mix study with relaxation, drink plenty of water, eat sensibly, and get fresh air and exercise – all these things will help more than you could imagine. If you are tired, sluggish or dehydrated, it is difficult to see how concentration is even possible.

Higher Human Biology exam tips

These tips apply specifically to Higher Human Biology. Remember that your assignment is worth 20 marks – the other 100 marks come from the examination.

Section A: multiple choice (20 marks)

- Do not spend more than *30 minutes* on this section.
- Answer on the grid inside the question paper.
- *Do not leave blanks* – complete the grid for each question as you work through.
- Try to answer each question in your head *without* looking at the options. If your answer is there, you are home and dry!
- If not certain, choose the answer that seemed most attractive on *first* reading the answer options.
- If you are guessing, try to eliminate options before making your guess. If you can eliminate three, you are left with the correct answer even if you do not recognise it!

Section B: restricted and extended response (80 marks)

- Spend about *120 minutes* on this section.
- Answer on the question paper. Try to write neatly and keep your answers on the support lines if possible – these are designed to take the full answer.
- Another clue to answer length is the mark allocation. Most questions are restricted to 1 mark and the answer can be quite short; if there are 2 or 3 marks available, your answer will need to be extended and may well have two, three or even four parts.
- The questions are usually laid out in unit sequence but remember that some questions are *designed* to cover more than one unit.
- Grade C (less demanding) questions usually start with 'State', 'Give' or 'Name'.

- Grade A (more demanding) questions usually begin with 'Explain' and 'Describe' and are likely to have more than one part to the full answer.
- Some more demanding questions begin with 'Suggest' – here, you need to demonstrate and apply your knowledge in a new context.
- Abbreviations like DNA and ATP are fine, as is referring to the nucleotide bases as A, T, G and C, unless you are asked to 'name' them in the question.
- Don't worry that some questions are in unfamiliar contexts. This is deliberate. Just keep calm and read the questions carefully.
- If a question contains a choice, be sure to spend enough time making the right choice.
- Remember to *use values from the graph* if you are asked to do so.
- Draw graphs using a ruler and use the data table headings for the axes labels.
- Look out for graphs with two *y*-axes – these need extra concentration as they can easily lead to mistakes.
- Answers to calculations will not usually have more than two decimal places.
- If there is a space for calculation given it is very likely that you will need to use it.
- Do not leave blanks. Have a go, using the language in the question if you can.

Glossary

The terms included here appear in the SQA Assessment Specification for Higher Human Biology. The Key Area in which a term first appears is given in the brackets after each term.

Where a term has an alternative name, can be abbreviated or has an unusual singular or plural, this is given in brackets with the definition.

You could make flash cards with the term on one side and the meaning on the other – a great resource for revision!

3'–5' (1.2) strand of nucleic acid running from a sugar to a phosphate

Acetyl group (1.7) produced by breakdown of pyruvate; joins with oxaloacetate in the citric acid cycle

Acetylcholine (2.6) neurotransmitter released by parasympathetic nerve fibres

Activation energy (1.6) input of energy required to start a chemical reaction

Active site (1.6) region on an enzyme molecule where the substrate binds

Adenine (A) (1.2) DNA base that pairs with thymine

Adjuvant (4.4) substance added to a vaccine to enhance the immune response

ADP (1.7) adenosine diphosphate; molecule that is phosphorylated to produce ATP

Adrenaline (epinephrine) (2.8) hormone that stimulates the release of glucose from glycogen during stress or exercise

Agonist (3.3) chemical neurotransmitter or a drug that mimics one

Allele (2.4) form of a gene coding for a version of a characteristic

Allergy (4.2) immune response to a normally harmless antigen

Alternative respiratory substrates (1.7) substrates for respiration other than glucose

Amino acid (1.3) unit of polypeptide structure

Amniocentesis (2.4) prenatal test to assess health of fetus using cells from amniotic fluid

Anabolic (1.6) metabolic pathways that consume energy in synthesis of complex molecules

Angina (2.7) chest pain occurring when blood supply to heart muscle is restricted

Anomaly scan (2.4) antenatal ultrasound scan that checks for physical abnormalities

Antagonist (3.3) drug that inhibits transmission of nerve impulses

Antagonistic (2.6) opposing actions of the sympathetic and parasympathetic systems

Antenatal screening (2.4) use of tests to identify risk of a disorder before birth

Anticodon (1.3)   sequence of three bases on tRNA that codes for a specific amino acid

Antigen (4.2)   molecule that can produce an immune response in the body

Antigen-presenting cell (4.2)   cell that has been infected by pathogens and displays their antigens on its surface

Antiparallel (1.2)   parallel strands in DNA that run in opposite directions in terms of chemical polarity

Antisepsis (4.3)   methods aimed at preventing growth of infectious agents such as bacteria

Apoptosis (4.1)   advantageous death of infected cells

Arteriole (2.5)   branch of an artery leading to capillaries

Artery (2.5)   blood vessel that carries blood away from the heart

Artificial insemination (AI) (2.3)   insertion of donated sperm directly into the uterus

Atheroma (2.7)   swelling on inner wall of artery made up of fatty material and connective tissue

Atherosclerosis (2.7)   potentially serious condition in which atheromas clog the arteries

ATP (1.7)   adenosine triphosphate; molecule used for energy transfer in cells

ATP synthase (1.7)   membrane-bound enzyme that synthesises ATP

Atrial diastole (2.6)   part of the cardiac cycle in which the heart muscle of the atria relaxes

Atrial systole (2.6)   part of the cardiac cycle in which the heart muscle of the atria contracts

Atrio-ventricular node (AVN) (2.6)   nervous tissue found at the junction between the atria and the ventricles

Atrio-ventricular (AV) valve (2.6)   heart valve found between the atria and the ventricles

Attachment site (1.3)   site on a transfer RNA molecule to which a specific amino acid binds

Autoimmunity (4.2)   abnormal immune response to self antigens, which leads to autoimmune disease

Autonomic nervous system (ANS) (2.6)   controls involuntary action of smooth and cardiac muscle and glands

Autosomal dominant (2.4)   allele on chromosomes 1–22; always expressed in phenotype

Autosomal recessive (2.4)   allele on chromosomes 1–22; expressed in phenotype if the genotype is homozygous for the recessive allele

Axon (3.3)   neural fibre that conducts impulses away from the cell body

B lymphocyte (4.2)   white blood cell with specific cell surface receptors; secretes antibodies into blood and lymph

Base (1.2)   nitrogenous substance that is a component of DNA nucleotides

Binocular disparity (3.2)   difference between the distance from an image to one eye and the other

Bioinformatics (1.5)   use of computers and statistics in analysis of sequence data

Blastocyst (2.1)   cellular structure that implants and becomes the embryo and the placenta

Body density (2.8)   quantitative measure used to calculate body mass index

Body mass index (BMI) (2.8)   relative measurement based on height and weight

Cancer cell (1.1)   grows and divides in an unregulated way to produce a tumour

Capillary (2.5)   narrow, thin-walled blood vessel that exchanges materials with the tissues

Cardiac cycle (2.6)   contraction and relaxation of the heart muscle in a heartbeat

Cardiac muscle (2.6)   muscle that makes up the heart walls

Cardiac output (2.6)   volume of blood expelled from one ventricle of the heart per minute

Cardiovascular diseases (2.7)   diseases affecting the heart and circulation

Catabolic (1.6)   metabolic activity that releases energy in breakdown reactions

Cellular respiration (1.7)   release of energy from respiratory substrates

Central nervous system (CNS) (3.1)   brain and spinal cord

Cerebellum (3.1)   area of the brain that contains the balance and coordination centres

Cerebral cortex (3.1)   cells of the cerebrum

Cerebral hemispheres (3.1)   two regions into which the cerebrum is divided

Cerebrum (3.1)   region of the brain that has motor, sensory and association areas

Cholesterol (2.7)   lipid molecule needed for cell membranes and in synthesising steroid hormones

Chorionic villus sampling (CVS) (2.4)   prenatal test to assess health of the fetus using cells from the placenta

Chromosome (1.4)   rod-like structure that contains the genetic material of an organism encoded into DNA

Chunking (3.2)   method for the expansion of the STM span

Citrate (1.7)   citric acid; first substance produced in the citric acid cycle

Citric acid cycle (1.7)   second stage of aerobic respiration occurring in the matrix of mitochondria

Clinical trials (4.4)   methods of obtaining data about new drugs or treatments

Clonal selection theory (4.2)   selection of lymphocytes to produce clones when exposed to specific antigens

Clone (4.2)   group of genetically identical cells produced from one parent cell

Codon (1.3)   sequence of three bases on mRNA that codes for a specific amino acid

Coenzyme A (1.7)   substance that carries acetyl groups into the citric acid cycle

Competitive inhibition (1.6)   slowing of reaction rate due to the presence of a substance resembling the substrate

Connective tissue (1.1)   tissue that supports, connects or separates other body tissues

Contextual cues (3.2)   aids to the retrieval of information from LTM

Converging neural pathway (3.3)   pathway in which impulses from many neurons are passed to one neuron

Coronary heart disease (CHD) (2.6)   condition caused by blockage of coronary arteries

Corpus callosum (3.1)   band of tissue in the brain that connects the two cerebral hemispheres

Corpus luteum (2.1)   formed from a follicle after ovulation; produces progesterone

Creatine phosphate (CP) (1.8)   molecule that serves as a source of phosphate and energy in muscle cells

Cytokines (4.1)   category of defence proteins secreted from cells; involved in signalling to other cells

Cytosine (C) (1.2)   DNA base that pairs with guanine

Decay (3.2)   degradation of quality of STM

Deep (elaborative) processing (3.2)   use of semantic methods of transfer of information to LTM

Deep vein thrombosis (DVT) (2.7)   blood clot in a deep vein, often in the leg

Dehydrogenase (1.7) enzymes that remove hydrogen from their substrates; important in the citric acid cycle

De-individuation (3.4) passing responsibility for an individual action to a group

Deletion (of genes) (1.4) chromosome mutation in which a sequence of genes is lost from a chromosome

Deletion (of nucleotides) (1.4) single-gene mutation involving removal of a nucleotide from a sequence

Dendrite (3.3) neural fibre that conducts impulses towards the cell body

Deoxygenated blood (2.6) blood, usually in veins, that carries little oxygen

Deoxyribose (1.2) pentose sugar that is a component of DNA nucleotides

Desensitisation (3.3) decrease in number or sensitivity of synaptic receptors as a result of exposure to drugs

Diastole (2.6) part of the cardiac cycle during which cardiac muscle is relaxed

Differentiation (1.1) changes to cells that allow them to specialise for different functions

Diploid (1.1) refers to a cell having two sets of chromosomes

Discrimination (3.4) application of different responses to a variety of closely related stimuli

Displacement (3.2) loss of items from STM

Diverging neural pathway (3.3) pathway in which impulses from one neuron are passed to many

DNA (1.2) deoxyribonucleic acid; molecule that holds the genetic code in living organisms

DNA polymerase (1.2) enzyme that unwinds and unzips DNA; adds free nucleotides during DNA replication

DNA probe (1.5) short piece of DNA complementary to a target sequence of DNA

DNA profiling (1.5) use of DNA probes to produce a 'fingerprint' of an individual's DNA

Dopamine (3.3) neurotransmitter involved in inducing the feeling of pleasure and other actions

Double-blind protocol (4.4) method in which neither trial participant nor experimenter knows the treatment given

Double helix (1.2) the three-dimensional shape of a DNA molecule

Duplication (1.4) chromosome mutation in which a sequence of genes is repeated on a chromosome

Elaboration (3.2) method of encouraging transfer of information to LTM by adding meaning

Electrocardiogram (ECG) (2.6) record of electrical activity in the heart; used to detect abnormalities

Electron transport chain (1.7) group of proteins embedded in membranes of mitochondria and chloroplasts

Embolus (2.7) any detached mass of material carried by the circulation

Embryo (2.4) stage of development up to about 8 weeks that leads to the formation of a fetus

Embryonic stem cells (1.1) stem cells from embryos that can divide and become any type of cell

Emotional memories (3.2) memories related to feelings

Endemic (4.3) infectious disease that occurs regularly in a particular area

Endocrine gland (2.2) gland that produces and releases hormones

Endometrium (2.1) inner lining of the uterus

Endorphin (3.3) neurotransmitter involved in reducing intensity of pain and other actions

Endothelium (2.5) layer of cells that lines the inner surface of blood vessels

Epidemic (4.3) infectious disease that affects individuals in unusually high numbers

Epidemiology (4.3) study of the transmission of infectious disease

Episodic memory (3.2) memory of an event

Epithelial tissue (1.1) tissue that lines tubes and surfaces within the body

Ethical issue (1.1) issue affecting human attitudes and decisions regarding various choices

Excitatory signal (3.3) signal that affects a receptor and which can be passed on

Exon (1.3) sequence of DNA that codes for protein

Experience (3.4) events of the past that contribute to learning

Extinction of behaviour (3.4) removal of behaviour that has not been reinforced

FAD (1.7) hydrogen carrier important in the citric acid cycle

Familial hypercholesterolaemia (FH) (2.7) inherited condition in which LDLs are at a higher than normal level in the blood

Fast-twitch (type 2) fibre (1.8) type of muscle fibre used in short bursts of activity

Feedback inhibition (1.6)   enzyme inhibition caused by the presence of an end product of a metabolic pathway

Fermentation (1.7)   progression of pyruvate in the absence of oxygen

Fetus (2.4)   stage of a baby after 8 weeks of development

Fibrin (2.7)   protein that helps form a blood clot

Fibrinogen (2.7)   blood protein that is converted to fibrin during the blood clotting process

Fluorescent labelling (1.5)   method of making a fragment of DNA show up under ultraviolet light

Follicle (2.1)   cluster of cells in the ovary that matures to release an ovum

Follicle stimulating hormone (FSH) (2.2)   pituitary hormone that controls development of follicles in ovaries and sperm production in males

Follicular phase (2.2)   first stage in the menstrual cycle during which a follicle develops

Frameshift mutation (1.4)   gene mutation in which all amino acids coded for after the mutation are affected

Gamete (2.1)   sex cell containing the haploid chromosome number

Gel electrophoresis (1.5)   method for the separation of DNA fragments using an electric current in a gel

Gene expression (1.3)   transcription and translation of a gene to synthesise proteins

Generalisation (3.4)   application of a response to a variety of closely related stimuli

Genome (1.5)   total genetic material present in an organism

Genome sequence data (1.5)   information about the nucleotide sequence of the entire human genome

Germline cell (1.1)   cell that can give rise to gametes

Glial cell (3.3)   cell in the nervous system that physically supports neurons and produces myelin sheaths

Glucagon (2.8)   hormone produced by the pancreas that stimulates the conversion of glycogen into glucose in the liver

Glucose (1.7)   sugar that is the main respiratory substrate in cells

Glycogen (2.8)   storage carbohydrate located in the liver and muscle tissues

Glycolysis (1.7)   first stage in cellular respiration

Guanine (G) (1.2)   DNA base that pairs with cytosine

Haemophilia (1.4) inherited disease in which blood clotting fails or is very slow

Haploid (1.1) describes a cell having one set of chromosomes (e.g. gametes)

Heart attack (2.7) serious medical emergency in which blood supply to the heart muscle is blocked

Heat-tolerant DNA polymerase (1.5) enzyme from bacteria in hot springs, used in PCR

Herd immunity (4.4) principle by which many vaccinated individuals protect those unvaccinated

Heterozygous (2.4) having two different alleles of the same gene

High-density lipoprotein (HDL) (2.7) 'good' cholesterol that transports fats away from cells and artery surfaces

High-energy electrons (1.7) electrons that can yield energy as they pass through an electron transport chain

Histamine (4.1) substance released by mast cells that causes the inflammatory response

HIV (4.4) virus that attacks lymphocytes, often leading to AIDS

Homeostasis (2.8) maintenance of a steady state in the cells of a living organism

Homozygous (2.4) having two identical alleles of the same gene

Hormone (2.2) protein released by an endocrine gland into the blood that acts as a chemical messenger

Hydrogen bond (1.2) weak chemical link joining complementary base pairs in DNA

Hypertension (2.6) abnormally high blood pressure in arteries

Hypothalamus (2.2) region of the mammalian brain that secretes releaser hormone at puberty

Identification (3.4) copying the behaviours or beliefs of a role model

Imitation (3.4) process of copying of a behaviour that has been observed

Immune surveillance (4.2) monitoring of the tissue for infection by white blood cells

Immunological memory (4.4) existence of memory lymphocytes, allowing rapid response to re-infection

***In vitro* fertilisation (IVF) (2.3)** medical procedure involving fertilisation of eggs by sperm in laboratory containers

Incomplete dominance (2.4) when an allele is not completely masked by a dominant allele, thus affecting an individual's phenotype

Induced fit (1.6)   change to an enzyme's active site brought about by its substrate

Infant attachment (3.4)   result of the successful bonding process between infant and carer

Inference (3.2)   process that can assist optimum perception in uncertain situations

Inflammatory response (4.1)   response to damage or infection involving vasodilation and cytokine release

Influenza (4.4)   viral infection that can become pandemic

Inhibitory signal (3.3)   signal that affects a synaptic receptor but is not passed on

Insertion (1.4)   single-gene mutation in which an additional nucleotide is placed into a sequence

Insulin (2.8)   hormone produced by the pancreas that stimulates the conversion of glucose into glycogen in the liver

Inter neuron (3.3)   conducts impulses within the CNS, linking sensory and motor neurons

Intermediate (1.7)   substance in a metabolic pathway between the original substrate and the end product

Internalisation (3.4)   changes in behaviour or beliefs as a result of persuasion

Interstitial cell stimulating hormone (ICSH) (2.2)   hormone from interstitial cells that stimulates sperm production in seminiferous tubules

Interstitial cells (2.1)   cells in testes found between the seminiferous tubules; produce ICSH

Intracytoplasmic sperm injection (ICSI) (2.3)   injection of sperm directly into an egg during IVF

Intron (1.3)   non-coding sequence of DNA

Karyotype (2.4)   display of matched chromosomes produced for medical purposes

Lactic acid (1.8)   produced by the fermentation of pyruvate in mammalian muscle cells

Lagging strand (1.2)   DNA strand that is replicated in fragments

LDL receptor (2.7)   receptor that recognises LDLs and encourages their uptake

Lead strand (1.2)   DNA strand that is replicated continuously

Learning (3.4)   modification of behaviour in light of experiences

Ligase (1.2)   enzyme that joins DNA fragments

Limbic system (3.1) area of the brain that contains LTM and other centres

Lipoprotein (2.7) assembly of protein with lipid that enables movement of lipid in water and through membranes

Long-term memory (LTM) (3.2) receives information from short-term memory and stores it permanently

Low-density lipoprotein (LDL) (2.7) 'bad' cholesterol, which is associated with high levels of atheromas

Lumen (2.5) central channel of a tube such as a blood vessel

Luteal phase (2.2) second stage of the menstrual cycle in which a corpus luteum is present

Luteinising hormone (LH) (2.2) pituitary hormone that triggers ovulation and corpus luteum development

Lymph fluid (2.5) fluid made up from tissue fluid collected into lymph vessels, which circulates the body

Lymph vessels (2.5) tiny vessels in which lymph circulates around the body

Lymphatic system (2.5) system of vessels and nodes that deals with lymph in the body

Lymphocyte (1.1) type of white blood cell involved in a specific immune response

Lysis (4.2) breakdown of cells

Malaria (4.4) globally important disease caused by a protozoan infection

Mast cells (4.1) cells that produce histamine in response to tissue damage

Matrix (1.7) central cavity of a mitochondrion in which the citric acid cycle occurs

Medulla (2.6) part of the brain with centres controlling breathing, heart rate and peristalsis

Meiosis (1.1) type of cell division resulting in four haploid gametes

Memory cell (4.2) lymphocyte remaining in the body for many years after recovery from an infection

Memory span (3.2) capacity of short-term memory for items

Menstrual cycle (2.2) approximately 28-day cycle in the middle of which ovulation occurs

Menstruation (2.2) removal of the endometrium and an unfertilised egg cell at the end of a menstrual cycle

Messenger RNA (mRNA) (1.3) carries a copy of the DNA code from nucleus to ribosome

Metabolic pathway (1.6) enzyme-controlled sequence of chemical reactions in a cell

Missense (1.4) substitution mutation; a single nucleotide change results in a codon for a different amino acid

Mitochondrion (1.7) cell organelle in which the aerobic stages of respiration occur (plural: mitochondria)

Mitosis (1.1) division of the nucleus of somatic or germline cells, giving two diploid daughter cells

Molecular interactions (1.4) various chemical links (e.g. sulfur bridge, ionic bond, van der Waals forces) joining amino acids and giving protein molecules their shape

Motor neuron (3.3) carries impulses from the CNS to muscles or glands

Motor skill (3.4) ability to carry out a task involving skeletal muscle

Multipotent stem cell (1.1) stem cell that has the potential to make almost all cell types found within a particular tissue

Muscle fatigue (1.8) painful condition caused by the accumulation of lactic acid in muscles

Muscle tissue (1.1) tissue making up skeletal, smooth and cardiac muscle

Mutation (1.1) random change to a DNA sequence

Myelin sheath (3.3) layer of fatty insulation round a nerve fibre

Myelination (3.3) insulation of nerve fibres with myelin sheaths

Myocardial infarction (MI) (2.7) medical term for a heart attack in which blood flow to the heart is reduced

Myoglobin (1.8) protein in muscle tissue that can bind with oxygen

NAD (1.7) hydrogen carrier important in the citric acid cycle

Natural killer (NK) cell (4.1) cell that releases cytokines and can cause apoptosis in infected cells

Negative feedback (2.2) system of maintaining a steady state in various body systems

Nervous tissue (1.1) tissue making up the nervous system

Neuron (3.3) conducting nerve cell

Neurotransmitter (3.3) chemical released into a synaptic cleft to transmit impulses to the next cell

Non-competitive inhibition (1.6) enzyme inhibition by a substance that permanently alters the active site of the enzyme

Nonsense (1.4) substitution mutation in which a codon is changed to a stop codon, shortening the resulting protein

Non-specific defence (4.1)   general response to infection, including phagocytosis

Non-verbal communication (3.4)   communication by means other than by words and language

Nor-adrenaline (nor-epinephrine) (2.6)   hormone and neurotransmitter

Nucleotide (1.2)   component of DNA consisting of a deoxyribose sugar, a phosphate group and a base

Nucleotide sequence repeat (1.4)   repeated sequence of nucleotides, which can be expanded by some gene mutations

Observation (3.4)   the process of seeing an event occurring

Oestrogen (2.1)   hormone produced by the ovary that helps in the repair and thickening of the endometrium after menstruation

Organisation (3.2)   method of encouraging transfer of information to LTM by adding structure

Osmosis (2.5)   water movement from high water concentration to lower water concentration through a selectively permeable membrane

Ovaries (2.1)   female sex organs in which ova are produced

Oviduct (2.1)   fine tube connecting an ovary to the uterus; location of fertilisation

Oxaloacetate (1.7)   substance that combines with the acetyl group in the citric acid cycle to form citrate

Oxygen debt (1.8)   builds up during fermentation in muscle cells

Oxygenated blood (2.6)   blood containing a high level of oxygen

Pandemic (4.3)   worldwide epidemic

Parasympathetic nerves to the heart (2.6)   nerve fibres which result in a decrease in heart rate; part of the autonomic nervous system (ANS)

Parasympathetic nervous system (3.1)   fibres of the autonomic nervous system that prepare body systems for rest

Pathogen (4.3)   biological agent of disease, such as a bacterium, virus, protozoan or fungus

Pedigree chart (2.4)   diagram showing the occurrence of phenotypes of a particular gene in a family tree

Peptide bond (1.3)   strong chemical link between amino acids in the primary structure of a polypeptide

Perception (3.2)   capacity to take in and make sense of sensory information

Perceptual constancy (3.2) capacity to appreciate the unchanging dimensions of an object as it moves

Perceptual set (3.2) factors influencing perception, including experience, context and expectation

Peripheral nervous system (PNS) (3.1) all peripheral nerves

Peripheral vascular disorder (2.7) condition caused by blockage to arteries other than coronary arteries, the aorta or those in the brain

Peristalsis (3.1) involuntary muscular movements of food through the digestive system

Personalised medicine (1.5) development in which treatment is based on an individual's genome

Phagocyte (1.1) defence white blood cell that can engulf and destroy foreign material

Phagocytosis (3.3) process by which phagocytes engulf and destroy foreign material

Phenotype (1.3) outward appearance of an organism

Phenylketonuria (PKU) (2.4) metabolic disorder that is tested for by postnatal screening

Phosphate (1.2) component of DNA nucleotide

Phosphate (Pi) (1.7) inorganic phosphate used to phosphorylate ADP

Phosphofructokinase (PFK) (1.7) enzyme that regulates glycolysis and synchronises it with the citric acid cycle

Phosphorylation (1.7) addition of phosphate to a substance

Phylogenetics (1.5) study of evolutionary relatedness of species

Pituitary gland (2.2) gland in the brain that releases many hormones

Placebo-controlled protocol (4.4) procedure that involves giving certain participants a blank instead of the drug under trial

Plasma (2.5) liquid component of the blood

Plasticity (3.3) capacity to form new neural pathways

Platelets (1.1) blood cell fragments important in blood clotting

Pluripotent stem cell (1.1) stem cell that has the potential to make almost all differentiated cell types of the body

Polymerase chain reaction (PCR) (1.5) method of amplifying sequences of DNA

Polypeptide (1.3) short strand of amino acids

Postnatal screening (2.4) diagnostic testing of newborn babies

Post-synaptic membrane (3.3) membrane of the neuron that contains receptors for neurotransmitters

Post-translational modification (1.3) changes made to polypeptides following translation

Pre-implantation genetic diagnosis (PGD) (2.3) genetic profiling of embryos prior to implantation during fertility treatments

Prenatal diagnosis (2.4) identification of the risk of disorders in unborn babies

Pressure filtration (2.5) passage of molecules through membranes under pressure

Pre-synaptic membrane (3.3) membrane of the neuron that releases neurotransmitters

Primary transcript (1.3) molecule made when DNA is transcribed

Primer (1.2) short complementary strand of DNA

Procedural memory (3.2) memory related to a skill

Product (1.6) substance resulting from an enzyme-catalysed reaction

Progesterone (2.1) hormone produced by the ovary that thickens and vascularises the endometrium

Prostate gland (2.1) produces fluid that makes up part of the semen

Protein (1.4) large molecule made up of chains of amino acids linked by peptide bonds

Prothrombin (2.7) blood component important in clotting; it is converted to thrombin during clotting

Protozoan (4.4) a single-celled organism; some protozoans can cause disease

Pulmonary embolism (2.7) an embolism (blood clot) in the pulmonary circulation

Pyruvate (1.7) the end product of glycolysis

Quarantine (4.3) enforced isolation of an infected individual to prevent further infection

Randomised (4.4) describing protocols in clinical trials that are the result of chance selection

Receptor (3.3) protein found in the post-synaptic membrane that binds neurotransmitter

Recreational drug (3.3) substance that changes neurochemistry; many are illegal

Red blood cell (1.1) blood cell containing haemoglobin, which can carry oxygen in the bloodstream

Regulatory signal (1.1) molecular signal that can be received by a cell to modify its activity

Rehearsal (3.2) practice by repetition of an item of information

Reinforcement (3.4)   the process by which behaviours are rewarded or not

Repetitive DNA sequence (1.5)   sequence of DNA that is repeated many times; these are highly individual

Replicate (4.4)   repeat experiment in an investigation or clinical trial

Replication (1.2)   formation of copies of DNA molecules

Retrieval (3.2)   recall of information from memory

Reverberating neural pathway (3.3)   pathway that recycles impulses round the same route

Reward pathway (3.3)   neural pathway that produces pleasure

Rhesus antibody testing (2.4)   testing to show if a person carries rhesus antibodies in their blood

Ribosomal RNA (rRNA) (1.3)   type of RNA that makes up ribosomes

Ribosome (1.3)   site of protein synthesis; composed of rRNA and protein

RNA (1.3)   ribonucleic acid; occurs in several forms in cells

RNA polymerase (1.3)   enzyme involved in synthesis of primary transcripts from DNA

RNA splicing (1.3)   joining of exons following the removal of introns from a primary transcript

Secondary exposure (4.2)   a second exposure to the same infective agent

Secondary tumour (1.1)   cancer formed from a cell transported from a primary tumour

Segregation of objects (3.2)   capacity to distinguish between an object and its background

Semantic memory (3.2)   memory of the meaning of something

Semi-lunar valves (2.6)   valves leading into the main arteries leaving the heart

Seminal vesicles (2.1)   glands producing fluid that forms part of the semen

Seminiferous tubules (2.1)   very narrow tubes in the testes in which sperm cells are produced

Sensitisation (3.3)   increase in number or sensitivity of receptors as a result of exposure to drugs

Sensory memory (3.2)   storage of sensory input that lasts a few seconds

Sensory neuron (3.3)   neuron that carries impulses into the CNS from a sense organ

Sequence data (1.5)   information concerning amino acid or nucleotide base sequences

Serial position effect (3.2) capacity to recall items presented in a sequence

Sex-linked recessive (2.4) recessive allele carried on the X chromosome

Shallow processing (3.2) use of non-semantic methods of transfer of information to LTM

Shaping (3.4) use of reinforcement in trial-and-error situations to produce desired behaviours

Short-term memory (STM) (3.2) receives information from sensory memory and has a limited span

Sickle cell disease (1.4) disease caused by a substitution mutation in the gene encoding haemoglobin

Signal molecule (1.6) molecule that brings about changes in a cell's metabolism

Sino-atrial node (SAN) (2.6) region of nervous tissue in the wall of the right atrium; receives impulses from the medulla

Skeletal muscle (1.8) muscle attached to the skeleton that brings about locomotion

Slow-twitch (type 1) fibre (1.8) type of muscle fibre used in endurance activities

Social facilitation (3.4) enhanced performance in competitive or audience situations

Somatic cell (1.1) body cell that divides by mitosis to form more body cells

Somatic nervous system (SNS) (3.1) controls the voluntary action of skeletal muscle

Spatial memory (3.2) memory of where something is located

Sphygmomanometer (2.6) instrument used to measure blood pressure

Splice-site mutation (1.4) mutation at a point where coding and non-coding regions meet in a section of DNA

Sporadic (4.3) referring to an infectious disease that occurs occasionally and unpredictably

Statin (2.7) a medicine that helps lower LDLs in the blood

Stem cell (1.1) unspecialised cell that can divide and then differentiate

Stroke (2.6) life threatening condition that occurs when blood supply to part of the brain is cut off

Stroke volume (2.6) volume of blood expelled from one ventricle during one cardiac cycle

Substitution (1.4) single-gene mutation in which one nucleotide is replaced by another

Substrate (1.6)   substance on which an enzyme works

Sugar–phosphate backbone (1.2)   strongly bonded strand of DNA

Sympathetic accelerator nerve (2.6)   nerve fibre that stimulates an increase in heart rate; part of the autonomic nervous system (ANS)

Sympathetic nervous system (3.1)   fibres of the autonomic nervous system that prepare body systems for action

Synapse (3.3)   junction between neurons

Synaptic cleft (3.3)   gap between neurons at a synapse

Synaptic vesicle (3.3)   tiny vacuole containing neurotransmitter; found in pre-synaptic neurons

Systematics (1.5)   study of the diversification of living organisms past and present

Systole (2.6)   part of the cardiac cycle in which cardiac muscle is contracted

T lymphocyte (4.2)   type of white blood cell; some kill infected cells while others stimulate the immune response

Template strand (1.2)   DNA strand on which a complementary copy is made

Testes (2.1)   male sex organs responsible for the production of sperm

Testosterone (2.1)   steroid hormone produced by interstitial cells

Therapeutic (1.1)   used as part of a medical therapy

Thrombin (2.7)   produced from prothrombin during blood clotting

Thrombosis (2.7)   blood clot within a blood vessel

Thymine (T) (1.2)   DNA base that pairs with adenine

Tissue (adult) stem cells (1.1)   stem cells from tissue that divide and differentiate to become cells of that tissue

Tissue fluid (2.5)   fluid which bathes cells in tissues; derived from blood

Transcription (1.3)   copying of DNA sequences to make a primary transcript

Transfer RNA (tRNA) (1.3)   transfers specific amino acids to the mRNA on the ribosomes

Translation (1.3)   production of a polypeptide at a ribosome using information encoded in mRNA

Translocation (1.4)   chromosome mutation in which part of a chromosome becomes attached to another

Trial-and-error learning (3.4)   type of learning that relies on reinforcement

Trypanosomiasis (4.4)   disease caused by a protozoan

Tuberculosis (TB) (4.4) disease caused by a bacterium that can survive within phagocytes

Tumour (1.1) collection of cancer cells produced by excessive, uncontrolled cell division

Ultrasound scanning (2.4) diagnostic procedure used for various prenatal checks, such as establishing the stage of pregnancy and the date that the baby is due

Uracil (U) (1.3) RNA base not found in DNA

Vaccination (4.4) using an antigen that has been made harmless to produce an immune response and memory cells

Vasoconstriction (2.5) narrowing of blood vessels to reduce blood flow

Vasodilation (2.5) widening of blood vessels to increase blood flow

Vector organism (4.3) organism that can carry or transfer a stage of a disease parasite into the body

Vein (2.5) blood vessel with valves that transports blood back to the heart

Ventricular diastole (2.6) part of the cardiac cycle in which the cardiac muscle of the ventricles relaxes

Ventricular systole (2.6) part of the cardiac cycle in which the cardiac muscle of the ventricles contracts

Venule (2.5) small branch of a vein

Verbal communication (3.4) communication using words and language

Zygote (2.1) fertilised egg cell